# ·THE·

# RAILWAY

# ·DATA FILE·

# ·THE·
# RAILWAY
# ·DATA FILE·

**Blitz**
**Editions**

This edition published by Blitz Editions,
an imprint of Bookmart Ltd, in 1999

Bookmart Ltd
Desford Road,
Enderby,
Leicester LE9 5AD

Produced by Eaglemoss Publications
Based on *The World of Trains*
Copyright © Eaglemoss Publications Ltd 1999

Cover artworks by Graham Dorsett,
Dennis Griffiths, Duncan Kitson and Paul Kellett.

Printed in Dubai

ISBN 1 85605 499 3

10 9 8 7 6 5 4 3 2 1

# • Contents •

## STEAM ENGINES

How a steam engine works..........................6
Valve working............................................7
Valve gear working....................................8
The locomotive firebox..............................9
Water gauges............................................10
Locomotive tenders..................................11
Locomotive water......................................12
Locomotive coal........................................13
Tank locomotives......................................14
Self-cleaning smokeboxes........................15
Blastpipes..................................................16
Smokebox numberplates..........................17
Locomotive whistles..................................18
Superheating..............................................19
Compounding..............................................20
Compound locomotives..............................21
Cylinder pressure......................................22
Vertical boilers..........................................23
Vacuum ejectors........................................24
Live-steam injectors..................................25
Exhaust-steam injectors............................26
Smoke deflectors......................................27
Steam headcodes......................................28
Locomotive lubrication..............................29
Locomotive cabs........................................30
Sentinel locomotives................................31
Drummond's Greyhounds..........................32
GWR 0-6-0s................................................33
Claughton 4-6-0s........................................34
GWR heavy tanks......................................35
LMS Beyer-Garratts....................................36
Private locomotive builders' plates..........37

## DIESEL ENGINES

The diesel engine......................................38
Diesel engine components........................39
Turbochargers............................................40
Diesel-electric drive..................................41
Diesel-hydraulic drive................................42
Diesel headcodes......................................43

## ELECTRIC ENGINES

EMU fronts..................................................44
AC electrics................................................45
Catenary......................................................46
Pantographs................................................47
Thyristors....................................................48
Tap-changers..............................................49
Dual-voltage trains....................................50
Electric braking..........................................51

## WHEELS, AXLES & BOGIES

Wheel arrangements (steam locos)..........52
Wheel arrangements
    (diesel and electric locos)....................53
Unusual wheel arrangements....................54
Articulated locomotives............................55
Steam sanding............................................56
Tyres and profiles......................................57
Disc wheels................................................58
Suspension systems..................................59
Plain and roller bearings..........................60
Buffers........................................................61
Manual couplings......................................62
Automatic couplers....................................63
BR coach bogies........................................64
Air suspension............................................65

## TRAINS & WAGONS

Atmospheric railways................................66
Streamlining................................................67
Dynamometer cars....................................68
Gas turbines..............................................69
Mixed freight trains..................................70
Brake vans..................................................71
British diesel railcars................................72
Passenger train make up..........................73
Tavern cars................................................74
Railway bottles..........................................75
Restaurant cars..........................................76
Observation cars........................................77
Doubledeck trains......................................78
Class 08 0-6-0............................................79
4-sub roofs................................................80
EPB Class 415............................................81
Class 156....................................................82
BR coach seating......................................83
BR coach air-conditioning........................84
Modern wagons..........................................85
Tank wagon design....................................86
Bulk powder wagons..................................87
Hopper wagons..........................................88
MGR operation............................................89
Coaling locomotives..................................90
Low-loading wagons..................................91
Open wagons..............................................92
Service wagons..........................................93
High capacity wagons................................94
Covered vans..............................................95
Flat wagons................................................96

## TRACK & TRACKSIDE

Rail..............................................................97
Gauge..........................................................98
Sleepers......................................................99
Rail fasteners............................................100
Ballast........................................................101
Water troughs............................................102
Rail lubrication..........................................103
Track circuits............................................104
Third-rail pick-up......................................105
Early rail types..........................................106
Points and crossings................................107
Changing tracks........................................108
Rack railways............................................109
Track rationalization................................110
Learning the road......................................111
Clearing House maps................................112
Single-lead junctions................................113
Single line tokens....................................114
Grade separation......................................115
Cuttings and embankments......................116
Mileposts....................................................117
Lineside signs............................................118
Locomotive water supply..........................119
Mail on the move......................................120

## RAILWAY BUILDINGS

Steam locomotive depot layout..............121
Steam depot equipment............................122
Testing stations........................................123
Hump yards................................................124
Manual signalboxes..................................125
Manual level crossings............................126
Automatic crossings..................................127
Bridges and viaducts................................128
Swing bridges............................................129
Tunnels......................................................130
Turntables..................................................131
Modern traction depots............................132

## TIMING & RECORDS

Times and timetabling..............................133
Railway company timetables....................134
Station clocks............................................135
Steam speed records................................136
World diesel speed records......................137
Electric speed records..............................138

## APPENDIX

Train resistance........................................139
Tractive effort............................................140
TE and HP - steam....................................141
TOPS letter codes....................................142
Cost-benefit analysis................................143

Picture acknowledgements......................144

# How a steam engine works

The heart of the steam locomotive is its boiler. Working under strong induced draught it is the most compact of all types of boiler in relation to the amount of steam produced. Its traditional form of construction is suitable for pressures up to about 300lb per sq in. It is usually fired by coal, though oil has been widely used and in special circumstances wood, sugar cane waste and even peat have been burned.

Solid fuel is burned on the grate (**1**) within the inner firebox (**2**). This is surrounded by **water**, in the outer firebox shell, to absorb radiant heat from the fire. To resist the pressure in the boiler the inner and outer fireboxes are joined by many hundreds of stays.

Air to support combustion is of two kinds. Primary air is admitted below the grate, controlled by damper doors (**3**) in the ashpan, and is drawn through the firebed. This makes the fuel incandescent but is not sufficient to burn all the constituents of the coal. Secondary air is admitted above the firebed, usually through the firehole

door (**4**) but sometimes also through tubes or hollow stays through the side water spaces.

The brick arch (**5**), constructed of firebrick or refractory concrete, serves three purposes: being incandescent it encourages combustion of gas distilled from the firebed; it lengthens the path of those gases to give more time for combustion; and it prevents cool secondary air reaching the tubes.

The hot gases are drawn through long tubes (**6**), surrounded by water in the barrel of the boiler, to the smokebox (**7**). In a modern boiler these tubes are of two types, small ones about 1¾-2¼in diameter and large flues about 5-5½in diameter.

The **saturated steam** generated collects above the water in the boiler (**8**). Its passage to the cylinders is controlled by the regulator valve (**9**), operated from the cab and usually placed in a dome (**10**) at the highest point of the boiler. It travels via the main steam pipe (**11**) to the superheater header (**12**), which is a box divided into two separate spaces. The saturated steam (at 250lb per sq in pressure its temperature is about 405°F/207°C)

flows through superheater element pipes (**13**) fitted inside the large flues to the superheated side of the header.

By this time it has become **superheated steam** and its temperature may have been raised to 600-700°F (316-371°C). From the header it flows via steam pipes (**14**) through the valves to the cylinders (**15**).

The **hot gases** from the fire, now much cooler after giving up heat to the water and steam, are ejected through the chimney (**16**). This is done by the **exhaust steam** from the cylinders, which passes to the chimney through the reduced orifice of the blastpipe (**17**) at high speed, entraining the gases on the way. In this way the smokebox maintains a partial vacuum which provides the draw on the fire.

Replacement water is forced into the boiler by injectors or pumps to maintain a safe level above the top of the firebox. Safety valves (**18**) on top of the boiler open to release steam if the pressure tends to rise above a safe level.

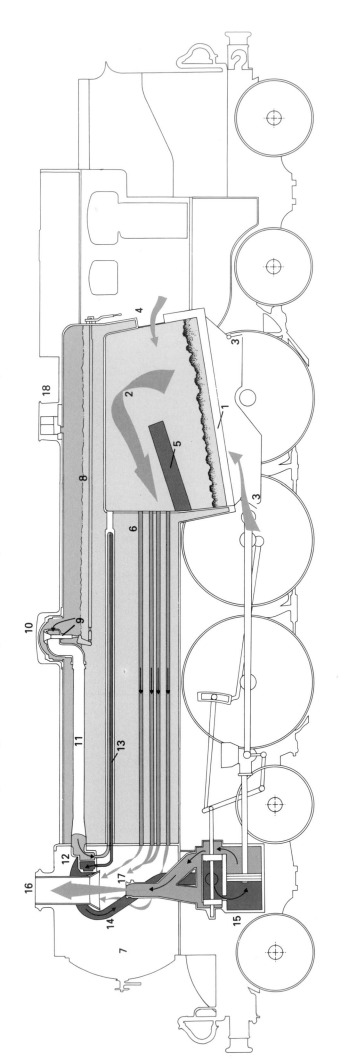

water | saturated steam | superheated steam | exhaust steam | hot gases | air flow

# Valve working

In a steam locomotive, steam has to be admitted to, and exhausted from, the cylinders at the right moment in the cycle. This is achieved by a valve arrangement inside the steamchest, which is located next to each cylinder.

Typically the cylinder has an aperture (port) at each end, and the function of the valve is to admit fresh steam under pressure at one end, while allowing used steam to escape at the other. The later main line engines were fitted with piston valves, in which the cylindrical steamchest contains two heads on a piston that cover and uncover the ports in sequence.

## Laps and leads

The amount of overlap between the valve and the port is known as the **lap**. In slow moving locomotives a long lap on the exhaust port is common. The delayed opening of the port gives time for the steam trapped in the cylinder to make best use of its stored energy and expand fully, pushing against the piston.

On fast running locomotives, exhaust clearance (allowing the port to open early when the valve is in mid-position) helps the steam to escape faster, so reducing back pressure.

Higher speed locomotives also have long lead, meaning that the admission port is already open when the piston is at the end of its movement (sweep) to the front or back of the cylinder, so assuring good steam pressure immediately it begins its next movement.

## Cut-off

This is the term used to denote the position of the piston in its path, at the moment the valve is closing the port to stop steam being admitted to the cylinder.

When the locomotive is working hard and slowly, long cut-off can admit steam for most of the stroke of the piston, but at higher speeds this overtaxes the boiler and leads to back pressure. To prevent this, cut-off can be reduced at high speeds until steam is admitted for only 15% of the stroke, its expansive properties being used to push the piston for the remainder of the stroke.

▲Most steam engines have between two and four sets of valve gear and cylinders. These are usually placed at the front of the locomotive, ahead of the driving wheels and under the smokebox. They are either visible on the side of the engine, as shown here, or hidden between the frames behind the wheels.

## The working cycle of valve and piston

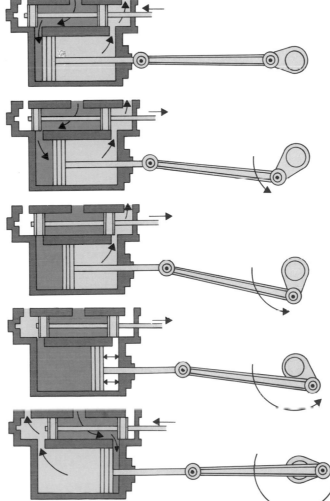

1 The valve head is in front of the forward port, allowing steam under pressure into the cylinder to push the piston back.

2 As the piston continues to move backwards, used steam from the previous stroke is exhausted through the back port at the rear of the cylinder.

3 After about 30% of the piston's full stroke the valve head cuts off the steam supply. The steam continues to expand and pushes the piston back.

4 The front port opens to exhaust the steam while the back port is closed, creating some back pressure before the next stroke is made.

5 Fresh steam under pressure enters by the back port and the process begins again. The piston and valve move forward to begin a new sweep.

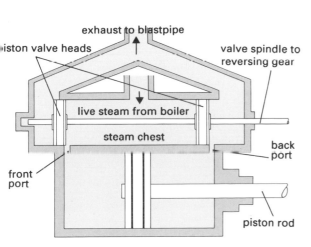

exhaust to blastpipe
piston valve heads
valve spindle to reversing gear
live steam from boiler
steam chest
back port
front port
piston rod

# Valve gear working

The function of locomotive valve gear is to regulate the movement of the valves so that steam is admitted to and exhausted from the correct end of the cylinder at the right time. It enables the driver to choose the duration (cut-off) of steam admission and to reverse the locomotive.

In the Walschaert valve gear, common on UK built locos, fore-and-aft movement of the valve spindle, whose valve heads open and close the steam ports, depends on the movement of both the combination lever (which is worked by the crosshead) and the expansion link. These two sources of fore-and-aft motion are joined at the point where the combination lever and radius rod are pinned together.

The movement of the expansion link is obtained from an eccentric rod attached to the crank axle. The front of the rod is pinned to the bottom of the expansion link, which is made to rock backwards and forwards.

Adjustment to the length of valve travel is obtained by raising or lowering the position of the radius rod in the expansion link. This is done by operation of the reversing rod from the cab.

The length of travel of the radius rod, and hence of the valve spindle, depends on the rod's position in the expansion link. Maximum valve travel (longest cut-off and maximum steam admission) is obtained when the radius rod is positioned furthest from the centre of the expansion link.

Moving the radius rod up and down from one half of the expansion link to the other reverses the movement of the locomotive by admitting steam into what otherwise would have been the exhausting side of the piston at that particular point in the cycle.

In the diagrams opposite, fresh steam under pressure is shown as orange and exhaust steam is coloured yellow.

## Cycle of operation

The valve spindle is drawn back as the radius rod is pulled by the oscillating expansion link. This opens the admission and exhaust ports.

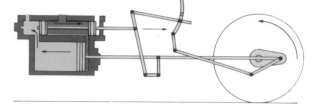

Moderated by the rear-moving radius rod, the advancing combination lever now ensures forward movement of the valve spindle.

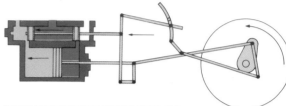

The combination lever continues to push the valve spindle forward, opening the rear port to exhaust.

The rear stroke begins, with the radius rod moving the valve spindle further forward to begin steam admission at the front of the cylinder.

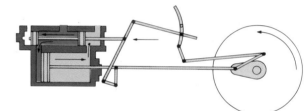

The rear-moving combination lever, regulated by the advancing radius rod, draws back the valve spindle, cutting off admission.

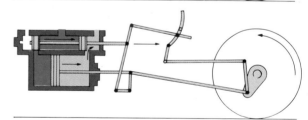

The combination lever continues to draw back the valve spindle, beginning to uncover the forward port for exhaust.

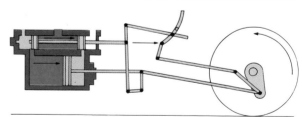

## The Walschaert system

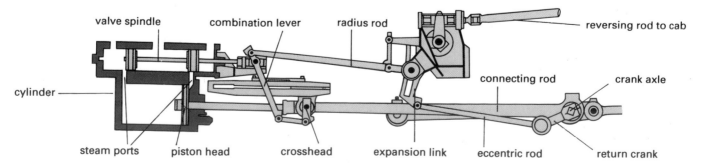

valve spindle · combination lever · radius rod · reversing rod to cab · cylinder · connecting rod · crank axle · steam ports · piston head · crosshead · expansion link · eccentric rod · return crank

# The locomotive firebox

The steam locomotive firebox is designed to burn fuel efficiently and produce adequate heat to boil water and create steam. The firebox must be large enough to burn sufficient fuel for the heaviest duty without forcing the fire to the point where unburnt fuel is drawn off the firebed in large quantities.

## Firebox types

Fireboxes may be wide and extend over the engine frames and wheels, or narrow, waisting in to fit between the frames – this limits their width to about 4ft. The firebox can be round topped and follow the circular profile of the boiler barrel, or Belpaire with the top roughly square. The Belpaire is more costly to produce but makes direct staying simpler and provides more steam space at the top of the firebox where it is needed most.

The locomotive firebox consists of an outer and inner shell. The outer firebox, an integral part of the boiler shell, is made of steel. The inner firebox is either of copper or steel construction. The plates of the two fireboxes need to be stayed together to resist boiler pressure – a large boiler contains well over 1000 stays.

Between the inner and outer fireboxes,

boiling water under pressure prevents the inner firebox plates melting in the intense heat from the fire. At their sides and ends these two fireboxes are 3-4in apart but above the inner firebox there is typically a 1½-2ft space to collect steam. At the base is the foundation ring which seals the gap between the two fireboxes.

As a safety feature to protect the firebox, fusible plugs of low melting-point alloy are provided in the crown; these melt and extinguish the fire should it be uncovered by a low water level.

Unburnt fuel drawn off the firebed could produce unwanted smoke and block the boiler tubes, which would impair steaming. To ensure the maximum combustion of gases within the firebox, air from the firehole is guided towards the fire by the deflector (baffle) plate. This air combines with the hot gases whose path to the boiler tubes has been extended by the brick arch, encouraging complete combustion.

Boilers using solid fuel need a grate at the base of the firebox. In order to clear wheels and axles this may be level, sloping or a combination of the two. In general the deeper the firebox the easier it is to fire efficiently, but this is not

always practicable.

The amount of air admitted through the grate to the underside of the fire is regulated by dampers, a series of openings cut into the sides and ends of the ashpan and controlled by doors.

The grate consists of cast iron firebars with air spaces between. To clean the fire it is necessary either to remove several bars, using heavy tongs, to give an opening through which the clinker and ashes can be pushed into the ashpan, or to paddle (lift) the remnants out through the firehole door with a long shovel.

To make the task easier, many locomotives are provided with a drop section, manually lowered, or a rocking grate, operated from the cab, allowing ash to be shaken out of the fire during the journey and the remains of the fire dumped during disposal over the ashpit.

Grates over 50sq ft are beyond the capacity of one fireman to handle. This led to the use of mechanical stokers which brought crushed coal by screw conveyor from the tender to a table plate inside the firehole door. Here it was blown by adjustable steam jets on to the fire. This device was particularly popular in the USA.

## Function and design

Fuel and air combine in the locomotive firebox to create an intense heat. This heat boils water and creates the steam to give the engine its power. The size and design of a firebox depends on the type of locomotive and the tasks it was intended to perform.

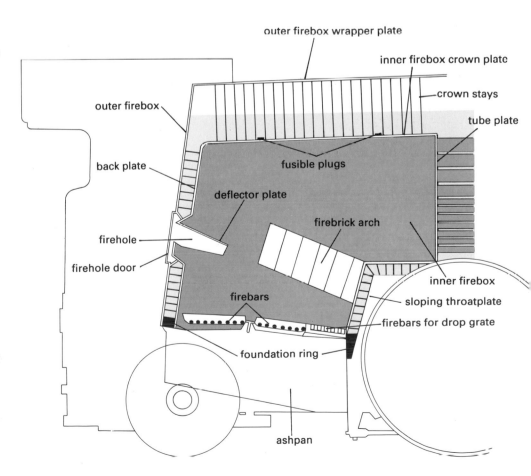

# Water gauges

The **inner firebox** of a steam locomotive is in the rear of the boiler and surrounded by water. The firebox is subject to intense radiant heat and it is essential that the **water level**, which must be above the crown (top) of the firebox, is controlled within a limited range of about 6in.

If the water level falls too low, the **firebox crown** will be uncovered, bringing the danger of overheating and collapse. This is despite the fitting of **fusible plugs** which would melt if exposed and let water from the boiler pour into the firebox to dowse the fire. Should the water level become too high, the **steam space** between the water and the top of the boiler becomes unduly restricted. This could result in water carrying over to the cylinders – also with serious results.

## Gauge fittings

It was vital that the crew could see the level of water above the firebox and a **water gauge** was fitted for this purpose. It took the form of a vertical glass tube about 6in long, connected to the boiler by fittings at the top and bottom. Water just visible in the bottom of the tube meant that there would be about 3-4in of water above the firebox crown.

The top and bottom gauge fittings, made of gunmetal and fixed to the firebox backplate, were fitted with rotary **gauge cocks** which could be shut off if the glass

tube burst – a common occurrence. A **glass protector**, which could easily be removed for cleaning, was usually fitted round the gauge glass to stop flying glass and boiling water hitting the crew should this happen.

It was normal practice to provide two water gauges, so that if a gauge glass burst on the road, the fireman had another to work with until the glass could be replaced (a five minute job; most engines carried a spare glass in the locker).

Many shunting engines had just one gauge and test cock. Until World War II, the Great Western Railway (GWR) provided a single gauge. The top and bottom fittings were cast in one piece, with an integral hollow column behind the glass on which test cocks were fitted.

The use of a **drain cock** at the bottom of the gauge, along with the other two cocks in turn, allowed the connections to the boiler to be blown through. This operation proved that these vital passageways were clear and free from scale build-up.

## Safety improvements

There were at least five boiler explosions in Britain during and after World War II, due either to crew unfamiliarity with a new type of shut-off cock (on US-built 2-8-0s) or a malfunction of a gauge due to incorrect assembly.

Various improvements were made over

the years to the basic gauge. It became common for the top and bottom fittings to be provided with **restrictor** or **ball valves** to shut off the sudden flow of water and steam in the event of a burst glass, giving safer access to the handles of the shut-off cocks. Some railways also coupled the top and bottom cock handles by a connecting link so that one movement shut both cocks.

In order to make the level in the glass clear, it was common practice for the **backplate** of the protector to have diagonal slots or painted stripes; these were unchanged when seen through steam, but refracted by about 60° through water.

### On the road
In service, the water level in the boiler could change quite suddenly and some care was necessary in controlling it. When the regulator was shut, the level of water would fall about 1in due to the reduced steam-bubble content of the water. Changes of gradient caused rapid movement due to the length of the boiler. To go over a summit from a severe up to a severe down, could bring the level in a long boiler down as much as 5in. It was essential that the fireman anticipated such changes on the road.

The water gauge told the crew of a steam locomotive the level of water above the top of the firebox – which must be covered. Two cocks, top and bottom, connected the gauge with the steam and water spaces in the boiler. A third, the drain cock, helped ensure the glass gave the correct reading. Should the glass shatter for any reason, ball valves would restrict the supply of water and steam. At the back of the gauge was a backplate with slots or diagonal stripes to make the water level easy to read.

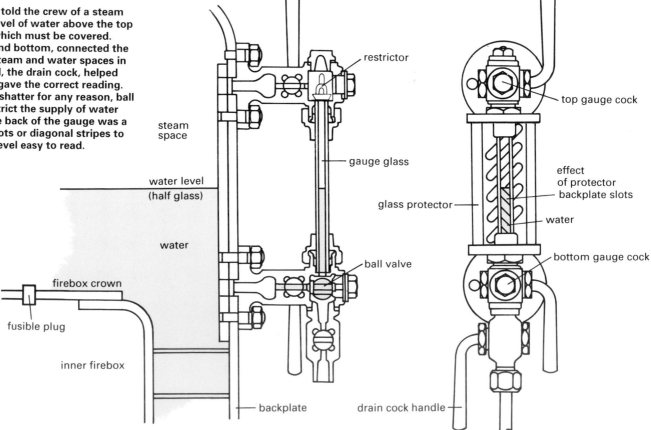

steam space

water level (half glass)

water

firebox crown

fusible plug

inner firebox

restrictor

gauge glass

ball valve

backplate

drain cock handle

top gauge cock

effect of protector
backplate slots

glass protector

water

bottom gauge cock

# Locomotive tenders

The tender carries enough fuel and water to enable the locomotive to pull its train between fuelling and watering points. Until the end of the 19th century, a tender load of less than five tons of coal was sufficient on Britain's railways, while water capacity was as much as 3500 gallons. But with the long non-stop runs and the higher rates of steam production in the 20th century, some tenders carried up to 10 tons of coal and others up to 6000 gallons of water.

Originally the water tank was of a horseshoe shape, with its open end facing the locomotive firehole and the coal piled on the flat floor in its centre. Later, the floor was raised to accommodate extra water, and the tank was given a sharp upward slope to the rear. This inclination encourages the coal to move forward on to the low horizontal part of the water tank, where it is easily picked up by the fireman's shovel.

Supports inside the tank, known as baffles, also serve as breakwaters to moderate surges of water that otherwise could be destabilizing. At the rear, the roof of the tank has a filling hole wide enough to take the leather downpipe of lineside water cranes. The hole has a heavy, hinged lid.

With the exception of the Southern, most main line locomotives had a water pick-up scoop with a screw arrangement for lifting and lowering. The rush of water which was forced up the scoop from the track troughs required generous air vents and a dome-shaped deflector over the top of the water scoop's standpipe. Where there were no water troughs the tenders were larger, often needing eight rather than the usual six wheels to support them.

Because of its weight and the big weight difference between full and empty condition, the main design problem with tenders was the springing. Heavy leaf springs were provided; most designers preferred to place these below the level of the water tank so that the tank could be as wide as possible.

Tenders were detached only at times of major repair, so the coupling between the tender and engine was made much stronger (and therefore heavier) than normal couplings. Water was taken from the tender to the locomotive's injectors by simple flexible pipes.

The LNWR used timber-framed tenders into the 20th century; an argument in their favour was that in collisions they became 'crumple zones' (a term not then used but now familiar to car designers).

One limitation on tender size was the length of turntables; for this reason some large locomotives had small tenders. At the other extreme, Nigel Gresley built some exceptionally large tenders for the non-stop London – Edinburgh service. These were supported by eight wheels, carried 5000 gallons of water and eight tons of coal, and included a narrow corridor so that engine crews could be changed without stopping the train.

American style mechanical stokers were not considered necessary in Britain, where the firing rate was well within the capacity of the fireman – though there were four applications in Britain: one SR Merchant Navy and three Class 9Fs. Steam operated coal pushers to move the coal forward were also considered a luxury except for the very longest through running.

## Tender capacity

The coal and water capacity of a tender increased steadily with the development of the steam locomotive. Apart from the Southern, expresses on all regions picked up water on the move – perhaps 2000 gallons in 500 yards of trough. Where water supplies were scarce – for example on African lines – locomotives sometimes hauled an extra tank behind the tender.

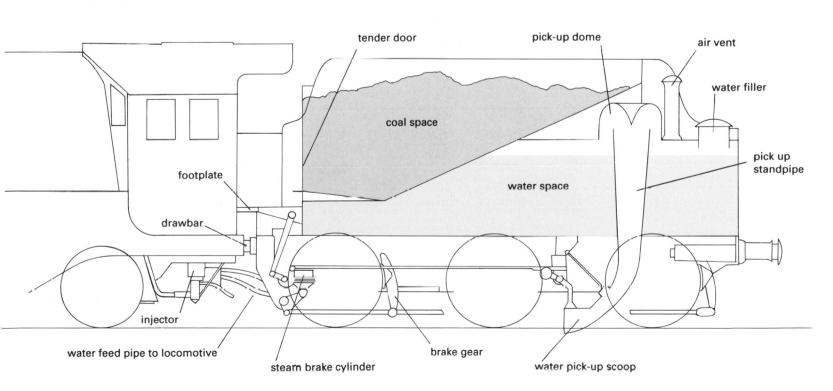

# Locomotive water

From the early days of steam the quality of water used in the locomotive has been of prime concern. No water is perfect. That obtained from rivers, lakes and reservoirs often contains organic matter; water from boreholes, while pure, is usually very hard.

Hardness, caused by calcium and magnesium salts, is a major problem. As boiler temperature and pressure rise, the previously soluble salts become insoluble. Some salts are deposited on hot surfaces where they are baked to form scale; others sink to the bottom of the boiler as sludge.

Scale has low heat conductivity and therefore hampers the transfer of heat from the fire to the water. If left too long it can lead to the firebox and tubes overheating, resulting in buckling and, in extreme cases, collapse.

Another scale, less common but more harmful, is silica, and several other constituents are troublesome. Even carbon dioxide, especially noticeable in surface water, is undesirable because under the influence of heat it gives off pure oxygen which causes pitting and corrosion.

▲At King's Cross in 1963 observers of A4 No 60015 *Quicksilver* are showered by sooty, wet steam sprayed from the boiler as a result of priming. This occurs when water is carried from the boiler into the cylinders.

▼Hard water contains salts which solidify, causing scale, when they come in contact with hot surfaces. The effect is seen clearly on the boiler sides of BR 9F No 92209 at Woodford Halse, in October 1964.

All steam locomotives need periodic boiler washouts, when jets of cold (sometimes hot) water under pressure are injected through plug holes in the firebox sides. In Britain, water quality varies quite widely and the mileage allowed between washouts ranged from 500 to 5000 miles; a typical engine would be stopped for washout every eight or ten days.

Organic impurities can be removed by filtration, while lineside chemical plants were used where the local water was hard. These varied in complexity, but their basic purpose was to soften the water by adding hydrated lime, sodium carbonate or sodium aluminate.

Many patents were awarded for equipment to soften the water on the locomotive itself. A totally perfect feedwater was neither necessary nor possible; even so, few of these systems justified their expense. A simple solution existed on some BR Standard locomotives, where water softening blocks were placed in a perforated cylinder suspended in the water space.

In recent years, excessive nitrates have caused serious problems with preserved locomotives. Acidic water is harmful because it is corrosive. Reducing acidity by chemical means is simple, but in practice some degree of acidity is needed – below a certain acidity level water tends to foam inside the boiler causing priming (when water is carried over with the steam into the cylinders).

# Locomotive coal

With a few short term exceptions, British steam locomotives burned coal. However, from the varieties of coal obtainable, only a few types were suitable and many railway companies designed their locomotives with a particular quality of coal in mind.

The heat produced by coal comes from its carbon and hydrogen content, and coals with a high proportion of these (known as high calorific) were always preferred.

Coals have a tendency to form a hot mass (cake) over the fire which hinders air circulation. If its chemical composition is satisfactory, a coal which cakes needs only a little more work by the fireman to break up the crust. This tendency to cake is an inherent property in the coal which cannot be removed.

Clinkering is a hard deposit that has to be chipped off the firebars. It occurs because ash and sulphur fuse together at a lower temperature than is reached in the firebox to sustain steam pressure. The best locomotive coal has a low ash and sulphur content – ash tends to clog boiler tubes and also, can pit and score metal surfaces as it is swept up by hot gases at speeds up to 200mph.

A high sulphur content is detrimental. Combined with the moisture content of coal, it will form acids both in the smokebox char and in the residual ash in the firebox. The acids then attack the metal surfaces of these areas.

The size of coal is only important when high steaming rates are required from relatively small grate areas. Combustion rates of any type of coal depend on how large the lumps are. Small sized pieces of coal increase the total surface area of coal in the firebox. Poor quality coal, which was too often supplied after 1939, has a high proportion of coal dust and slack. Most coal dust is carried straight up the chimney, unburned, and the slack tends to block air flows in the boiler tubes.

In general, a smoky exhaust means inefficiency. To achieve complete combustion, a high firebox temperature is needed and this demands a good air flow and only a thin layer of unburned coal on top of the fire. When the firebox temperature is low – as in lighting up – certain coals emit yellow smoke. However, smoke consists of the hydro-carbon contents of the coal, and hydrogen has four times the calorific value of carbon. Black smoke is very wasteful. Heaping coal into the firebox at long intervals was a sure way to produce black smoke and wasteful consumption.

Bituminous coals, a class that includes house coal, were widely used for locomotives, but only those varieties that were non-caking, hard and with low ash content were favoured. Some railways were supplied by just one or two favourite collieries in Yorkshire and Lancashire.

Welsh coal – used in particular by the GWR – was semi-bituminous, having more carbon and burning with a shorter flame. But it did not necessarily burn more efficiently – this depended entirely on the skill of the fireman with his use of dampers, firehole door, flap openings and firebed thickness.

Coal which was handled too often (especially in mechanical coaling plants where it was dropped into large hoppers) tended to break into small pieces, and for that reason hard coals were preferred by most railways. The GWR designed its locos to suit the high calorific value, low volatility Welsh coal available in its region. To reduce degradation it stayed with hand/tub coaling – a dirty and time-consuming method.

Inferior coals of the soft or lignite type were used in some countries, notably Germany and South Africa; locomotive designs frequently allowed for this.

▼Black smoke may look very impressive but is often a sure sign of wasted fuel. A low firebox temperature, or a deep firebed, means coal remains unburned and particles are sucked along the boiler tubes and up the chimney, producing the clag so beloved of photographers.

## Coal constituents

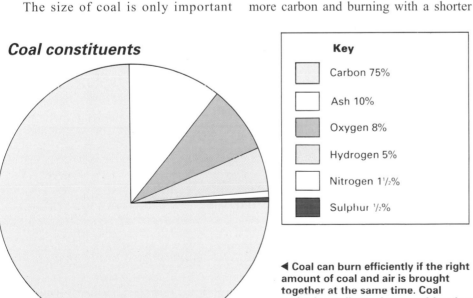

| Key | |
|---|---|
| ☐ | Carbon 75% |
| ☐ | Ash 10% |
| ▨ | Oxygen 8% |
| ☐ | Hydrogen 5% |
| ☐ | Nitrogen 1½% |
| ■ | Sulphur ½% |

◀ Coal can burn efficiently if the right amount of coal and air is brought together at the same time. Coal varies in quality and composition, but it consists mostly of carbon – the remainder being composed of gases and ash. The best coal for locomotives has a high carbon and hydrogen content and is known as high calorific.

# Tank locomotives

Instead of carrying coal and water on a separate tender, the tank locomotive has integral coal bunkers and water tanks. The elimination of the tender not only reduced capital cost but also made operation more convenient and cheaper. If a locomotive could replenish its water supplies at short intervals, there was no point in hauling a heavy tenderful of water. Operations which lent themselves particularly well to tank locomotive service were suburban passenger railways, where runs were only 20 miles or so, shunting work and branch lines.

Tank locomotives carry their coal behind the cab in a bunker, which often covers a supplementary water tank. Most carry their main water supply in tanks that flank the boiler in a variety of positions. These compact locomotives were once popular for yard work because they afforded the driver a better view forward.

The most common type was the **side tank**, which carried two narrow, vertical tanks that rested on the running plate on each side of the boiler. The **saddle tank** is a curved tank draped around the top of the boiler. On the GWR the saddle tank was developed into the **pannier tank**. Pannier tank locomotives have two rectangular tanks slung at the sides of the boiler, in most cases giving better visibility than the saddle tank.

Saddle and pannier tanks do not extend downwards as far as the running plate; this leaves a useful gap through which inside connecting rods and valve gear may be inspected and lubricated.

Other, rarer tank engines were the **well tank**, in which the water was carried in tanks between the frames, and the **Forney tank**, an American type with the water carried in a tank behind the cab. There were also a few **tender tanks**, which were tank locomotives with a small form of tender, usually on just two closely spaced axles, for the coal supply.

Use of a tank engine avoided the time consuming trip to a turntable at each end of a short run. Branch lines – including many colliery branches – usually did not have a turntable, and so often employed tank locomotives.

These engines were also very useful in yard operations, where locomotives spent as much time in backward motion as in forward. In shunting, the better visibility when in reverse offered by a tenderless locomotive made coupling and uncoupling easier and safer.

Another advantage of the tank locomotive is the better protection afforded to the crew – except in the case of the few elderly 'half cab' tank engines, which lacked the rear half of the cab roof and weatherboard.

Tanks may be internally divided to solve the problem of surging water. The express tank locomotive was especially subject to this – the disastrous 1927 Sevenoaks derailment, for example, was thought to result from high speed and bumpy track giving rise to destabilizing water surges.

Such large express tank locomotives were built by a few companies with passenger routes of 50 miles or so, the Brighton line being a notable example. The highly successful LMS and BR 2-6-4T, carrying 2000 gallons of water and 3½ tons of coal, was also a large engine.

With its short distances and high population density, Britain made good use of tank locomotives. For example, in 1923 the GWR had 3944 locomotives, of which 2442 were tank locomotives. But US railroads did not favour the type; they had a few for commuter trains but shunting was entrusted to six- and eight-wheel tender locomotives.

## Tank engine types

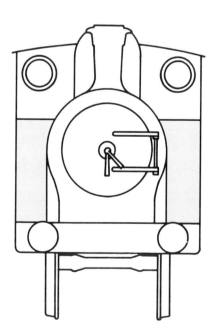

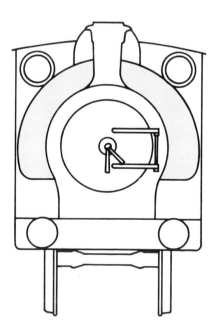

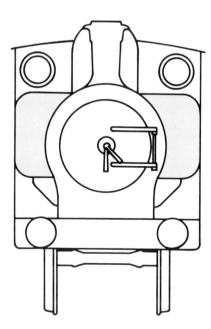

▲Side tanks were alongside the boiler and supported from the frames. As boiler diameter increased, side tanks alone could not hold enough water and were often supplemented by an additional tank below the coal bunker.

▲Saddle tanks were mounted on top of the boiler and firebox and were usually horseshoe section but occasionally had straight sides and top. It was not normally possible to provide enough capacity for duties other than shunting. Filling involved climbing on top, which was not always safe.

▲Pannier tanks were rectangular in cross-section with rounded outer corners, extending from smokebox front to cab. The tops were flush with the top of the boiler, leaving the driver a good forward view.

# Self-cleaning smokeboxes

The golden age of steam is typified by pictures of locomotives pounding along the rails, a trail of exhaust from the chimney hanging in the air behind. What these pictures do not show is the particles of unburnt, or partly burnt, coal from the fire which were drawn through the boiler tubes and emitted by the strong upward draught through the chimney.

These were sometimes ejected as hot cinders, possibly starting lineside fires, or stayed in the smokebox. An engine working hard on a long run could build up several hundredweights of char in the smokebox. This was enough to block some of the bottom tubes and, ultimately, impair steaming.

To ensure that ejected char was broken down to a size too small to cause lineside fires, various forms of wire mesh spark arresters were fitted between the blastpipe and the chimney cowl. These screens did not prevent char building up in the smokebox - indeed they may have contributed to it - and, because of their necessarily small mesh area, could sometimes become blocked themselves.

In the USA, with their use of mechanical stokers, these problems were particularly acute. Following extensive tests at the turn of the century, the American Railway Master Mechanics Association formulated a device which would not only break up the char, but which would also scour the smokebox clean. This device comprised a nearly vertical baffle plate in front of the tubeplate and a horizontal table plate, at the level of the blastpipe cap, with a shallow downward apron on its leading edge.

The combustion gases were drawn through a relatively shallow opening below the apron at high speed, preventing any char from falling out. The gases were then drawn through the mesh screens in front of the blastpipe and chimney, breaking the trapped char into small and harmless particles before it went up the chimney.

This method was quickly adopted by US railways and known as the Master Mechanics' front end. Railways in Britain were reluctant to adopt this device, since it hindered access to the front of the tubes for cleaning purposes. Churchward on the Great Western Railway, and later Stanier on the London Midland & Scottish (LMS), did adopt baffle and table plates on their locomotives, but without the mesh screens; with hand firing in Britain the large coal was less prone to shedding small pieces during combustion.

It was left to H G Ivatt, Chief Mechanical Engineer of the LMS, to use the Master Mechanics' front end on new locomotive designs from 1946. The device went under the label self-cleaning smokebox and was intended to speed up disposal duties at sheds.

From 1951, self-cleaning smokeboxes were adopted by R A Riddles for his BR Standard locomotives. Engines so fitted carried a plate with the letters SC on the smokebox door to show disposal staff that the door did not need to be opened between washouts (every 12-16 days in most cases). It was usual to reduce the blastpipe orifice by about $1/8$in to counteract the loss of draught passing though the screens.

chimney

smokebox door

wire mesh screen

superheater header

tubes

apron

baffle plate

blastpipe

table plate

draught

## Three-cylinder problems

The self-cleaning smokebox worked effectively on two- and four-cylinder engines which had four strong exhaust beats per revolution. Its successful application to three-cylinder engines, with six lighter beats, proved more difficult. The ex-London & North Eastern Railway Class V2 2-6-2s needed considerable alteration to the draughting, when self-cleaning plates were fitted, before steaming and smokebox cleanliness were satisfactory. A successful layout for the ex-LMS rebuilt Royal Scots was never produced. One attempt so impaired the steaming of the locomotive that it was removed. When the letters SC were seen on the smokebox door by one driver, he would mutter 'Short of steam'.

◄The self-cleaning smokebox was designed to stop large particles of unburnt coal from being ejected through the chimney and to help servicing at locomotive depots. A baffle plate, fitted in front of the tubeplate, and a table plate, placed at the level of the blastpipe cap, directed boiler gases through a mesh screen. This broke up the trapped char into small pieces before it went up the chimney.

# Blastpipes

Steam production in a locomotive boiler is self regulating. The exhaust steam from the cylinders, in passing through the smokebox to the chimney, creates a draught which draws the smoke and gases along the boiler tubes and pulls fresh air through the firegrate. The harder the engine works the more steam is used, which means a bigger draught, hotter fire, and faster steam production.

## Ejecting the steam

The steam from the cylinders is ejected from the blastpipe, which is a vertical nozzle at the bottom of the smokebox facing the chimney exit. Up to a point, the narrower the nozzle the greater the steam velocity and the stronger the draught.

However, although a high velocity steam jet may create a strong draught, it is uneven and tends to draw out lumps of half burned coal with the smoke from the fire. These lumps may make picturesque sparks when the locomotive is working hard at night, but are the outward sign of inefficient combustion.

While a constricting nozzle increases steam velocity, it also creates back pressure in the cylinder because the used

steam cannot escape fast enough. An ideal blast is strong but slow and steady, and provides a fast passage for the steam leaving the cylinders.

## Improving the draught

Because the strength of the draught is directly related to both the steam velocity and the total area of the steam jet in contact with the gases in the smokebox, it is possible to improve the draught by changing the configuration of the steam jet. Around the turn of the century there were several experiments to this end, but it was not until the 1930s that good arrangements were achieved.

The simplest and easiest method to improve the draught is to have two blastpipes, each exhausting through a different orifice in a double chimney. This method was favoured by the LMS Railway, where it produced a startling improvement in the performance of the Royal Scot class locomotives. After nationalization it was also applied to GWR Castle and King locomotives, making similar improvements.

Another method, favoured by the Southern Railway, was the Lemaitre exhaust, whose outward sign was a very

large diameter chimney. Beneath the chimney was a blastpipe, divided into five nozzles, producing five steam jets. This doubled the area of steam in contact with the gases, whereas the double blastpipe only improved the ratio by approximately 50%.

## The Kylchap

Probably the most advanced method of draught improvement was the Kylchap, perfected by the French engineer Andre Chapelon. This had two blastpipes, but each nozzle had a cross-section formed of four circles joining in the centre, so steam emerged in the form of four jets that met in the middle. Beneath each chimney were two extra petticoat pipes, shaped to split the four jets and then combine them again into a single jet which was exhausted through the chimney.

Engines fitted with Kylchap exhausts were exceptionally free running. The exhaust from the chimney was so soft that the non streamlined engines needed deflector plates to lift the smoke into the air away from the cab windows. The ultimate development of the Kylchap exhaust was Chapelon's last locomotive, a SNCF 4-8-4, with a unique triple chimney.

## Three stages in blastpipe development

In the last decade of steam, three types of blastpipe arrangements were common: single, double and Kylchap. The choice of blastpipe depended on the tasks the locomotive was designed to perform.

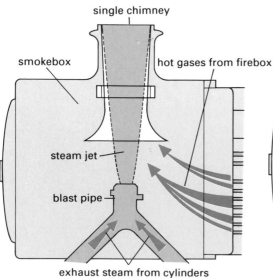

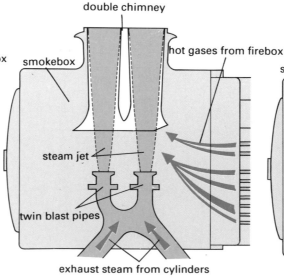

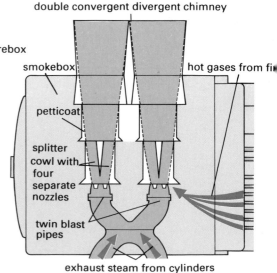

The **single blastpipe** combined exhaust steam from the cylinders to form a powerful jet. This drew hot gases through the boiler and air across the firegrate which assisted the fire in boiling water to produce steam.

The **double blastpipe and chimney** arrangement was favoured for large engines designed to haul heavy loads. It produced more steam in the boiler by improving the draught across the firegrate.

The **Kylchap** was usually given to fast express engines which travelled long distances at high speeds. Designed to have an even effect on the fire, it produced a soft, steady exhaust and improved coal consumption.

# Smokebox numberplates

The smokebox numberplate came about because of a change in the design of engine sheds. Originally, sheds were laid out on parallel lines, but in the early years of this century shed design on some railways changed and there was a tendency to house locomotives at one main depot, laid out on the roundhouse principle – engines grouped round a central turntable, like the spokes of a wheel.

This meant that crews looking for their locomotive were faced with a circle of smokeboxes devoid of identification. Most railways solved this problem by painting the engine number on the buffer beam, but the Midland Railway (MR) made cast-iron numberplates and bolted them on to the smokebox door. Appearing in 1907, these were the first smokebox numberplates.

Following the Grouping in 1923, the London Midland & Scottish Railway (LMS) continued the MR system.

Unfortunately, no MR smokebox plate is known to exist, and LMS plates are exceedingly rare, since, after nationalization in 1948, all the engines were renumbered.

BR standardized smokebox number plates, which were made of cast iron, and fitted them to all new and existing engines. The Western Region, as the Great Western Railway (GWR) had become, at first made its plates in cast brass, with ornate figures, but this practice was quickly stopped by the Railway Executive, and thereafter Western Region engines had the standard plates. It is not thought that any of the brass plates survive.

In most cases, the BR plate was bolted directly to the smokebox door. The exceptions were BR standard locomotives and ex-GWR types, where the plates were fixed to a pair of brackets welded on to the smokebox door.

## Collecting smokebox numberplates

The only smokebox numberplates available to the collector today are those manufactured by BR since 1948. However, the variety and quantity of the BR plates gives plenty of scope for collectors, as examples are available from all the regions at most auctions and swop-meets. Prices start at about £100 but can shoot up to several thousands for examples from, say, a King or Duchess locomotive.

These prices have prompted a stream of fakes in recent years, so buyers need to be on their guard. Plates purchased in ex-loco condition, complete with chipped paint, oil and grime, are now much more highly regarded than restored examples, and should be left as they are.

▲Above: the numberplate of LMS 8F 2-8-0 No 48773, of Polmadie shed, Glasgow, has an angled back to allow for the convex smokebox door. Right: the plate off London, Brighton & South Coast L2X 0-6-0 No 32449 has mounting collars for four corner bolts; the plate off LMS 3P 2-6-2 No 40001 – this was the first London Midland Region number – has the standard two bolt holes; the plate off Caledonian Railway 2P 0-4-4T No 55219 has bevelled corners, another variation; the plate off GWR Hall 4-6-0 No 6929 is of standard flat design with two fixing holes. Those for LMS Class 5 4-6-0 No 44995 and Lancashire & Yorkshire Railway 3F 0-6-0 No 52309 are shaped to fit closely to the smokebox door.

# Locomotive whistles

Whether it's an express locomotive giving out a warning as it approaches a crossing or tunnel, or a shunting locomotive piping out its code as it goes about its humbler duties, the sound of the steam locomotive whistle evokes memories of a past era.

While the steam locomotive whistle can still be heard on main line steam specials and on preserved lines, the golden age now exists only in the memory or captured on tape or disc. However, this doesn't detract from the attraction of owning a locomotive whistle – even though it will now be a cherished item to be seen – and regularly cleaned – rather than heard.

Locomotive whistles come in a variety of shapes and sizes, and when in working order produce very different sounds, from the deep throaty bass of a Stanier hooter, as found on the LMS's star performers, through to the shrill chime of the Gresley Pacifics.

Whistles comprise a valve, pressure chamber, cylinder or domed bell plus a top chamber. The sound is caused by the force of steam entering the top chamber and causing vibration in the chamber's base. They were made to produce specific notes – similar to organ pipes. The multi-note chime whistle features variable length chambers to create the distinctive double or treble tones.

Whistles were controlled by either a valve in the cab, a push rod from a valve at the base of the whistle, or a top lever.

Three note chimes survive in use thanks to the steam locomotives of South Africa. Some South African whistles have found their way to the UK for use on preserved lines and to give a bigger voice to locomotives on miniature railways.

Five- and even six-note chimes were used widely on the American continent. Of the three different designs of American multi-note chime whistles, the castellated variety shows best the different-sized chambers, while the flat top and domed bell types have their variable length chambers cast inside.

Particularly sought after examples are the chime whistles from LNER locomotives. The story goes that these were introduced by Sir Nigel Gresley after a visit to the Romney, Hythe & Dymchurch Railway where he heard a miniature locomotive which had been presented with an American whistle.

The domed bell whistle and valve found on the Southern Railway's Bulleid Pacifics are also in demand, as are whistles from the BR Standard Britannia and Clan Pacifics.

▲A London & North Eastern Railway (LNER) B1 class brass locomotive whistle. This whistle is complete and has been highly polished. The only identification mark it carries is a small number 2.

▼An industrial locomotive brass whistle from an engine at Manvers Main colliery. It is complete with its lever and is 13in (33cm) high.

◀This more unusual whistle is from an LNER Class J94 locomotive. It is made from brass and is of a type known as an organ-pipe whistle. It has been highly polished and mounted for display.

# Superheating

After the steam locomotive had reached its definitive form in the middle of the 19th century, the introduction of superheating was the most important single development. Superheating enables the power output of a locomotive to be increased by up to 25%, with equivalent savings in coal and water, compared to non-superheated machines. Its widespread introduction from 1910 onwards, gave a new impetus to steam locomotive design and coincided with demands from railway operators for heavier trains to be hauled at higher speeds.

## Basic principles

Steam generated in a boiler at a given pressure and temperature is known as saturated steam, as it is in contact with the water. When additional heat is applied it becomes superheated. In a saturated locomotive, steam passes through the regulator valve, main steam pipes and valves to the cylinders, where its pressure is applied to the pistons.

Its expansion in the cylinder results in some being condensed to water. The cylinders themselves are cooler than the steam, producing more condensation. Condensed steam produces little power.

When sufficient superheat is applied to saturated steam to raise its temperature high enough it will keep it above saturation point throughout its working cycle, until it is discharged from the blastpipe in the smokebox. This eliminates loss of power through condensation.

The other great benefit from superheating is that steam approaches the condition of a perfect gas, progressively expanding in volume as more heat is absorbed. The heat taken up in the superheater elements slightly reduces the saturated steam production rate of the boiler, but this is far less important than the increased steam volume and power output resulting from superheating.

## History

Ideas for giving superheat to saturated steam date back to the beginning of the 19th century. The first design for a locomotive superheater capable of giving a reasonable degree of superheat, as distinct from steam drying which only raises its temperature by a small amount to overcome initial moisture, was put forward in 1850.

The French locomotive engineer Montcheuil proposed that saturated steam from the boiler should be passed through U-shaped element tubes, running out and back through one or more of the flue

▼The Schmidt superheater is the most common type used in locomotives. The regulator valve allows saturated steam to enter the main steam pipe from the steam dome. From here the steam passes to the superheater header, then through the superheater elements inside the large flue tubes, where the saturated steam is heated to become superheated. The steam then returns to a separate section of the header and through the steam pipe to the cylinders.

tubes in the boiler barrel, before being delivered to the valves and cylinders.

Nearly 50 years elapsed before developments in metallurgy and lubricating oils – capable of withstanding the carbonising action of highly superheated steam – enabled superheaters to become a practical proposition. Success was finally achieved, due largely to the work of Dr Wilhelm Schmidt, known as 'hot steam Willie' to his friends, supported by Dr Robert Garbe, Chief Mechanical Engineer (CME) of the Berlin division of the Prussian State Railways, and Jean Baptiste Flamme, CME of the Belgian Railways.

Flamme suggested that the best arrangement would be to place the superheater elements in three rows of flue tubes which passed through the boiler barrel.

### Why superheat?

Superheating increases the heat content and volume of the steam, making it more fluid and using less for a given work output. It normally eliminates condensation in the steam circuit and resultant loss of power.

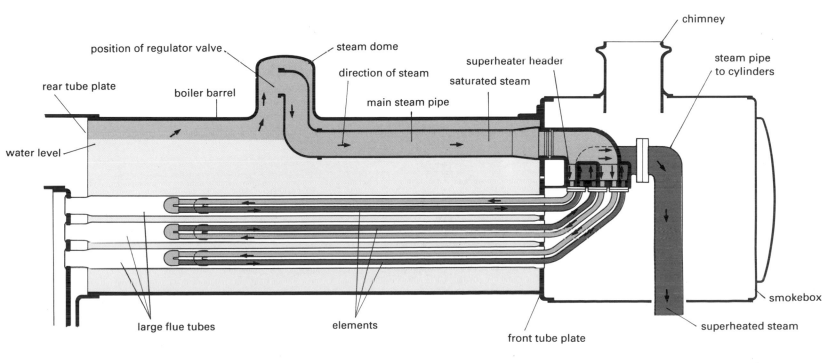

chimney

position of regulator valve

steam dome

direction of steam

superheater header

saturated steam

steam pipe to cylinders

rear tube plate

boiler barrel

main steam pipe

water level

large flue tubes

elements

front tube plate

smokebox

superheated steam

# Compounding

In compound drive locomotives, steam from the boiler is expanded in a high-pressure cylinder group, and then conveyed to a second, low-pressure group.

The aim of compounding is to extract the maximum power and efficiency out of the steam raised in the boiler. In compound locomotives, steam is admitted to both high- and low-pressure cylinders for a greater percentage of the piston stroke, for a given overall expansion, than in simple locomotives. Conventional valve gears restricted the opening of steam ports to the cylinders at short cut-offs (when steam is admitted only for a small percentage of the piston stroke). This frequently resulted in steam being severely throttled – leading to a pressure drop in

delivery to the cylinders and power loss in simple locomotives.

Improved valve gears with larger steam port openings at short cut-offs in modern simple expansion locomotives reduced this advantage in compounds, but other important factors also apply.

Larger port openings at longer cut-offs result in softer exhaust beats when steam is discharged from the blastpipe in compounds. This reduces the amount of unburned coal drawn through the tubes when the locomotive is working at a high power output – especially important where small, powdery coal is used. Longer cut-off working in compounds also gives a more uniform steam pressure on the pistons, resulting in more even

turning moment on the coupled wheels and less stress in the driving mechanism.

Where steam expansion is divided into two stages, there is a reduction in the difference in temperature between steam entering and leaving the cylinders and at the cylinder walls, resulting in a higher initial temperature drop in simples. Leakage losses are reduced and any steam leaking past the HP piston rings goes to the low pressure side and does useful work.

However, after 1905, the superiority of compound locomotives was challenged with the introduction of Wilhelm Schmidt's firetube superheater. This largely overcame the major problem of power loss due to condensation in the cylinders of simple expansion locomotives, and so increased their maximum power by up to 20%. From 1908, superheating was introduced on compound locomotives, resulting in equally large savings.

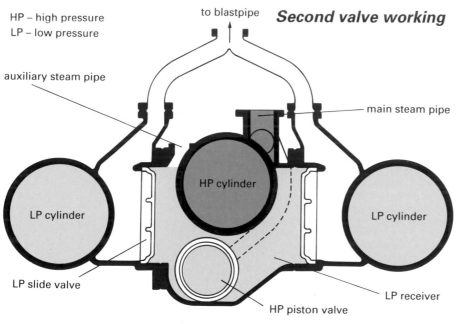

HP – high pressure
LP – low pressure

to blastpipe

### *Second valve working*

auxiliary steam pipe

main steam pipe

HP cylinder

LP cylinder

LP cylinder

LP slide valve

LP receiver

HP piston valve

### *Compound benefits*

The first successful compound locomotives were three 0-4-2 tanks built in 1876, for the Bayonne and Biarritz railway in south-west France and built to the designs of the Swiss-born engineer Antole Mallet. Tests carried out in France from 1913 to 1950, between compound and simple types, showed a coal and water economy of 12-15% for the compounds, whose maximum power was also about 20% greater than equivalent simples.

▲ ▶ Shortly before World War II, LMS 4P 4-4-0 No 1101 hauls a local train at Penrith. This class of 240 locomotives were the only compound engines to be built in any number in the UK. These engines had a single high pressure (HP) cylinder between the frames and two low pressure (LP) ones outside.

When the engine moved off, it worked as a simple expansion locomotive, with HP steam being admitted to the LP steam receiver. Compounding started with the opening of the second valve of the regulator. Live steam (orange) was admitted only to the HP cylinder. It was then admitted as LP steam (yellow) into the two LP cylinders via the LP receiver. The used steam (cream) is then exhausted.

# Compound locomotives

### Two-cylinder cross compounds

These locomotives were pioneered by the Swiss engineer Anatole Mallet in 1876 and since then 14,000 have been built worldwide. Other notable designers included the Prussian August von Borries and the Austrian Karl Gölsdorf. In all of their designs, the wide central European loading gauge allowed the large low pressure cylinder to be placed outside the frames. Because of tighter clearances in Britain, the two-cylinder compounds built for the NER had cylinders between the frames.

Between 1924 and 1930, three two-cylinder compound 2-8-0s, with water tube firebox boilers working between 350-500lb psi, were built in the USA. Their efficiency was up to 30% higher than contemporary American simple machines.

### Three-cylinder compounds

From 1881 onwards, 210 three-cylinder compound locomotives were built to the designs of Francis Webb for the London & North Western Railway. These locomotives had two small high pressure (HP) cylinders outside the frames and one large low pressure (LP) cylinder inside. The preferred layout, with one inside HP cylinder and two outside LP cylinders, was first applied by Edouard Sauvage of the Nord Railway in France to a small 2-6-0, in 1887. In 1896, William Mackersie Smith's 4-4-0, for the NER, appeared. This engine was a fore-runner of the 240 Johnson and Deeley compounds.

In the three-cylinder compound, steam is only admitted twice to the HP cylinder for every wheel revolution (compared with four times in a compound with two HP cylinders), resulting in a considerable drop in pressure. André Chapelon's 4-8-4, of 1946 solved this problem by using a large HP steam chest with twin-piston valves. This feature helped the engine to develop 5500hp.

### Four-cylinder tandem compounds

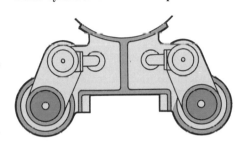

In these, all four cylinders were on the outside of the engine. The HP cylinder was mounted directly in front of the LP one on each side, and the piston rods for each pair were inter-connected. This design appeared first in 1868. A class of 160 2-10-2 machines were constructed in 1903 for the Santa Fé Railway and at the time they were the world's largest locomotives.

### Four-cylinder Vauclain compounds

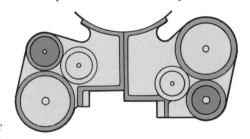

Developed by Samuel Vauclain of the Baldwin Locomotive works, these engines had all the cylinders placed outside the frames. One cylinder was placed above the other on each side, with a common steam chest between them, driven through a shared crosshead and connecting rods. Some 1500 of this type of locomotive were built.

 High pressure steam

### Four-cylinder balanced compounds

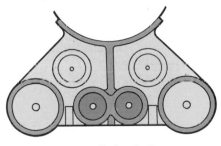

▲cylinders in-line
▼staggered cylinders

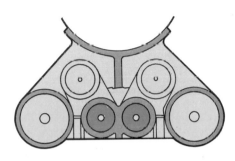

So called because the driving mechanism of the locomotive – rods, weights and cranks – was virtually self-balancing. In two-cylinder machines, the moving parts were only partially balanced and produced a pounding hammer blow effect on the track, causing it much stress.

The four-cylinder balanced compounds had two inside and two outside cylinders and most European designs had a separate steam chest to each cylinder. The concept was first applied in 1883 by Charles Sandiford to an Indian Railway 2-4-0 and later in 1886, by Alfred de Glehn of the Nord Railway. No fewer than 11,000 of this type of engine were built, including over 7000 in France – some capable of 3500-4000hp.

**Mallet compounds** These long-wheel-based locomotives were jointed to give them greater flexibility when going round curves. Two LP cylinders were mounted outside the engine on the leading frame unit and the HP cylinders were placed in the trailing frame. The type was most fully developed in the USA, culminating in the Norfolk & Western Railways' 2-8-8-2s. These compounds were the most powerful low speed, heavy freight engines ever and 3000 were built.

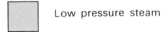 Low pressure steam

# Cylinder pressure

In the days of steam, indicator diagrams presented in graphic form what takes place inside the cylinder. These diagrams made it possible to compare the horsepower exerted in the cylinder with the horsepower produced at the locomotive drawbar. The results gave an indication, at various speeds and cut-offs, of the locomotive's efficiency in converting the steam's energy into useful pulling power.

Testing indicators were fitted inside the forward and rear cylinder covers of a locomotive. The indicators consisted of a special pressure gauge and a means of presenting the readings in a diagram. Throughout most of the steam era mechanical indicators were used, but electrical devices were tried in the post-war period.

With **mechanical indicators**, the diagram was made at the cylinder, necessitating the attendance of engineers on the buffer beam. To protect them from the elements, indicator screens were erected, but these merely transformed hell into purgatory for the technicians, who had to perform their task on a bucking engine, assailed by penetrating winds on one side and the searingly hot smokebox on the other. The indicator operators informed the dynamometer car staff when an indicator reading was made by means of a speaking tube or electric bell, so that appropriate marks could be made on the paper roll registering the pull at the drawbar. From these readings a graph was made.

**Electric indicators** were derived from equipment developed to measure pressures inside aero-engines, and had the advantage that their readings were passed directly to the dynamometer car. This electrical version was ingenious, dispensing with the pen used in mechanical indicators. It emitted a spark when the steam pressure reached a certain point, which burned a tiny hole in the recording paper. The chosen pressure changed constantly, so after several cycles of steam entry, expansion and exhaust the sparks had traced a series of holes.

Whatever the type of indicator, the resulting diagram was in the shape of a boot. The highest part showed the pressure as the steam entered the cylinder, while along the side the line fell to show the reducing pressure as the steam did its work by expanding in the cylinder. The line (like the piston) then reversed course and showed low pressure as the steam was exhausted. At the end of this return stroke there was a rise, registering the compression caused as the remaining steam found the exhaust port closed. Irregular diagrams would reveal defects.

▲To take accurate readings of what was going on inside the cylinder of a steam engine it was often necessary for engineers to ride on the buffer beam of a locomotive. To protect them from the elements, an indicator screen was erected around the front of the smokebox. During one such session, ex-LNER V2 class 2-6-2 No 60845 hauls a test train of 16 coaches and dynamometer car on the Western Region in early BR days.

▶ Steam admitted to the cylinder is shown as an even horizontal line. When the steam is cut off, the pressure falls as the steam expands and pushes against the piston. After the exhaust port opens, the line (like the piston) reverses and shows low pressure as the steam is exhausted. At the end of the return stroke the line rises, registering the compression caused by the remaining steam left in the cylinder after the exhaust port has closed. As fresh steam is admitted into the cylinder the line rises once again.

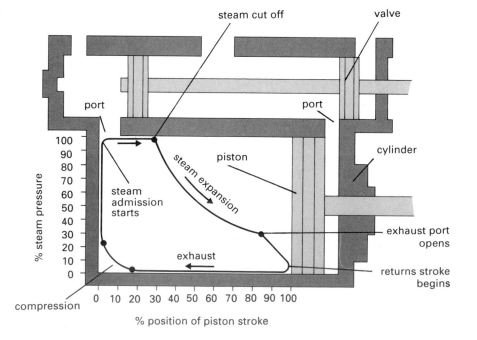

# Vertical boilers

In 1829, at the Rainhill trials of the Liverpool & Manchester Railway (LMR), two of the three competing locomotives had vertical boilers. Although it was the horizontally boilered *Rocket* which won, the vertical boiler had great appeal. It was cheap and easy to construct, promised faster steam raising, occupied less space and therefore permitted a locomotive with a shorter wheelbase – and it made ash disposal easier.

As locomotives became bigger, the horizontal arrangement of the boiler became accepted as normal. This was simply because height limitations of track structures made it impossible to install large vertical boilers. However, even at the time of the Rainhill trials, the Stephensons had been experimenting with locomotives carrying two vertical boilers, one behind the other. The LMR's 0-6-0 freight locomotive, *Twin Sisters*, was constructed in this way.

## Boilers in line

Although it was theoretically possible to build a locomotive with several vertical boilers, this had little advantage and would have placed a heavy burden on a single fireman. From the 1830s, the vertical boiler locomotive was confined to a few specialized uses where low power and a short wheelbase were specified.

This meant that almost all vertical boiler locomotives were built either as four-wheel trams or industrial shunting engines. In both these roles, the ability to travel round sharp curves was important, demanding a short wheelbase and light loads. The vertical boiler also powered many steam railcars and was the basis of the sophisticated Sentinel locomotives.

A number of vertical boiler locomotives were also built as inspection vehicles. Fitted with a forward-facing seat, such a locomotive was ideal for making track inspections. The first locomotive to be completed at Ashford works in 1850

was a vertical boiler machine for the use of the South Eastern Railway's chief engineer.

## Variations on a theme

Although it would be hard to imagine a simpler kind of locomotive, there were many variations. One basic difference was the transmission. Most of these engines had two small, vertical cylinders which drove the wheels through gears, but some had horizontal cylinders and cranked axles, as in conventional locomotives. There was at least one locomotive, working on the Plynlimon & Hafan line in Wales, that had both horizontal and vertical cylinders.

Because they were simple and cheap to build, many firms produced these

engines. Often, a general engineering factory requiring a shunting locomotive would build its own vertical boiler machine, rather than order a locomotive from one of the main builders.

Of the specialized locomotive builders, Beyer-Peacock was the biggest supplier of vertical boiler locomotives, mainly for tramway service. However, most other big builders were not interested in designing and constructing such small engines, but manufacturers of lawnmowers, steam-rollers, steam-cranes and steam-lorries were among those that built them as a sideline.

A few vertical boiler shunters arrived in Britain towards the end of the steam era on industrial railways. A handful of these locomotives have been preserved.

### Street level

Locomotives designed for hauling passenger trailers on street tramways sometimes had an arrangement whereby the steam was condensed in cold water tanks – the aim being to avoid covering pedestrians and traffic in clouds of steam. The same goal led to the unusual, and not very successful, fitting of superheaters to raise the temperature of the steam after it left the cylinders, so that it would condense into water vapour at a slower rate.

▶ Vertical boiler engines made their first appearance alongside the horizontally boilered *Rocket* at the Rainhill trials. From then on, they were confined to a few specialized uses where low power and a short wheelbase were specified – particularly around factory works and quarries. Vertical boilered engines were cheap and easy to construct, having two small, vertical cylinders which drove the wheels through gears.

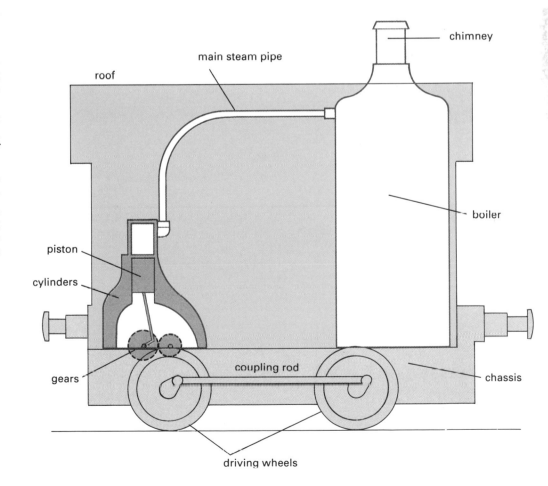

# Vacuum ejectors

In the steam era, ejectors were used – in most cases – to create the vacuum in locomotives and rolling stock fitted with vacuum brakes.

In this system, if air was allowed to be drawn into a vacuum in a brake cylinder, it would force the piston inside upwards. This piston was connected to a set of levers and its movement would apply the brakes. To maintain the vacuum in the brake cylinder, air had to be forced away by using a vacuum ejector.

The basic principle of an ejector is quite simple. The edge of any rapidly flowing jet of fluid – in this case steam from the locomotive's boiler – will mix with the air around it and make it move in the same direction.

When the driver moved the brake valve to the running position, it enabled the air to be exhausted from the train-pipe and the brakes would come off. When the brakes were applied, the movement of a valve isolated the ejector, allowing air to be admitted into the train-pipe, thus applying the brakes.

## Large and small ejectors

If the steam and air mixture is confined inside a cone, the ejection process becomes more efficient. Vacuum ejectors are provided with steam direct from the boiler. Various designs were used by the Big Four companies and in most cases there were two separate systems inside the equipment.

A small ejector was operated continu-ously to maintain the vacuum in the train-pipe. A large ejector was used to speed up the release of the brakes by recreating the vacuum as quickly as possible.

Each ejector had its own steam supply from the boiler, with controls to enable the driver to operate each one separately or together. When a locomotive was working a train, the steam supply to the small ejector would be turned on at the start of a journey, but the driver would only open the cock to the large ejector when he wanted to release the brakes quickly.

## Other features

To make the ejectors operate reliably, they had to be provided with a number of other features. The most important of these features was a non-return valve on the vacuum pipe. This ensured that gases and soot from the smokebox were not drawn into the brake system when the steam to the ejectors was shut off.

Some railways used equipment which combined the ejectors with the brake valve. The movement of the control han-dle in one direction applied the brake and, pushing it back past the running position, brought the large ejector into operation.

On locomotives like the LNER Pacifics, the system also connected the small ejector to the top of the brake cylin-ders on the locomotive and tender during an application to increase their effective-ness. Others, such as Bulleid's Pacifics, sometimes had vacuum 'stored' in tanks mounted on the tender. This was extra vacuum which was used to quick-release the brakes on the engine.

### Sooty shower

Drain valves were provided in the bottom of the ejector to get rid of any water that may have condensed inside them. A ball-valve, held against its seat by steam pressure, stopped air being pulled through the drain pipes when the ejectors were working. If this equipment was not working properly when the driver created the vacuum at the start of the journey, it was not unknown for water, blasted up the chimney, to descend on anyone nearby.

### Vacuum finale

The end of steam on BR also spelled an end to widespread use of vacuum braking on the system. The construction of the steam locomotive, with its use of steam in the ejectors, meant that vacuum brakes were easier to use – air brakes tended to be temperamental and were prone to being invaded by grit and ash. However, with much vacuum-braked stock on BR's books, many diesel locomotives were also fitted with vacuum brakes. The last BR trains (Paddington – Oxford) to be braked by this system were hauled by Class 47s.

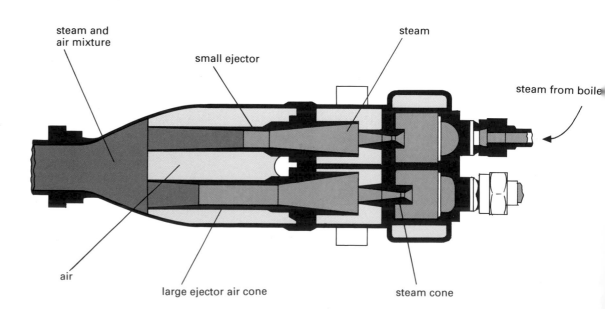

► A vacuum ejector usually formed part of the braking system. Steam from the boiler helped draw air out of the system and created a vacuum. The brakes did not come on until air was let back into the train-pipe. The twin cone ejector was used on the BR Standard locomotives and was mounted on the side of the boiler. The small cone let the brakes come off slowly; the larger one allowed the process to be speeded up. Its exhaust was discharged through a ring at the base of the chimney, in order that the blast would assist in drawing air out of the ejector pipe.

# Live-steam injectors

Every steam locomotive needed a constant supply of water from its tender or side tank (known as feed-water), which had to be injected into the boiler against the pressure inside it. When a large Pacific was working hard it could use well over 2500 gallons of water an hour, and boiler pressures of 250lb psi were common.

## Feed-pumps
The earliest locomotives had feed-pumps. These consisted of a piston in a cylinder, driven by the motion, which forced the water into the boiler through a non-return (clack) valve.

When a given amount of water is boiled, it produces a greater volume of steam. If this had not been the case, the feed-water pump would have used more steam from the boiler to work it than the amount of water it was putting in – making the steam engine impossible. Feed-water pumps like this only operated when the locomotive was moving, which made it difficult if more water was needed in the boiler should the engine be stationary.

## Cone injector
In 1859, the French engineer H Giffard invented the cone injector, which enabled water to be forced into the boiler without mechanical pumps. Although it also used steam, it operated on a very different principle.

As with the vacuum ejector, a jet of steam was used, which mixed with cold feed water from the tender or tanks. A lot of heat is required to turn water into steam, and this was liberated again in the injector as the steam was condensed.

The injector adopted by BR consisted of three types of cones – steam, combining and delivery. The shape of these cones – wide at one end and narrow at the other – turned heat into kinetic (velocity) energy and then into pressure energy.

Steam from the boiler was forced through the **steam cone** where it expanded – causing a drop in pressure. The energy was not lost but converted to give velocity to the steam as it moved into the **combining cone**. Here, the steam was mixed with the cold feed water and condensed. The steam and water were then completely combined in the cone as a solid jet of hot water – the steam having transferred its energy to the water as velocity energy. Between the combining cone and the **delivery cone** was an overflow gap, where excess steam and water could drain away.

The jet of water entered the delivery cone through its small opened end. As the delivery cone widened out, the momentum of the jet slowed down. The energy was then converted from velocity into pressure. This was then sufficient to overcome the pressure in the boiler which the injected water entered via the clack valve.

## Peculiarities
Getting an injector to pick up could be tricky. It might flood if the proportions of steam and water were not correct, so the overflow was needed. When an injector was working it had a characteristic sing, which told the footplate crew that all was well. Even so, the fireman could often be seen leaning out of the cab window, making sure that water was not being wasted from the overflow.

Some injectors were notoriously temperamental and, as it was always vital to keep sufficient water in the boiler, it was usual for locomotives to be fitted with a pair of them. Problems arose with scale forming inside the cones, so access was provided for inspection and cleaning.

There were more complicated designs of injector, with an overflow and a flap on the cone which combined the steam and water. Others used the exhaust from the cylinders, as well as live steam.

### Condensing problems
Because an injector relied on the water being cold enough to condense the steam, it would not work if the water in the tanks or tender got warm. Problems arose with locomotives provided with condensing equipment for use in tunnels. Some of the last of these were the GWR 97XX Pannier Tanks which were fitted with feed-water pumps. These were driven by their own independent steam cylinders, so they could operate even when the locomotive was stationary.

▼The live-steam injector used fresh steam, not yet used in the cylinders, to put water into the boiler. The injector that BR used on its Standard locomotives contained three cones which changed the energy of the steam and used it to force the water into the boiler against the pressure already in there. It was important for injectors to combine the correct amount of steam and water and some could be quite complicated.

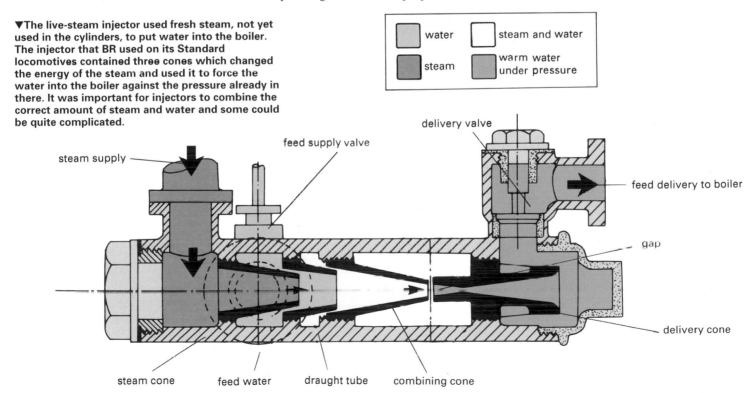

# Exhaust-steam injectors

An exhaust-steam injector uses steam which has been exhausted from the cylinders to force water into the boiler. With a live-steam injector, the supply comes straight out of the boiler but, when a locomotive is working, the exhaust steam from the cylinder is a much more economic source. Although its pressure is less than a tenth of that of the boiler, it is still has the same latent heat, so it can be used in a suitably designed injector.

## Live-steam use

An injector which relies solely on exhaust steam cannot work when the locomotive is stationary, or when it is running with the regulator closed. Therefore, exhaust-steam injectors have to be designed to use live steam as well and are much more complicated – especially as they have to change over auto-matically from one source to another. To ensure reliability, exhaust-steam injectors fitted in the later days of BR steam used a small jet of live steam all the time they were operating.

When the exhaust-steam injector is needed by the fireman when the locomotive is not working, he turns on the live steam supply to it. As there is no pressure in the steam line from the steam chest, next to the cylinder, to the change-over control system (automatic shuttle valve), it allows the live steam to flow through auxiliary live-steam ports as well as through the supplementary live-steam cone. The injector then operates like an ordinary live-steam one.

An exhaust-steam injector is a more complicated and expensive item than the live-steam type, and there must be enough energy savings to offset the extra costs, so they were usually fitted only to main line locomotives.

## Keeping it clean

Live steam from the boiler is clean, but on its way through the cylinders it picks up lubricant oil. If this were returned to the boiler, any organic matter present could cause foaming – making the boiler prime and carrying water into the cylinders. In addition, when the boiler is drained, oily scum could deposit on the heat-transfer surfaces, reducing their efficiency. To prevent this, an exhaust-steam injector has a ball-shaped grease separator in the steam pipe from the smokebox. Its internal vanes make the steam swirl, throwing out any droplets of oil by centrifugal force. They collect in the bottom of the separator, and are discharged by an automatic drip valve.

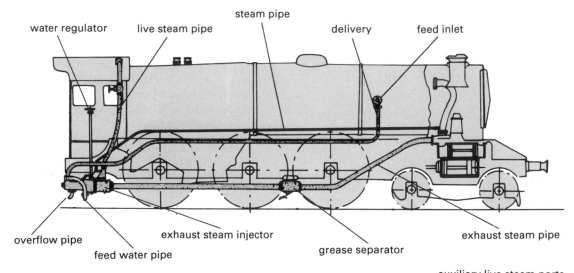

water regulator    live steam pipe    steam pipe    delivery    feed inlet

overflow pipe    feed water pipe    exhaust steam injector    grease separator    exhaust steam pipe

◀ Because exhaust steam is at a lower pressure than live steam, larger pipes are needed to convey it from the blastpipe, in the smokebox, to the underside of the cab where the injectors are installed. Here, their operation can be monitored by the crew. The grease separator prevents oil in exhaust steam from the cylinders going into the boiler. The live-steam supply comes from the back of the boiler.

## *Operation*

Once the regulator is opened, steam enters the cylinders' steam-chest and the pressure from here activates the change-over control system in the exhaust-steam injector. The valve inside cuts off the supply of live steam to the auxiliary live-steam ports and pressurizes the exhaust-steam valve control piston, opening the large exhaust-steam valve at the back of the injector.

The inner valve, which prevented live steam flowing back to the cylinder exhaust, is pushed by the flow, letting the exhaust steam into the large exhaust-steam cone. The injector then uses steam which would otherwise have gone up the chimney.

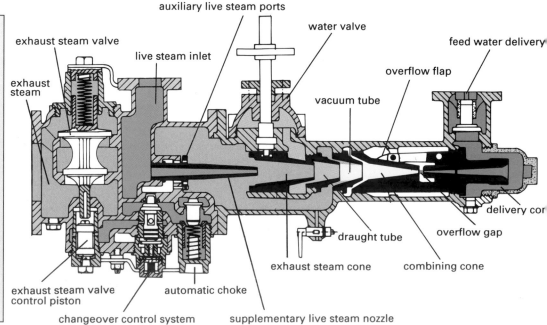

auxiliary live steam ports    water valve    feed water delivery

exhaust steam valve    live steam inlet    overflow flap

exhaust steam    vacuum tube

delivery cor

exhaust steam valve control piston    changeover control system    automatic choke    supplementary live steam nozzle    draught tube    exhaust steam cone    combining cone    overflow gap

■ exhaust steam    ■ live steam    □ water    □ exhaust steam, live steam and water    ■ warm water under pressure

# Smoke deflectors

In the days when a man with a red flag proceeded before a train, tall chimneys reached high above the rest of a locomotive, and smoke was not considered a problem – not even to the environment.

But as locomotives became larger and more powerful, chimneys had to be shorter to clear bridges. With higher speeds, smoke exhaust could become caught in the whirlpool of air formed behind the smokebox, pulling it downwards. The potential danger was of smoke obscuring the driver's vision of the road and signals ahead.

### Exhaustion point

Engineers turning their attention to the problem of drifting exhaust smoke adopted smoke deflectors – also known as smoke lifting plates and smoke baffles. The theory was that plates, suitably positioned, could offer resistance to the lateral flow of air from the front of the smokebox, inducing an upward current, thus lifting exhaust smoke clear of the engine.

The first locomotive in the UK to have deflectors was the Southern King Arthur class *Sir Percivale*, fitted with German-style side shields in 1927. Whilst effective, many disliked the looks, and for a few years a series of alternatives were tried, many quite hideous. Eventually the Southern settled on somewhat smaller plates, and by 1929 most of the class had been so fitted, gaining the distinction of being the first British class to be adorned with deflectors.

From the 1930s, deflectors became common on larger locomotives. Some classes had them fitted retrospectively, and engineers often included them into the design of new locomotives. But they were by no means universal; the Great Western never found the need for them even on their largest locomotives and the front of the LNER streamlined A4s, designed with the help of wind tunnel tests, proved effective at lifting smoke clear without any further aid.

### Uplifting experience

Like so many other steam locomotive developments, the pursuit of a common goal led to a variety of lifting plates, not one standard design. The most familiar type turned out to be oblong plates on either side, and just ahead of, the smokebox, typified by the deflectors fitted to the British Rail standard types after 1950.

But many still thought deflectors less than attractive, and all sorts of shapes were tried to minimize the obtrusion. Two LNER A3s were the subject of much experiment in the 1930s, but when the fitting of Kylchap double chimneys in the late 1950s led to increased smoke drift (because of their softer exhaust), the outcome was German style wings – the 'elephant's ears'. The design of the Bulleid Merchant Navy class caused such smoke drift that experiments quickly took place shortly after their introduction in the 1940s, resulting in a host of deflectors of varying shapes and sizes.

The 'trial and error' approach adopted by some engineers meant that the success of smoke deflectors could be rather hit and miss, and on some locomotives the plates could be more of a hindrance to the driver's vision than the smoke itself.

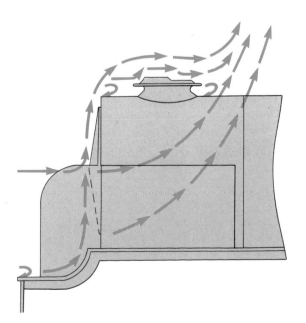

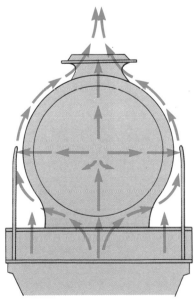

▲ The first smoke deflectors were used in Germany and here the Witte-style smoke deflectors on this German Pacific are certainly doing their job in lifting the exhaust well clear of the boiler. These deflectors are noticeable in that they are placed as far away from the sides of the boiler as the loading gauge structure will allow, thus providing the widest possible air passage. This style of deflector was also used on Gresley's A3 Pacifics.

◄ The air which came into contact with the front of a moving locomotive spread out at right angles to the direction of travel. This 'spreading out' of the air caused a partial vacuum all around and just behind the edges of the locomotive's front face. Because of this, exhaust was caught up in the swirling currents of air created along the front part of the boiler. Smoke deflectors contained the spread of air, creating an strong up-draught in the rear of the chimney.

# Steam headcodes

The function of headcodes during the steam era was to help lineside staff, particularly operators in signalboxes, to identify the type of train. This enabled them to check that passing trains were running to the scheduled order and allocate priority if necessary.

Different codes were shown by the particular arrangement of lights at the front of the locomotive. Although these lights were called headlamps, they were not intended to light the way ahead for the engine crew and were only for identification by lineside staff. In most cases, the lights were oil lamps, hung by the crew on the appropriate lamp irons, but some later locomotives had electric lighting powered by a steam generator.

At the time of Grouping in 1923, many smaller constituent companies had their own forms of headlamp codes and the four new companies naturally desired some standardization for the sake of both their own and inter-regional services. Eventually, the Railway Clearing House decided on a series of codes which lasted in basic form well beyond the end of steam.

The Southern Railway was something of an exception. It used large white discs (with route numbers on them) in place of lights during the day, and also had many variations on the standard headcode conventions.

**With Grouping in 1923, the railways agreed to a standard system of train identification. This was based on the fact that locomotives could run light and haul passenger or freight trains. These two categories were sub-divided by the type of train and proportion of vehicles with vacuum or air brakes. At first, the trains were classified from A to H, and J and K. After 1962, the numbers one to nine were substituted to describe the revised nine categories.**

▶ **A - express passenger, fast ECS, newspaper or breakdown train; snowplough duty**

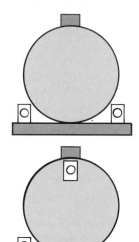

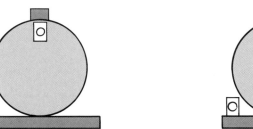

▲ **B – ordinary stopping passenger or mixed train; breakdown train not on duty**

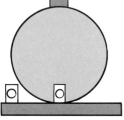

▲ **C – parcels, newspapers or perishable goods train composed of coaching stock**

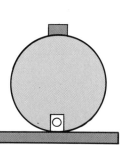

▲ **D – express perishables, over 1/3 wagons fitted with continuous brakes; ECS train**

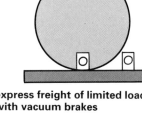

▲ **E – express freight of limited load not fitted with vacuum brakes**

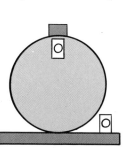

▲ **F – express freight or ballast, less than 1/3 of wagons with continuous brakes**

▲ **G – light engine or engines coupled with not more than two brake vans**

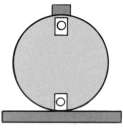

▲ **H – through freight or ballast train not included under the other categories**

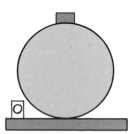

▲ **J – through mineral or empty wagon train not stopping at any intermediate stations**

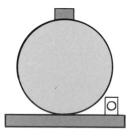

▲ **K – main line or branch pick-up freight train calling at intermediate stations**

# Locomotive lubrication

Electric locomotives, whose internal movements are almost entirely rotating, are easily lubricated. Diesel engines have rocking and sliding movements which are lubricated by well-tried automotive techniques. It is steam locomotives which present the widest range of problems.

The big-end bearing transmits great force from the connecting rod to the driving wheel and is easily overheated. The traditional practice is to provide a corked oil-cup in the top of the big-end, whose motion throws up oil, some of which falls on a worsted plug where it permeates to a felt inserted in the bearing surface.

The ability of worsted threads to soak up oil and pass it along their length is the solution for many lubrication problems of providing oil drip by drip over a long period. The frequency of the oil drops depends on the number of strands used in a trimming, while different trimmings can be led to different delivery pipes so one oil box can lubricate several points. On piston rods, mops of worsted, fed from an oil box, brush the rod.

Lubricating the sliding surfaces inside the cylinder and steam chest, that is, the piston and valves, can be done by conveying the oil in a steam jet, using an atomiser fed from a sight-feed or mechanical lubricator.

Mechanical lubricators, typically placed on the running board above the cylinders, consist of an oil box and several small pumps, powered by a link from the crosshead or valve gear. These pumps deliver the oil through very narrow pipes at a rate of about 2oz per pump per hundred miles.

## Driver's aid

The sight-feed lubricator is located in the cab and is an ingenious device in which the drops of oil can be seen emerging from a nozzle and their frequency (about two to four drops per minute) regulated by adjusting a valve.

With both the sight-feed and mechanical lubricators the drops of oil pass to an atomiser, which uses a steam jet to break them down before they pass down a tube to the delivery point.

It was always the driver's responsibility to ensure that all oil boxes and cups were well-filled. At major stopping points he would go round with an oil can, checking axlebox oil levels, while feeling vulnerable parts for overheating. Oil quality differed between superheated and unsuperheated engines, as superheated locomotives worked at higher temperatures and needed a more expensive oil that would not burn up.

### *Sprinkleman*
One of the locomotive designs of the revolutionary Soviet Railways in the 1920s was a 4-8-0 that repeatedly ran hot. Whether this defect resulted from a design fault, poor maintenance, or the wrong type of oil is uncertain. To keep the trains running, until a cure could be effected, locomotive crews carried an extra man called a sprinkleman. His job was to clamber around the engine while it was in motion, playing a watering can on parts that were hot.

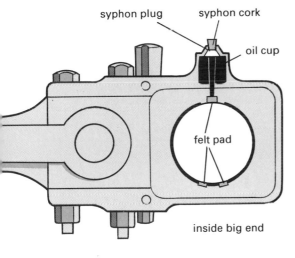

syphon plug · syphon cork · oil cup · felt pad

inside big end

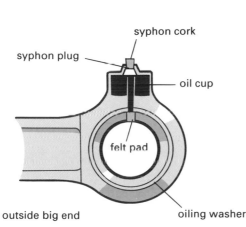

syphon cork · syphon plug · oil cup · felt pad

outside big end · oiling washer

◀ The big-end bearing has to be lubricated to stop the end of the connecting rod binding against the journal of the driving wheel. Usually, oil is poured into a corked oil-cup, in the top of the big-end, whose turning action throws up oil. Some of this oil falls on a worsted plug, or a metal restrictor, where it soaks into a felt inserted in the surface of the bearing, providing the necessary lubrication.

▼ A sight-feed mechanical lubricator helps to lubricate the sliding surfaces inside the cylinder and steam chest. It is located in the cab and the driver can check that oil is being delivered as drops can be seen emerging from a nozzle. The delivery is regulated by an adjusting valve. Steam is fed to the oil box and, after passing through the sight feed, the oil is carried to the pistons and valves by a steam jet.

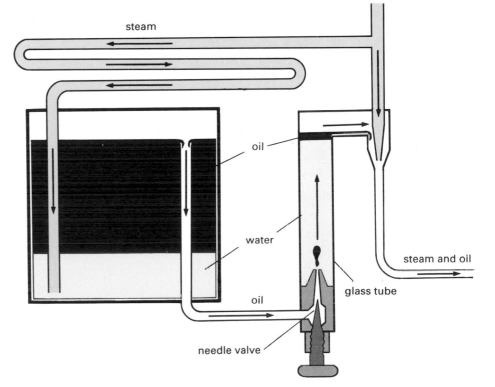

steam · oil · water · oil · needle valve · glass tube · steam and oil

# Locomotive cabs

On the world's first passenger locomotive, *Rocket*, the cab was placed in what became the traditional position, immediately behind the firebox. Although this was the most convenient place for the controls, from the point of view of construction and maintenance, it was probably the worst place in terms of the driver's view ahead.

As speeds on the railways increased, drivers endured the hazard of rain or hail striking their faces as they peered ahead. This led to the introduction of the spectacle plate in the 1850s. This feature consisted of a vertical frontage with glass windows facing forward.

In 1860, the Stockton & Darlington Railway imitated the roofed cabs which were popular on US railroads. Two engines, intended for work over the Pennines, were fitted with them, but this example was not followed. The railway companies held the view that if life was made too comfortable for the drivers, they might fall asleep. Enginemen protested that such cabs were fit only for wimps.

About the same time, the Midland Railway, plagued by stone-throwing boys on bridges, bent back the top of the spectacle plate to form a simple roof structure. But the roof, supported at its rear on two pillars, rattled badly, irritating the drivers, who raised strong objections to its presence. Soon the pillars were removed, leaving a short bent-over roof. This led to the short-roof cab favoured by most railway companies of the late 19th century.

## American ideas

In the 1880s, the American cab was reintroduced by the North Eastern Railway in Britain, but, apart from the Great Eastern Railway, other companies stayed with the short cab. Sometimes, however, a longer roof supported by strong uprights was preferred.

### Front end cabs

An Italian steam locomotive design, Class 500 4-6-0, and several US designs, had the cab placed in front of the locomotive. Although this was considered highly unorthodox, it was popular with lines of severe gradients and long tunnels, where smoke could contaminate the cab for long periods, making conditions for the crew impossible. No examples were built in the UK.

However, only with a long-roofed cab and side doors could the enginemen escape from becoming soaked in wet weather. It was not until the 1920s that the long-roofed cab with side windows became standard practice in Britain. Further improvements to the comfort of the locomotive crew were made by James Manson of the Glasgow & South Western Railway. He introduced hinged side doors between tender and footplate to block out draughts and increase safety. These improvements were highly popular with the crews.

## Designer's dilemma

Cab design was affected by the layout of the controls, which were placed more for the convenience of the designer than for the driver.

The Great Western Railway of Churchward's day was one of the worst in this respect. The huge reversing lever in many of the engines of his design was placed directly below the driver's forward facing window. To look ahead, the driver had to drape himself over this lever, and to operate it he had to step back, away from the window. Moreover, the heavy regulator lever was operated by his left hand.

Bulleid, the Chief Mechanical Engineer of the Southern Railway, was one of the first designers to take the comfort of the crew into consideration. He arranged the controls of his Pacifics so that they were close to the driver's right hand.

But it was only with the BR Standard classes, introduced in the 1950s, when the opinion of a mock-up was sought from firemen and drivers, that the cab layout could be described as user-friendly. Here, the relevant controls were grouped on either the fireman's or driver's side of the cab – and both had seats.

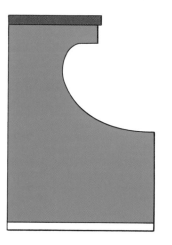

▲Short-roof cab favoured by most railway companies of the late 19th century, including the GWR.

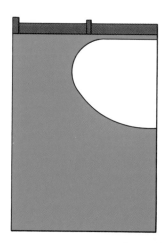

▲Full-roof cab with pillars. Although these rattled badly, some companies, including the Great Central Railway, preferred them.

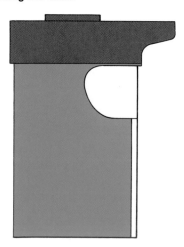

▲Long-roofed cab, introduced in the 1920s, and fitted to Midland Railway Compounds and Class 2P 4-4-0s.

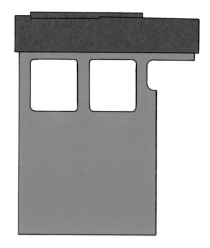

▲Side-window cabs offered the crew the most protection and could be seen on many of the Pacifics built by the LNER and LMS.

# Sentinel locomotives

This unorthodox type of locomotive was introduced by the steam lorry builder, Sentinel Waggon Works. The company advertised it as being suitable for yard and short-distance traffic where a high power-to-weight ratio, fuel economy, the ability to cope with bad track and small clearances were all required.

The locomotive combined several unusual features in a well-thought-out arrangement. The boiler was vertical, as were the cylinders. Drive was by means of chains, not rods, and the wheels were coupled by chains as well. Fuel and water were carried on board, making the Sentinels essentially tank locomotives.

The Sentinel company offered two broad types of locomotive: the railway type, where the work involved short- and medium-distance haulage, and the industrial type, for yard work. It was the industrial type which sold most and which seemed to fill a real need. This version was produced in 80, 100 and 200hp variants. The square vertical boiler was at the cab end and fired from the side. There was a superheater at the top and boiler pressure, at 275lb psi, was higher than in conventional steam locomotives. This enabled the boiler to carry the reserve of steam that some operators found neces-

sary. It also enabled small cylinders to be used. These warmed up faster and, unusually for a yard locomotive, a super-heater became worthwhile.

The central part of the locomotive was usually devoted to water storage and the two vertical cylinders were at the front. These had poppet valves which usually offered steam cut-off at 30% or 80% of the piston stroke; the change was made by sliding the camshafts.

With the smaller horsepowered versions, the pistons drove a transverse crankshaft which had sprockets at its ends. From these, the drive was transmitted to corresponding sprockets on the driving axle by roller chains.

Higher horsepowered Sentinels had pinions at each end of the engine crankshaft which drove a countershaft through gear wheels. From the countershaft there was chain drive to the driving axle. Chain drive and chain coupling gave a more flexible wheelbase and this was important for engines operating in yards on badly laid track.

Compared with the saddle tanks, which Sentinel units usually replaced, there was less pounding and nosing when in motion. Wheelslip was less likely, so heavier loads could be started. There was

also considerable fuel economy, largely because little coal was required to maintain boiler pressure in the long periods when yard locomotives were at rest. Controls were placed at both sides of the boiler so a one-man crew was possible.

The Somerset & Dorset Joint Railway, which used some 200hp units for difficult colliery sidings, found they needed only half a ton of coal daily. This was perhaps only one-third as much as a conventional yard locomotive used. Equally important, for the same power the Sentinel was smaller than the corresponding saddle tank locomotive. A 27 ton 200hp Sentinel would be less than 10ft in height, whereas the saddle tank would weigh about 33 tons and stand over 11ft tall.

Of the railway type, the biggest order was for 50 units of 2ft gauge supplied to the Egyptian Delta Light Railway, where they successfully hauled both freight and passenger services. Railway types were often double geared, the gear being changed when the locomotive was at rest. With single geared engines, the sprocket ratios could be varied: a 100hp unit at the lowest ratio could shift 400 tons on level track, while higher ratios enabled speeds up to 37mph to be attained, but with lighter loads.

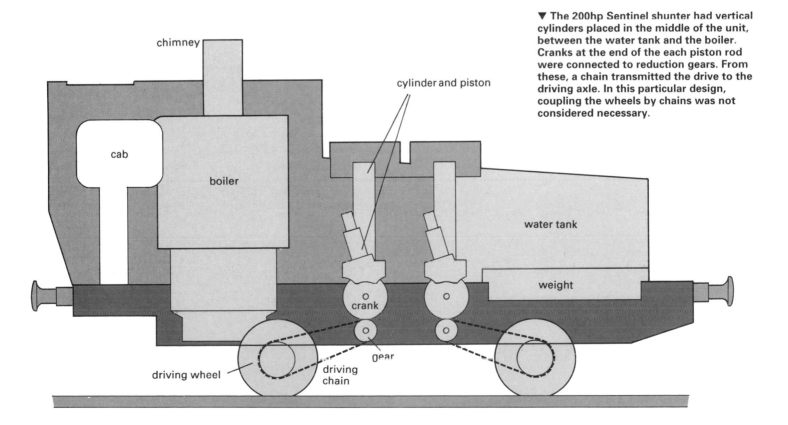

▼ The 200hp Sentinel shunter had vertical cylinders placed in the middle of the unit, between the water tank and the boiler. Cranks at the end of the each piston rod were connected to reduction gears. From these, a chain transmitted the drive to the driving axle. In this particular design, coupling the wheels by chains was not considered necessary.

chimney

cylinder and piston

cab

boiler

water tank

weight

crank

driving wheel

gear

driving chain

# Drummond's Greyhounds

As Locomotive Superintendent of the North British and then the Caledonian railways, Dugald Drummond had designed distinctive 4-4-0 locomotives. Upon moving to the London & South Western Railway (LSWR) in 1895, he soon introduced express 4-4-0 locomotives that closely resembled his Scottish engines.

Drummond's first design for the LSWR was miscalculated and proved too small for requirements and after 10 locomotives were built, he introduced a bigger version, the T9 class 4-4-0. This was immediately successful and 65 were constructed between 1899 and 1901, with an extra one specially built for the Glasgow Exhibition. They were among the handful of outstanding British turn-of-the-century classes.

## Classic outline

The T9s had a classic British layout, with two inside cylinders and 6ft 7in driving wheels. They were hard-wearing engines and easy on maintenance. Many of them had water-tubes across the firebox. This innovation worked well, but the thermal efficiency gained was balanced by the extra maintenance costs, so it was eventually removed.

Safety valves set in the dome were a characteristic Drummond feature, but the designer tried three locations for the sandboxes. Initially, some were incorporated in the driving wheel splashers but later, perhaps in order to ensure that the sand stayed dry, they were placed in the smokebox. This no doubt kept the sand warm, but in order to provide a near vertical drop for sandpipes, Drummond was obliged to deliver the sand not to the rail beneath the driving wheels, but beneath the bogie, where it served little purpose. Eventually, the sandboxes were placed between the frames and served the driving wheels.

The T9s produced sprightly performances on the undulating Salisbury – Exeter line and easily mastered the London – Bournemouth expresses, where the limit of eight bogie vehicles was soon

raised to 10. On the 172-mile London – Exeter run, where there was one stop to change engines at Salisbury, their trains were scheduled for 210 minutes.

But heavier trains and the introduction of steam train heating – instead of gas – which drew power from the engine, meant that the T9s soon became too small for the most arduous duties and they were succeeded by the L12 class, which was virtually a T9 with a bigger boiler.

Twenty L12s were built before Drummond decided to produce 4-6-0 locomotives as good as his 4-4-0s. But after failing to make a success of the 4-6-0, he was compelled to revert to the 4-4-0 and the 10 members of the D15 class may be regarded as the ultimate development of the T9. They were also Drummond's final design.

All these designs were modified in due course. Superheaters transformed the T9s and gave them a fresh lease of life. With extended smokeboxes to accommodate the superheaters and with their original chimneys replaced by stovepipe designs, their outward appearance was radically changed – although basically they remained the same.

After Grouping in 1923, the T9s were to be seen also in Kent and Sussex, although the former LSWR lines remained their main field of activity. They were especially useful for the extra trains that were a feature of the Southern Railway (SR) – ocean liner expresses and summer holiday traffic. In Cornwall, the class could be seen handling portions of the Atlantic Coast Express into the 1950s. But with one exception, now preserved as part of the National Collection, the class was scrapped in 1951-61.

### Royal Trains

After pulling the Royal Train to Portsmouth in 1935, No 119 was kept aside for Royal Train and other special duties. The locomotive was turned out with lined out wheels, burnished steel and copper work and the Royal coat of arms prominently displayed on its leading coupled splasher.

▶ The T9s were produced by the LSWR's own workshop at Nine Elms and the private locomotive builders Henry Dubs & Co in Glasgow. Most T9s had a life of around 60 years and following nationalization, many eked out their existence on the SR's 'withered arm' – the former LSWR secondary lines in Devon and Cornwall. On 31 October 1960, No 30338 calls at Halwell Junction with a Wadebridge to Exeter local service.

# GWR 0-6-0s

In the 19th century, the six-coupled locomotive was the standard British freight engine. On the Great Western Railway (GWR), Joseph Armstrong had designed a class of 310 double-framed 0-6-0s in 1866 and his successor, William Dean, produced a replacement of which 260 were built from 1863-99. These were the famous Dean Goods, which were still going in the 1950s and were the most long-lasting of the British 0-6-0 designs.

This success was probably won as much by good luck as good judgement. At a time when steam locomotive design was far from scientific, Dean had somehow achieved a combination of dimensions that was close to the optimum. Indeed, in BR days, when it was proposed to replace the surviving Dean Goods by modern 2-6-0 locomotives, it was found that the old engines steamed far better than the new.

## Long lasting engines

The Dean 0-6-0 was very similar to the earlier Armstrong 0-6-0, but with single frames and was therefore lighter. This lightness explains the longevity of the class, because its axleload meant that for many years it was the most powerful locomotive allowed on the Mid Wales line. With its 5ft 2in wheels it was quite suitable for the passenger as well as

freight trains on this and other routes.

Under Dean's successor, George Jackson Churchward, Belpaire boilers and superheaters were fitted to the class. The basic reliability, light weight, and thermal efficiency of the engines made it the first choice of the War Office in two world wars. In 1914, 62 engines were requisitioned for overseas service and the same fate awaited a further 100 in 1939, but many were captured by the Germans.

Although the six-coupled type was cheap to build and maintain, the absence of a leading guiding wheel made it hard on the track and a rough-rider at the higher speeds. For this reason, Churchward built 2-6-0s rather than 0-6-0s. When the ageing Dean Goods began to need replacement in the 1930s, it was at first intended to introduce a lightweight 2-6-0, but in the end the 2251 class 0-6-0 emerged; by that time Churchward had been succeeded by Charles Collett.

The 2251 class was really a Dean

Goods with a taper boiler, 200lb psi boiler instead of 180lb psi, and a more comfortable cab. Increased pressure gave it a tractive effort of 20,000lb against the 18,000lb of the Dean. The 2251 class was built through the 1930s and 1940s, offering the same cheapness and reliability as the Dean design, but only 120 were produced. Lasting into the 1960s, and basically a modernized edition of a type first built in the 1860s it represented the more acceptable face of the GWR conservatism. One example of each of the Dean and Collett 0-6-0s have been preserved.

## Wayward genius

William Dean was an authoritarian eccentric whose genius was mixed with a waywardness. Many of Dean's prototypes had great difficulty in staying on the rails, and his 4-2-4 tank engine, in which the side tanks protruded forward of the smokebox, appears to have run only a few paces before being hidden away. But the Dean singles and his 0-6-0 were among the great locomotives of their time. In his final years Dean retained his post as Locomotive Carriage and Wagon Superintendent, but had plainly lost his mental powers, a sad end for a once brilliant man.

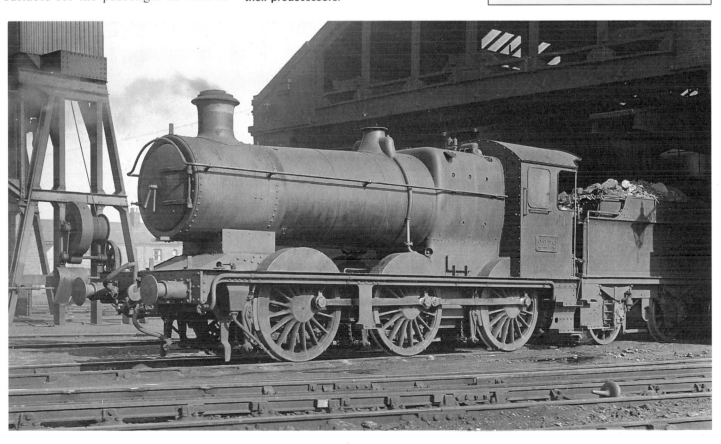

▼ On 4 September 1937, 2251 class No 2279 awaits its next turn of duty at Chester shed. This class was a development of the Dean Goods 0-6-0s but with a Belpaire boiler. However, a slight increase in axleweight meant that these 0-6-0s did not have the same wide route availability as their predecessors.

# Claughton 4-6-0s

In the early 20th century, some designers found that simply enlarging the traditional inside-cylinder 4-4-0 into a similar, but longer, 4-6-0, brought disappointing results. On the London & North Western Railway (LNWR), the two-cylinder 4-6-0s of the Experiment and Prince of Wales types performed little better than the 4-4-0s that preceded them.

So, in 1913 Charles Bowen Cooke, who became locomotive superintendent in 1909, decided to break from tradition and design a completely new 4-6-0 with four cylinders. Extra cylinders meant extra complication and expense, but it seemed the only way to produce a locomotive with sufficiently high horsepower for the increasingly heavy trains of the West Coast main line from London to Manchester and Scotland.

The good performance of the Great Western Railway's (GWR) four-cylinder Star Class 4-6-0 *Polar Star* when tried on the LNWR may have encouraged the LNWR directors to accept Bowen Cooke's proposal. However, when his new design was ready, the Company's civil engineer, ignoring the lower track stresses produced by four-cylinder locomotives, said that it was too heavy.

### Good performances

Bowen Cooke's revised design carried a smaller boiler therefore than he would have preferred, but the first locomotive, *Sir Gilbert Claughton*, performed very well on trial and was soon joined by nine others in 1913. During World War I, Crewe continued to build 4-4-0s, two-cylinder 4-6-0s and Claughtons in parallel; 130 Claughtons were built by 1921.

They were unlike the GWR Stars. The wheel diameter of 6ft 9in was similar, but the 175lb psi boiler pressure was considerably less than the 225lb of the Star. This may have eased boiler maintenance, but considerably reduced tractive power.

Over both the northern section of the West Coast main line, with its severe grades, and the more level southerly section, the Claughtons put up some stirring performances when new. However, their wide ring piston valves wore rapidly allowing severe steam leakage which resulted in deterioration in performance with increasing mileage.

Various adjustments were made, but the reputation of the class suffered and was not enhanced when, after the railway Grouping, the Claughtons were tried against other LMS types. It is now clear that these trials were not really fair and were a chapter in the LMS feuds of the 1920s. Nevertheless, the decision of the LMS management to order the new Royal Scot class 4-6-0 for the West Coast was completely justified.

The Royal Scots and the later Stanier Jubilees replaced the Claughtons on the prime passenger services. In the 1920s, 20 Claughtons were fitted with a larger boiler and this change, together with a redesign of the piston valves, produced such an improvement that the last of the big-boilered types survived until 1949, whereas the smaller-boilered examples were scrapped in the 1930s.

▼ In LMS days, Claughton No 5913 *Colonel Lockwood* climbs up Camden bank out of London's Euston station with the 16.00 Euston – Manchester express. A number of attempts to improve the Claughtons led to some of them being fitted with Caprotti valve gear, other improved piston valves and Kyala blastpipes. Eventually, a number were nominally rebuilt as Patriot three-cylinder 4-6-0s.

### Charles Bowen Cooke

Like so many British locomotive engineers, Charles Bowen Cooke was the son of a vicar, but he was unusual for the breadth of his culture (he spoke fluent German and contributed to the railway press) and for his gentlemanly behaviour. He was appointed Chief Mechanical Engineer of the LNWR in 1909, after a background of operating, rather than designing, locomotives. One of his first actions was to fit superheaters to the LNWR locomotives. He had been apprenticed to the autocratic Francis Webb, but in contrast to his mentor, was a patient colleague. His early death in 1920 was widely regretted, and may account for the failure to develop the Claughton, which was destined to remain a near-miss.

# GWR heavy tanks

The southern ends of the valleys in the South Wales coalfield were penetrated by several local railways, while the northern ends were tapped by the London & North Western Railway (LNWR). However, the dominant railway in the area was the Great Western Railway (GWR).

The GWR served few collieries, but sent forward many of the coal wagons brought down the valleys by the local railways. Some wagons went to the Midlands and some, through the Severn Tunnel, to the south. The GWR's very successful 28XX class 2-8-0 locomotives handled the long-distance coal trains, but in South Wales itself, there was a need for a short-haul locomotive of similar power to the 2-8-0s.

In 1910, Swindon built No 4201, a 2-8-0 tank engine. Two years later, a batch of similar locomotives appeared with a bunker coal capacity of 3½ instead of 3 tons. These 2-8-0Ts, and further batches, made up the 4200 class. The engines were said to be tank versions of the 2800 class, but this was not really true, for the boilers were smaller and the spacing of the driving wheels quite different. However, their pulling power was very similar. There were no problems when the heavy trains were hauled to Newport by one of the tank engines and handed over to a 2-8-0 for the journey to London.

Engines from No 5205 onwards were slightly different in having 19½in stroke by 30in diameter cylinders, instead of 18½in by 30in, giving them a tractive effort of 33,170lb. This meant that in BR days the later engines were classified 8F and the earlier engines 7F.

The class performed well, and a few were used for duties outside Wales. The China clay traffic of Cornwall, for example, presented heavy short distance trains and the class was successfully employed there. However, the design did have somewhat limited coal capacity and later batches had four ton bunkers.

The LNWR had a similar requirement for Wales, but filled it by building 0-8-2T locomotives and then, because of their limited coal capacity, enlarged the design to an 0-8-4T. The GWR eventually turned to another solution, spurred by the inter-war depression in the coal industry.

By extending the frames of the 4200 class to the rear and adding a pair of carrying wheels, it was possible to enlarge the coal bunker to hold six tons, equivalent to the tender of the 28XX class, and the water capacity to 2500 gallons.

Twenty engines, Nos 5275-5294, were built as 2-8-0Ts but never entered traffic as such, being converted to the 72XX class. Twenty others, Nos 5255-5274, were quickly brought back a few months after entering service and were similarly converted. The final members of the 72XX class, Nos 7240-7253, were rebuilt from older units of the 42XX class. All in all, the two classes of mineral tank amounted to 205 units, the last batch of the 2-8-0T variant was built in 1940.

### Horses for courses

When the South Wales railways amalgamated into the GWR, the GWR found it needed new or renovated locomotives for them. But the South Wales locomotive men, who were used to the 0-6-2T, were not at all in favour of replacing them with GWR 2-8-0Ts. They said the wheelbase of the 42XX class was too long for the twisting valley lines. So instead of increasing production of the 4200 class, the GWR adopted a crash programme for building an entirely new design of tank – the 56XX 0-6-2T.

▼ **On 28 October 1961, one of the 72XX class, No 7209, bides its time at Oxford shed. These locomotives were rebuilt from the earlier 42XX class, with their coal bunkers and water tanks extended to carry more fuel. Although primarily intended to haul coal trains between South Wales and London, many were involved in other duties and were sometimes pressed into passenger service on summer Saturdays. Three of this class have survived into preservation.**

# LMS Beyer-Garratts

Beyer-Garratt 2-6-0 + 0-6-2 articulated locomotives had two units pivoted at each end of the boiler and equalled two conventional engines. They did not need turning at the end of a run and provided space for a more effective firebox.

The London Midland & Scottish Railway (LMS) acquired 33 in the late 1920s for its ex-Midland Railway (MR) main line between the Nottingham coalfield and London. However, this route was very busy, so coal trains were few, but heavy. The old Midland Railway had used pairs of 0-6-0 locomotives and this practice had been continued by the LMS. Three of the class were delivered in 1927 and after long trials, 30 more were ordered.

The class had a number of defects and these were as a direct consequence of the managerial confusion then reigning on the LMS. The first Beyer-Garratt proposals originated with the LMS's Chief Mechanical Engineer, George Hughes, but behind his back a group of ex-Midland Railway operators was conducting its own set of negotiations with Beyer Peacock, the Garratt manufacturers.

After Hughes retired, his successor Henry Fowler, even though a former MR man, was similarly sidetracked by the Derby group, which took on itself the signing of a contract with Beyer Peacock. This tightly knit circle was stronger in ideology than imagination and was determined to get back to basics: the MR's 'small engine' tradition.

The Beyer-Garratt, unlike the conventional 2-8-2 that Hughes had originally suggested, could be fitted into the ideology because ex-MR officials could delude themselves that the design was really two small engines that happened to be joined together. But they insisted that the manufacturer incorporate MR small engine standards in these enormous machines. In particular the bearings which were no bigger than those of the MR's standard 0-6-0 freight engine, and obsolescent short-lap valve gear was specified.

## Poor investment

The result was a locomotive class with a distinct tendency to run hot and whose specific coal consumption was no better than that of the essentially 19th century 0-6-0s that it was designed to supersede. Oddly enough, the LMS authorities did not see fit to provide the crews with any information on the class and they had to cope as best they could. Although the LMS Garratts did their job and remained in service into the 1950s, they proved to be a poor investment.

Even if Hughes and Fowler had succeeded in obtaining Garratts to their own specification, it seems unlikely that this would have been the best solution. When the Stanier 2-8-0 appeared in 1934 its performance was not greatly inferior to that of the Garratts, with their fallibility and high maintenance costs. The last was withdrawn in 1958.

### Not suitable
The introduction of the Beyer-Garratts seemed to have taken the LMS's operating department by surprise. Despite their experience, the Derby men seemed to have forgotten that the new locomotives would need to run over the hump at the Toton marshalling yard; some urgent re-engineering was required when it was seen that the leading wheels lifted off the rails during this manoeuvre.

◄ The cylindrical rotating coal bunker is shown clearly in this mid-1930s view of LMS Beyer-Garratt No 4998 as it pulls out of Toton yard in Derbyshire. The Garratts' main sphere of work was hauling coal from Nottinghamshire to London. However, the class also worked between Toton and Washwood Heath yard in Birmingham.

# Private locomotive builders' plates

Each of the larger main line railway companies had its own locomotive works and, in many cases, these establishments built as well as repaired locomotives. However, many of the smaller lines lacked the resources to produce locomotives for themselves and had to look to private firms to fill this need.

Such businesses developed during the earliest days of steam locomotion, often springing from established engineering partnerships. One of these was founded by the great Robert Stephenson himself and continued to bear his name until the manufacture of steam locomotives came to an end in the 1960s.

All locomotive builders provided their products with builders' or works plates, usually one on either side. The majority of these plates were made of brass and listed information such as the builder's name, the year of manufacture and the works number of the particular locomotive. Occasionally, the name of the works was included, particularly if the manufacturer operated two or more factories.

Sometimes, locomotives were built under licence by one company to the design of another. This fact would be included on the works plate, together, perhaps, with the relevant patent number.

In the early days, the works plates were often hand made. Rectangular in shape, they would have been cut from a sheet of brass and engraved with the relevant details. In some cases, a more decorative basic shape was used.

By the 1870s, as both the output of locomotives and the number of manufacturers increased, the plates became generally oval. An exception was the North British Locomotive Company of Glasgow, which normally produced diamond-shaped plates, though for a time it preferred round ones.

Most plates, by this time, were made of cast-brass, with raised and generally polished lettering and borders. The background between the letters was left unpolished, perhaps even cast with a textured finish. This was then painted, usually either black or red, to show off the lettering to the best effect.

Some builders continued to use smooth polished plates with engraved lettering. Among them were Peckett & Co of Bristol, and Manning Wardle & Co and Hudswell Clark & Co, both of Leeds. These engraved plates, when properly polished, are the most attractive of all builders' plates.

In a few rare instances, plates included a whole range of information. Such was the case with two locomotives belonging to the Leek & Manifold Valley Light Railway, a Staffordshire narrow gauge line. The engines, No 1 *E. L. Calthrop* and No 2 *J. B. Earle*, had combined name, number and works plates, which also bore the name of the builders, Kitson & Co, as well as the name of the railway.

---

### Collecting private locomotive builders' plates

The best source of private locomotive builders' plates is the main railway auction houses, which sellers prefer to use in order to reach the largest potential market. A few years ago, a sale in Sheffield contained 20 or so such plates out of a total of 600 lots. Prices have risen considerably over recent years, and relatively common plates from manufacturers such as Hunslet & Co and the North British Locomotive Co, and dating from the 1920s to the 1950s, may cost several hundred pounds.

The older a plate is, the more expensive it will usually be. Pre-1900 examples will fetch the best prices; an 1897 plate from Dubs of Glasgow sold for £540 a few years ago. It is important to inspect the back of a plate before buying. Dirt and rust marks are a sign that the item is genuine.

---

▲▶Rebuild plates were rare, and indicated a different level of work. This example (above) is thought to come from an 0-6-0ST built by Manning Wardle in 1883. South African Railways was the principal customer for Garratt locomotives produced by Beyer Peacock.

▲The diamond-shaped plates of Dubs & Co were perpetuated by its successor, the North British Loco Co. This plate is off a South African 4-8-0.

# The diesel engine

The purpose of a diesel engine is to produce mechanical effort by converting heat into work, and is correctly known as the direct injection compression ignition oil engine. It was developed by a German, Dr Rudolph Diesel, around 1900 and was based on machines built by Dr Nicholas August Otto in 1878.

When air is highly compressed it becomes very hot. In a diesel engine, a mixture of fuel and air enters into a cylinder, which acts as a combustion chamber, and is compressed by a piston. Due to the high temperature of the compressed air, the mixture ignites and burns in a controlled explosion, which expands and forces the piston to move along the cylinder. The burnt gases then escape through an exit flue and out into the atmosphere.

As the piston slides up and down (a reciprocating action) inside the cylinder, it pushes a connecting rod which turns a large flywheel. A crankshaft, connected to the flywheel, transmits the power to the main generator, which in turn supplies the traction motors.

## Two main types

Diesel engines are divided into two groups known as two-stroke or four-stroke engines. This division reflects the way in which they carry out their operating cycle.

The simplest form of two-stroke engine has no valves to let the air and fuel mixture into the cylinder and burnt gases out. Compressed air is needed to fill the cylinders, as it is not sucked in by the piston (induction) as happens in the four-stroke engine. Air enters and leaves the cylinder through a port (opening) in its side, which is revealed and hidden by the reciprocating movement of the piston.

The four-stroke design is a more complex engine than the two-stroke, because rods, gears and timing mechanisms are needed to work the inlet and exhaust valves. The downward movement of the piston is either a power stroke or an induction stroke. Each upward movement is either a compression stroke or an exhaust stroke. This means that the crankshaft must rotate twice for a piston to produce a power stroke.

### Thermal efficiency

The heat energy (thermal efficiency) of a diesel engine is given off in different ways. The diesel engines which arrived on BR in the late 1950s gave off 37% of their energy in exhaust and radiated heat, 8% through internal friction, 25% was lost to the cooling water system and only 30% was available for work (on a steam locomotive 4% was usually considered nearer the mark for the average locomotive).

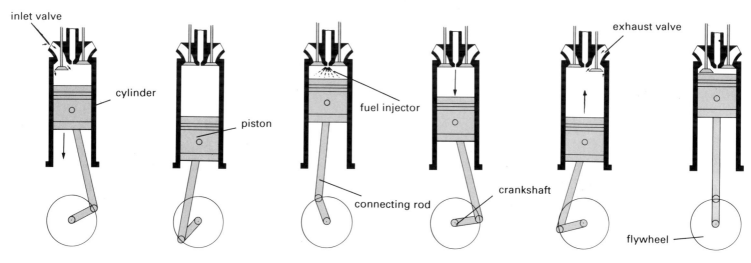

▲In the four-stroke cycle, a mixture of air and fuel is sucked in by the downwards movement of the piston (induction stroke).

As the piston returns back up the cylinder it squeezes the fuel mixture (compression stroke) causing an explosion, forcing the

piston back down (power stroke). The returning movement expels the burnt gases through the exhaust port (exhaust stroke).

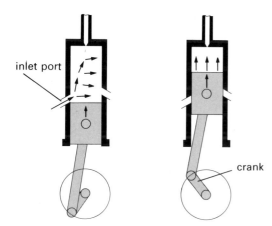
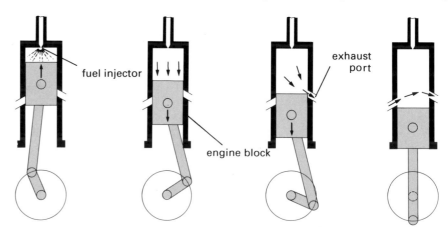

▲In the two-stroke cycle, air drawn into the cylinder is compressed and ignited

(induction and ignition stroke). The piston then moves down the cylinder exposing the

exhaust ports and turning the crankshaft (power and exhaust stroke).

# Diesel engine components

The engine in BR's most basic diesel locomotive, the Standard Class 08 shunter, introduced in 1952, was based on the EE6K 350hp engine and first used by the London Midland & Scottish Railway in 1936. It had a set of six upright cylinders placed in a line (bank). It is from this basic engine that the whole range of English Electric power units, which have been fitted into many of BR's diesels, were developed.

## Inlet and exhaust valves
In a four-stroke diesel, fuel and air is injected into the **combustion chamber** at the top (head) of each cylinder. Different sets of **valves** let the spent (exhaust) gas out and allow fresh air to enter. Two-stroke engines need non-return valves to prevent exhaust blowing back into the air inlet.

The movement of the piston from the top to the bottom of the cylinder is called a stroke. It is important that the valves open at the right time, to ensure that the piston is at the top of its stroke when combustion takes place and that the spent gas can leave quickly, to avoid loss of power and wasted fuel.

To open the valves at the right time, a range of shafts, **rods** and levers are used, with **springs** to return the valves to the closed position. Valve timing must be accurate as the smallest adjustment will affect the power output dramatically.

## Piston components
Each piston has an outer body, consisting of a **crown** and a **skirt**. Pistons are usually cast and then precision ground to give a perfectly balanced weight.

**Piston rings** are fitted around the body of the piston and these push against the sides of the cylinder. This seals the area above the piston where the combustion takes place. The top ring is usually made of chrome to resist carbon (the residue of the combustion) sticking to it. Around the bottom of the piston, scraper rings limit the amount of lubricating oil left behind in the cylinder.

A **gudgeon pin** fastens the end of the piston to a pivoting **connecting rod**, whose lower end (in two U-shaped halves and known as the big end) surrounds a crankpin fitted to a **crankshaft**. Both of these halves are lined with **bearing shells** of copper or lead. The movement of the pistons on the crankshaft turns the main generator which supplies power to the traction motors.

Metal surfaces which move against each other, such as big end bearing shells and crankpins, are kept apart by a thin film of lubricating oil.

## Lubrication and cooling
This oil, under pressure, is fed through a series of channels (oilways) which have been drilled in the engine block and inside the crankshaft connecting rods. These oilways take oil to all the main bearing surfaces. Once used, the oil finds its way to the bottom of the crankshaft and collects in a **sump**. From here, it is picked up by the pump and recirculated after passing through an oil cooler.

Both the compression of the air and the combustion of fuel causes a great deal of heat. Water keeps the engine cool and is pumped through cooling passages called **water jackets**, which surround the hottest part of the engine – particularly the cylinders, the inside of which are lined.

There are two kinds of cylinder liners: wet and dry. Wet liners have direct contact with the cooling water which flows between the liner and the cylinder block. Dry liners are in contact only with the block. Replacing worn liners is a much cheaper option than providing a new cylinder block.

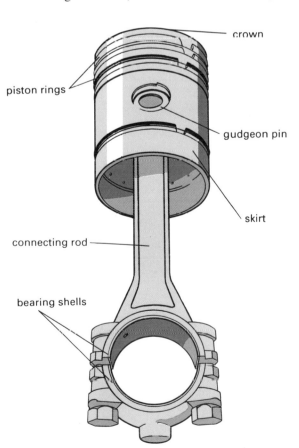

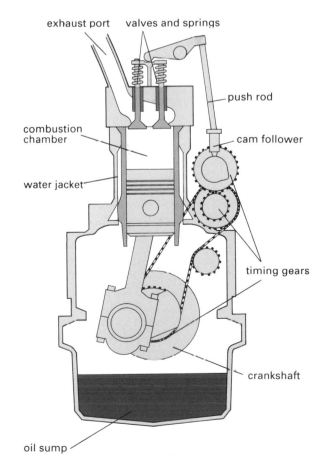

◀ The pistons transfer the heat of the combusting fuel into work. The body of a piston has a crown and a skirt. Piston rings seal the area in the cylinder where the combustion takes place. A gudgeon pin fastens the end of the piston to a pivoting connecting rod, whose lower end is attached to a crankshaft. A film of oil stops the bearing shells binding on the crankpin.

▶ In a four-stroke diesel engine, fuel and air is injected into the combustion chamber. Valves let the exhaust gas out and fresh air in. These are controlled by rods and levers, and are closed by springs. Water keeps the engine cool and is pumped through water jackets, which surround the cylinders. Used lubricating oil collects in a sump at the bottom of the crankcase.

# Turbochargers

Many of the power sources in the modern diesel fleet, including Classes 20, 37, 50 and many multiple units, are fitted with turbochargers. These are rotating devices which obtain extra power from an engine.

Diesel engines are powered by a mixture of air and diesel fuel. A turbocharger enables a greater concentration of oxygen to reach the cylinders than would otherwise be possible. This allows more fuel to be injected and the resulting combustion increases the force acting on the piston, and with it the power at the flywheel.

In 1909, Dr Alfred Buchi, a Swiss engineer, published information on his research into turbocharging. Two years later, the first practical experiments with turbochargers took place at Sulzer Brothers works in Winterthur, Switzerland.

A turbocharger consists basically of a **turbine** (similar to a windmill) and an **air compressor** (a device which squeezes air). The turbine is rotated by **exhaust gases** from the engine and, at the highest exhaust gas temperatures, 10,000 – 15,000 revolutions per minute are achieved.

As the turbine rotates, an air compressor on the same shaft also turns. As the **air from the atmosphere** is compressed it becomes hotter (charged) and, therefore, loses some of its density. Too little air would cause smoke and poor combustion. To restore its density, the **charge air** has to be cooled by passing it through an **intercooler**, where the heat is absorbed by cold water. Intercoolers often have their own separate cooling radiator system to chill their water supply. When the air has cooled, it contracts and takes up less space, resulting in more air being compressed into the cylinders.

## Idling problems

When the engine is idling, there is often insufficient air pressure in the compressor to prevent exhaust gas clinging to the bearing on the turbine side. Should this occur, the lubricating oil becomes contaminated and, if left unattended, will dry out, causing seizure of the main turbine shaft. To prevent this happening, some turbochargers receive a separate blast of air from the locomotive's air system to blow the fumes away through the exhaust outlet.

Factors which influence the design of a turbocharger include the type of duties the locomotive will perform and the lubrication oil and bearing type required.

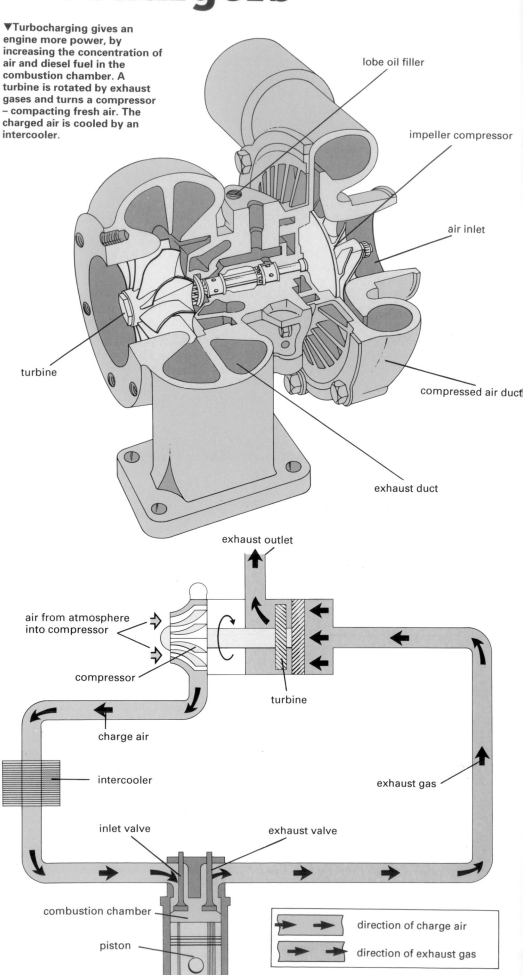

▼Turbocharging gives an engine more power, by increasing the concentration of air and diesel fuel in the combustion chamber. A turbine is rotated by exhaust gases and turns a compressor – compacting fresh air. The charged air is cooled by an intercooler.

lobe oil filler

impeller compressor

air inlet

turbine

compressed air duct

exhaust duct

exhaust outlet

air from atmosphere into compressor

compressor

turbine

charge air

intercooler

exhaust gas

inlet valve

exhaust valve

combustion chamber

piston

direction of charge air

direction of exhaust gas

# Diesel-electric drive

In the simplest terms, the transmission system of a diesel-electric locomotive consists of a diesel engine driving an electric generator, from which current is supplied to the traction motors. The diesel engine produces mechanical power at its crankshaft, which is converted into electrical power in the generator and back into mechanical power at the traction motors.

Electrical power, measured in kilowatts (kW), is the product of voltage (pressure) and current (quantity). As speed increases, the traction motors develop an electromagnetic force (EMF) which opposes the current from the generator. To maintain the tractive effort – which is moving the train – the generator voltage must be increased.

However, the generator voltage must be held at a level which does not overload the diesel engine. To prevent this happening, the voltage and current are continuously balanced by a load regulator to match the power being developed by the diesel engine.

## Power control

The driver determines the speed and power of the engine by moving the control lever (the power handle) in the cab. This lever operates a valve which applies air pressure to the spring of the engine governor. In principle, this is similar to a steam engine governor with spinning weights on a vertical shaft driven by the engine. As weights rise and fall under the effect of centrifugal force with varying engine speed, they operate a valve in the control system. The more the governor spring is compressed, the more power is produced from the engine.

The driver sets the controller so that the diesel engine runs at the speed required. Engine speed determines the power developed and is not directly tied to the speed of the train on the track. The driver selects the power according to the weight of his train, avoiding full power at first to prevent wheelspin on starting and often to prevent speed rising above the limit in a busy area.

While running on the open line with full engine power, the train speed changes according to conditions. On a rising gradient, the speed will fall. The governor will detect the increasing load and send a signal to the load regulator to protect the diesel engine by compensating for the rising current – achieved by reducing voltage from the generator.

A signal also goes to the fuel control shaft to increase the supply of fuel to the engine cylinders. Cranks on the shaft move the fuel racks to and fro. A fuel rack is a notched lever which engages with the fuel pump body and rotates it slightly in one direction or the other. This action varies the stroke of the pump plunger and consequently the amount of fuel delivered.

If the train reaches a speed at which the back EMF of the traction motors prevents them from taking more current even at maximum generator voltage, the load regulator moves further to weaken the motor field strengths, reducing the back EMF and allowing acceleration to continue. At length, an unloading point is reached at which the motors can no longer absorb the full engine power and the speed is stabilized.

### Balancing act
Load regulators protect the diesel engine. They take various forms, but are basically a variable resistance in the circuit supplying current to the generator magnets. Tappings from the resistance are brought out to contacts, over which a moving arm is driven by an oil servo motor or an electric pilot motor. An alternative is a special transformer with a moveable magnetic core, which is operated by oil pressure from the governor in the same way as the resistance regulators. Field weakening to attain full speed may take place in two or three steps.

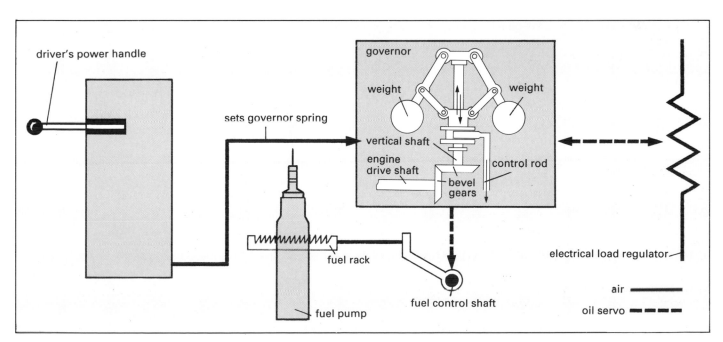

▲The speed and power of the diesel engine is determined by a power handle in the cab. This operates a valve which applies air pressure to the spring of the engine governor. Here, spinning weights, driven by the engine, rise and fall on a vertical shaft. This action sends messages to both the load regulator, to protect the engine, and to the fuel control shaft, to boost the power by increasing the supply of fuel. Notched fuel racks rotate the fuel pump body and this varies the stroke of the pump plunger and the amount of fuel delivered to the engine cylinders.

# Diesel-hydraulic drive

Diesel-hydraulic transmission returned almost unnoticed to British Rail in the second generation of diesel units. The Voith gearboxes incorporated hydraulic torque converters similar in principle to those of the Western Region diesel-hydraulic locomotives, which were phased out with the last of the Western class.

In a steam locomotive, the pressure of steam on the pistons acts through the connecting rods, coupling rods and cranks to exert torque (turning effort) on the wheels when the locomotive is at a standstill and thus sets it in motion. However, there is no torque at the crankshaft of a diesel engine until it is running. The transmission system must therefore enable it to run up to speed before it is connected to the wheels, where the torque appears as tractive effort (pulling power).

## The torque converter

In an hydraulic system, the engine power is transmitted through a torque converter, using oil as the transmission medium. The engine drives an impeller in an oil-filled casing, circulating the oil through the blades of a turbine wheel on the output shaft (which is unconnected with the input shaft, except through the oil). The impact of the oil on the turbine blades makes the shaft revolve.

If it were not for a ring of fixed blades inside the casing, this device would simply act as a coupling between the input and output shafts without increasing the torque. However, the fixed blades redirect the oil back on to the turbine blades and the torque is multiplied, turning the wheels and moving the train.

As the train accelerates, the tractive effort needed to move it decreases and the torque at the turbine must be reduced to prevent overloading the diesel engine. At all times, the tractive effort and the speed of the train on the track must be the equivalent of the horsepower being produced by the engine. This balance is maintained automatically in the torque converter – as the turbine speeds up, the impact on its blades of the oil returning through the fixed blades is reduced. A simple comparison is that of a collision between two cars in a traffic jam. If a driver fails to stop and the car ahead is stationary, the impact is more severe than if the car ahead is moving forwards.

In a practical hydraulic transmission, the turbine is coupled to the wheels by a cardan shaft with universal joints to allow relative movement between the converter on the vehicle underframe and the axle. A converter may have two or more stages, coming into action in sequence, to cover the required speed ranges. At some point in the transmission, a mechanical reverse gear must be provided because the diesel engine runs only in one direction.

**Key**
- impeller
- turbine
- fixed reaction blades and casing

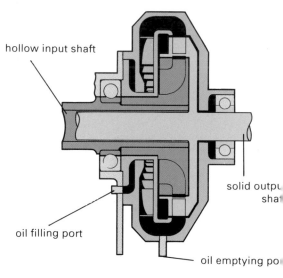

hollow input shaft

solid output shaft

oil filling port

oil emptying port

▼Diesel-hydraulic transmission, used on BR's second-generation diesel units. Many use Voith gearboxes which incorporate hydraulic torque converters. These are similar in principle to the Western Region diesel-hydraulic locomotives Classes 35, 42, 52 and Class 127 DMU 4-car sets.

▶ A torque converter transmits engine power to the final drive. An impeller in an oil filled casing circulates oil through the blades of a turbine mounted on a solid output shaft encased inside an input shaft. It is the impact of the oil on the blades which causes the shaft to move.

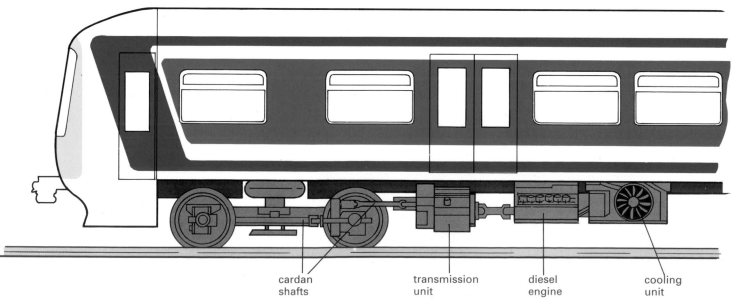

cardan shafts | transmission unit | diesel engine | cooling unit

# Diesel headcodes

At the time of the 1955 British Railways Modernization Plan, steam locomotives displayed either route headcode discs or white light lamps to help signalmen identify different trains. When diesel locomotives were introduced on many main lines in the 1950s, they were equipped with four position headcode discs – flapped discs attached to the front of the engine which showed white or a light when open.

In the 1960s, diesel and electric power became the norm and manual signalboxes began to be replaced by large power boxes with centralized control. In 1962, BR introduced the four-character system. In this, the identification number of the train was displayed as a headcode on the front of the locomotive and on the panel display in modern signalboxes.

The first number of the code showed the class of train, the letter in the second position signified the destination area, and the remaining two numbers identified a particular train number. Depending on the area in which the train was running, heavy traffic would mean insufficient numbers would be available to give every train a code, so route numbers were allocated.

While the British Rail network was divided into regions, many trains were classed as inter-regional. The letter for the area code was displayed as a universal code and was the same for a particular region, no matter where the train originated.

Modern central signal control means that trains as far away as 25 miles or more are often controlled from one panel. Although headcodes are no longer displayed for the benefit of signalmen, trains are still given the same four-character identification – principally the same as those used for headcodes. The signalbox describer apparatus allows signal operators to identify the train precisely as it passes through the sections they control, without seeing the headcode itself.

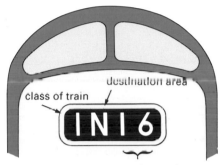

destination area
class of train
route or train number

▲From 1961, the identification number of a train was shown as a headcode on the front of the locomotive and each character gave different information. This system was abandoned in the 1970s, as centralized signalling became widespread.

| Code | Destination area |
|------|------------------|
| E | Eastern Region |
| M | London Midland Region |
| N | North Eastern Region |
| O | Southern Region |
| S | Scottish Region |
| V | Western Region |
| X | Excursion or Special |

▲Examples of universal codes used for inter-regional services circa 1967

▶ 1992 train class table

| Code | Class of train |
|------|----------------|
| 1 | Express passenger; breakdown or snowplough duty |
| 2 | Ordinary; suburban or branch passenger or mixed; breakdown train not on duty |
| 3 | Parcels or perishable goods train composed of bogie fitted vehicles |
| 4 | Freight timed at 75mph |
| 5 | Empty carriage stock |
| 6 | Freight timed over 50mph |
| 7 | Freight less than 45mph |
| 8 | Freight less than 35mph |
| 9 | Train not all fitted with continuous brakes |
| 0 | Light locomotive |

▼From the late 1950s, diesel locomotives displayed the four-aspect disc identification system. The disc was a flap; when opened it showed as a white circle or light. The back of the disc was painted the same colour as the front of the locomotive and did not show when closed.

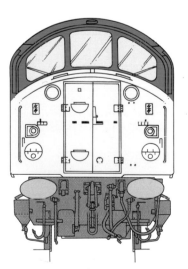

**express passenger train**

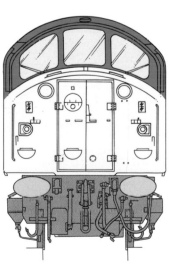

**ordinary stopping passenger train**

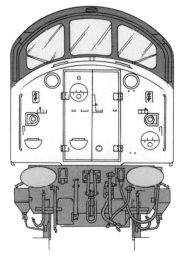

**freight without continuous brakes**

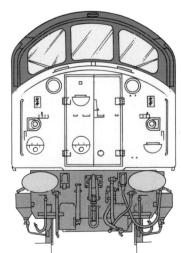

**empty coaching stock or parcels train**

# EMU fronts

The appearance of electric multiple units (EMUs) has long been influenced by operational requirements – particularly the need to couple two or more units together. This can be achieved only by using electrical, brake and ancillary connections, but often this meant cluttering the front of the unit with jumper cables and sockets.

Additionally, some front-ends require corridor connections to enable passengers to pass from one unit to another. These were originally introduced to enable passengers access to the buffet car on long trains where several units were coupled together.

## Looks count

A problem facing designers is how to make the units' ends more attractive, without losing the functional facilities which aid operation. Designs of the 1950s and 1960s followed the criterion that operation came before appearance.

Even where designers tried to improve the looks, by recessing equipment as in

the case of the 4-CIG and 4-BIG units, or by giving the units a more streamlined look as with the Eastern Region's Class 309 (which was otherwise based on the same carriage design), the hoses and connections were still prominent.

While the fronts of most types of EMU differ in some way, even with modern designs, useful comparisons can still be made. Good examples for contrast are the 4-CEP and 4-BEPs (designed for the Kent Coast electrification in 1956 and one of the early generation of entirely BR designed EMUs for the Southern Region) and the Class 508 (one of the new generation built in the 1970s also used on the Southern). While other designs varied, the treatment of functional equipment has been similar.

## Timely approach

Designs from the 1970s onwards have seen definite attempts to improve matters. With the introduction of the Tight Lock type coupling, the front-end could be tidied up.

The upper part of the coupling is the basic buckeye connection, which physically couples units together, while the lower box contains all the electrical and air connections. During coupling, the cover of the lower box automatically drops away as the units draw together. Such a system of coupling is now universally used, although not compatible with pre-1970 stock.

### Early connection
The first EMUs to have front corridor connections were the units built by R E L Maunsell in 1937 for the Portsmouth electrification. These were the celebrated 4-COR (corridor) and 4-RES (restaurant) units. But because a driving window was placed only on one side of the corridor connection – the other side being used for the route indicator – they soon became known as the one-eyed Nelsons.

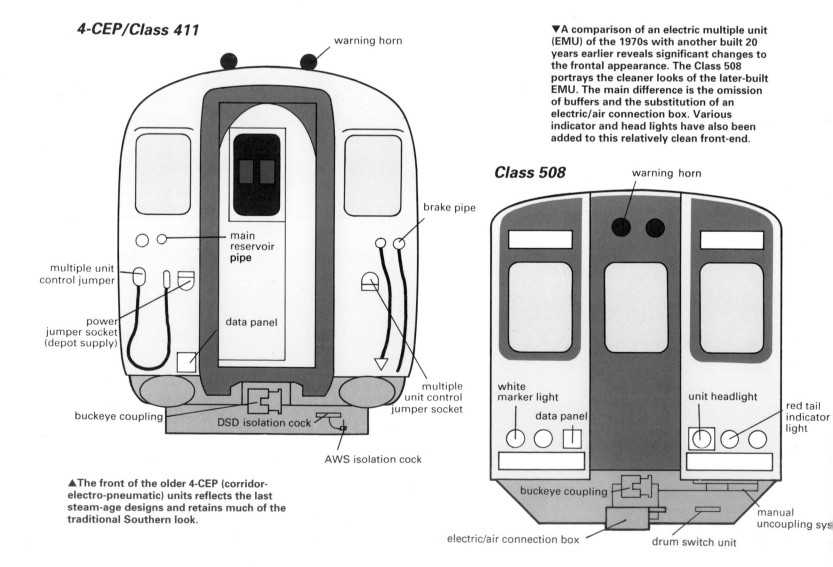

### 4-CEP/Class 411

warning horn · brake pipe · main reservoir **pipe** · multiple unit control jumper · power jumper socket (depot supply) · data panel · multiple unit control jumper socket · buckeye coupling · DSD isolation cock · AWS isolation cock

▲The front of the older 4-CEP (corridor-electro-pneumatic) units reflects the last steam-age designs and retains much of the traditional Southern look.

▼A comparison of an electric multiple unit (EMU) of the 1970s with another built 20 years earlier reveals significant changes to the frontal appearance. The Class 508 portrays the cleaner looks of the later-built EMU. The main difference is the omission of buffers and the substitution of an electric/air connection box. Various indicator and head lights have also been added to this relatively clean front-end.

### Class 508

warning horn · white marker light · data panel · unit headlight · red tail indicator light · buckeye coupling · electric/air connection box · drum switch unit · manual uncoupling sys

# AC electrics

Power reaches many electric locomotives by means of wires (**catenary**) suspended over the track and is supplied from small (feeder) power stations at intervals along the route which are connected to the National Grid.

A **pantograph** on the locomotive collects alternating current (AC) from the wire and passes it along a **power busbar** on the roof to the **circuit breaker** (a switch capable of handling high currents which opens automatically if there is an electrical fault in the locomotive, cutting off the power before further harm is done).

When closed, the circuit breaker passes current through a roof bushing to the **primary winding** (copper strip, wound round an iron core) of the **main transformer**. The return path of the current is through **axle brushes** to the wheels and so back to the feeder station along the running rails.

The current in the primary winding of the transformer induces a current at lower voltage in the adjacent **secondary winding**. This is still AC, but it is converted into direct current (DC) by the **rectifier** for driving the **traction motors**. Power would cause the powered wheels to spin, damaging the motors. So, on starting, the voltage from the transformer secondary winding is reduced.

In modern locomotives, the motors are fitted in the bogies. The stresses on the track caused by the motors being hung on the axles are relieved by resilient wheels with rubber blocks between the rim and the hub.

The older types of electric locomotives were fitted with an electrically operated switching device called a tap changer which could increase or decrease the AC voltage supplied to the rectifiers and therefore the DC voltage supplied to the motor circuits. In the latest practice, this control takes place in the rectifiers themselves which are solid state devices called thyristors with no moving parts. A tap changer controls the voltage in steps, but with thyristors the control is continuous and smooth. A thyristor, like other types of rectifier, allows current in one direction only, but it does so only when the voltage from the transformer reaches a certain value, which can be varied by the control system.

Traction motors must produce their maximum turning effort (torque) when the locomotive is at a standstill and then work efficiently up to the maximum speed of the train. The motor best suited to this duty is the series-wound DC commutator type. Most are relatively small to fit within a bogie frame and on locomotives they are ventilated by traction motor blowers (fans) to disperse the excess heat produced at high tractive efforts.

The combined torque of the motors acting through the gears to the wheels – the locomotive's tractive effort – has to overcome the resistance of the train to movement. This is greatest when starting or climbing a gradient but falls as speed increases or when running downhill.

The maximum voltage which can be applied to the motors depends on the number of turns on the secondary winding compared with the primary winding.

## Voltage control

The operating voltage of the locomotive is set by the number of turns forming the secondary winding of the transformer. Other windings incorporated within the transformer drive the air conditioning, heating (and cooking) on the coaches forming the train, and supply current to air compressors, cooling fans, doors or other auxiliary equipment.

▼A modern electric locomotive takes AC from the overhead wire and converts it into DC for use in its traction motors. The motors are fitted in the bogies and usually drive the axle through flexible couplings. If the drive is direct, stresses on the track caused by the weight of the motors hung on the axles are relieved by rubber blocks between the rim and the hub of the wheels. A Class 87 has four 1225hp motors, each more powerful than a single Class 25 diesel.

## How an AC electric locomotive works

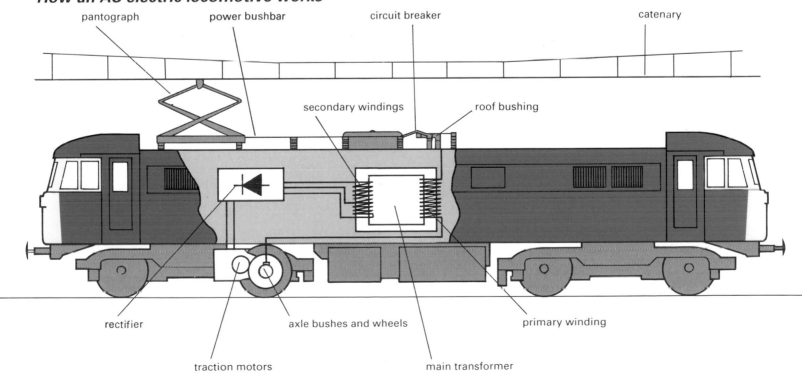

pantograph · power bushbar · circuit breaker · catenary · secondary windings · roof bushing · rectifier · axle bushes and wheels · primary winding · traction motors · main transformer

# Catenary

A cable hung between two supports droops in a curve created by gravity, known mathematically as a catenary. When used to supply overhead electric current, it is used in lengths of up to 6000ft (1.8km). On double track it is supported by masts alongside the line at intervals of up to 240ft (73m); on four-track and wider stretches, gantries or span wires are suspended across the line. In span wire construction, a cable is supported by masts on each side of the line. A second cable, suspended below it by droppers, carries arms to which the contact wire is attached. In this case, the contact wire is at right angles to the catenary.

Sections of catenary overlap so that the supply to the pantograph is not interrupted. At certain overlaps, the two sections are connected electrically by an isolator switch which can be operated from ground level to cut off the supply when the catenary needs inspection or maintenance. In each section, catenary is anchored at the mid-point but at the other masts, the arms which carry the contact wire can swivel to allow for expansion and contraction of the wire.

To even out the wear on pantographs, the contact wire is positioned alternately to one or the other side of the centre line above the track. The wire is attached to an arm which slides on a registration tube and is adjusted so that this 'zig-zagging' across the track occurs. There are two methods of positioning the contact wire, called 'pull-off' and 'push-off', and on straight track they are used at alternate masts.

## National Grid

Power is supplied to the catenary through feeder stations connected to the National Grid. They are spaced at intervals of 20 or 30 miles (32 or 48km). Half-way between two feeder stations there is a neutral section of catenary to separate the two supplies. This is formed by a length of contact wire separated from its neighbours by insulating beads of the same cross-section as the wire so that pantographs can slide easily over the neutral section. The circuit-breakers of locomotives and motor coaches open automatically at the approach to the neutral section and reclose on reaching the next section of live wire.

Further isolating switches, in this case remotely controlled, are housed in lineside cabinets at overlaps halfway between the neutral sections. The power supply is monitored from control rooms where the state of all switches and other information is shown on a large wall diagram.

When switches open because of a fault, the control room operators first try to reclose them by means of buttons on the panel (some faults clear themselves) and if unsuccessful send engineers to find and cure the trouble. The operators are also responsible for isolating sections of the catenary for maintenance and for organizing the supply of power when faults occur so that traffic can be kept moving.

On some sections of line, where return current from the trains flowing through the rails might interfere with underground telephone circuits, a return current cable is carried at the rear of the masts. Current is drawn out of the rails and into the cable by transformers.

### Live wire

On an electric railway with overhead current supply, the catenary is the whole system of upper cable, the droppers which support the contact wire and the contact wire itself from which the trains collect current through their pantographs. The whole of this system, not just the contact wire, is live and carries 25kV. Unfortunately, over the years some tragic accidents have resulted from not understanding this.

## Catenary fixings

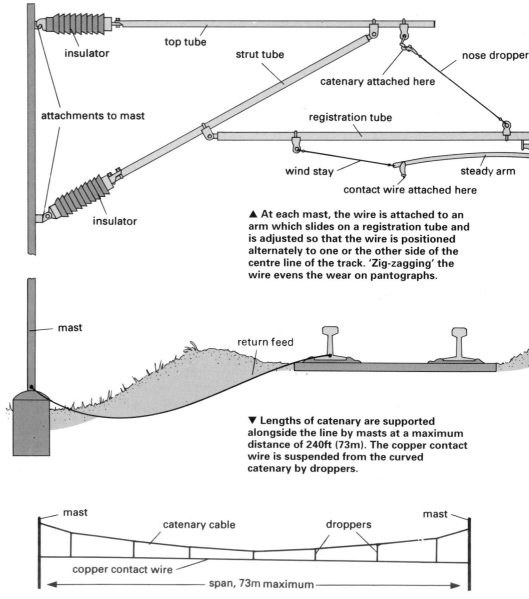

▲ At each mast, the wire is attached to an arm which slides on a registration tube and is adjusted so that the wire is positioned alternately to one or the other side of the centre line of the track. 'Zig-zagging' the wire evens the wear on pantographs.

▼ Lengths of catenary are supported alongside the line by masts at a maximum distance of 240ft (73m). The copper contact wire is suspended from the curved catenary by droppers.

# Pantographs

A dictionary definition of a pantograph is 'an instrument for copying drawings, plans etc on the same or a different scale'. The draughtsman's pantograph is a four-sided frame hinged at the corners so that it can be opened out or folded back. Railway pantographs at first took the same form, their purpose being to raise or lower a collector head or pan, which slides along the overhead contact wire to pick up electric current.

## Current collection

Today, the half pantograph is the usual form, consisting of a lower arm pivoted on the roof of the locomotive or motor coach, and either one or two upper arms pivoted at its outer end. These carry the head, which is mounted on springs in order to follow any unevenness in the contact wire.

A system of levers extends the upper arm as the pantograph is raised and keeps the head level so that it meets the wire squarely. Current is collected through metallized carbon strips on the head.

The contact wire zig-zags from side to side of the centre line of the track so that wear is spread evenly over the whole of the collecting surface. When the wire is lowered under bridges and through tunnels, the whole pantograph dips and rises, keeping a constant pressure on the wire.

When out of use, the pantograph is folded down on the roof. The up springs are stretched in this position. To raise the pantograph, air is let into the operating cylinder and the piston moves forward, pulling the control rod and moving a slotted link on the rod away from a stop. The springs are then free to pull on the cranked end of the lower arm and lift the head into contact with the wire.

During its stroke, the piston has also compressed the down spring (which is stronger than the two up springs). To lower the pantograph, air is exhausted from the cylinder, the down spring moves the piston back and the control rod engages with the stop and pushes the crank on the lower arm so that the frame folds down.

## Lowering the pantograph

In the first stage of lowering, the air is exhausted quickly until the frame is about 12in (30cm) from the down position. The rate then slows so that the pantograph settles gently on to its stops. While the pantograph is raised, air is piped to the head. If the head or a collector strip is damaged, the air leaks and the pantograph is lowered.

Some locomotives have a special pantograph designed for collecting currents at speeds over 125mph (200km/h). This type has no springs, but is raised by pressure supplied through a regulator that is set to maintain constant force on the wire. Air is added when the contact wire rises and is bled from the system when the level falls.

### Stone-Faiveley pantograph

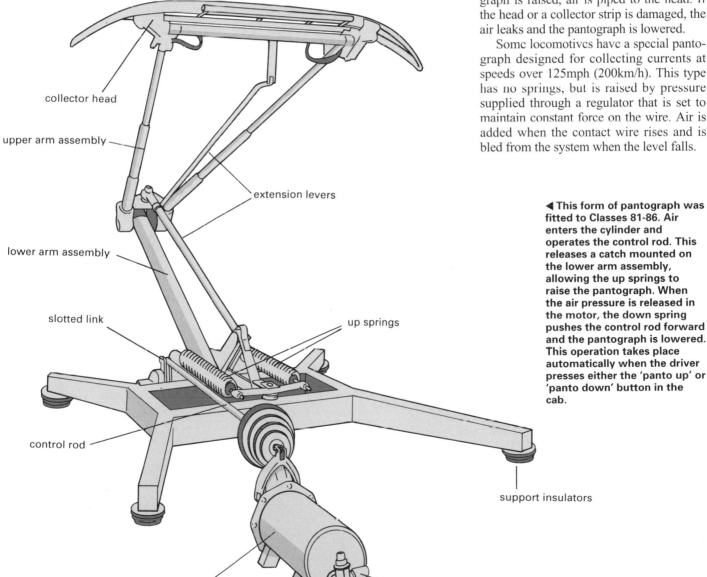

collector head

upper arm assembly

extension levers

lower arm assembly

slotted link

up springs

control rod

support insulators

air cylinder, piston and down spring

air inlet

◀ This form of pantograph was fitted to Classes 81-86. Air enters the cylinder and operates the control rod. This releases a catch mounted on the lower arm assembly, allowing the up springs to raise the pantograph. When the air pressure is released in the motor, the down spring pushes the control rod forward and the pantograph is lowered. This operation takes place automatically when the driver presses either the 'panto up' or 'panto down' button in the cab.

# Thyristors

The first semiconductor devices used in electric locomotives and EMUs were diode rectifiers. They converted the alternating current (AC) input from the overhead wire into a direct current (DC) output for the traction motors. The input voltage was controlled by connecting the diodes to different tappings on a transformer by means of an electro-mechanical tap-changer. A first step towards a diode that would both rectify and control was the silicon controlled rectifier (SCR). Beginning as a low-current device, the SCR was developed to handle high powers and is now known as a thyristor.

A simple diode passes current throughout the greater part of the positive half-cycle of the AC input voltage. During the negative half-cycle which follows, the flow of current is blocked. The thyristor has a similar blocking effect in the negative half-cycle but unlike the diode it does not pass current during the positive half-cycle until it has been switched on by a small voltage pulse applied to an extra electrode called the 'gate'. The point at which the pulse is applied can be varied, and the power delivered to the motors depends on the time for which current can flow. This is known as 'phase angle control' and is an all-electronic method requiring no mechanical switching.

If the thyristors are operated over their full range of control they may cause interference in the supply system. In motive power installations they are therefore divided into two groups, each covering half the voltage range and coming into action one after the other. With the thyristors of both groups fully conducting, the motors receive the full supply voltage.

## Applications in DC traction

The properties of the thyristor are also used in direct current (DC) traction. Switching full voltage on to stationary motors would cause a rush of current sufficient to burn out the windings. Standard DC practice has been to limit the current by means of resistances which are switched out in steps as the motors accelerate. But resistances heat up and waste energy. When they have to be kept in circuit for low-speed operation such as shunting, drivers have to work in this condition for as short a time as possible. The instruction manual for one of the older BR EMUs warned the driver that if he remained in the shunting notch for two minutes continuously, he must not return to it for ten minutes to allow the resistances time to cool down.

Thyristors can overcome this difficulty. When voltage is switched on to a circuit, it does not reach maximum at once. By using thyristors in a circuit called a chopper, the voltage can be switched off before it has fully developed. The chopper acts as an on/off switch with a variable 'on' period. At first the 'on' periods are very short and the switch opens while the voltage is still low. They are lengthened progressively until the chopper conducts continuously, the motors having reached the speed at which full voltage can be applied safely. Switching takes place at speeds far beyond anything possible with mechanical switches – on/off times are measured in fractions of a microsecond.

With standard thyristors, two are required in each chopper because once a thyristor has been switched on it passes current continuously until the voltage falls to zero. In AC practice this occurs automatically halfway through each cycle. In a DC chopper the second thyristor acts as a 'quenching' thyristor to switch off the other one.

It would obviously be simpler if a thyristor in a chopper could be switched off by applying a pulse in the same way as it is switched on. This has led to the development of the gate turn-off thyristor (GTO) which is operated by the application of a negative pulse.

The GTO has other uses apart from choppers. Using its on/off switching capability, a single-phase input can be converted into three single-phase outputs out of step with each other, in other words a three-phase supply. This type of circuit is called an 'inverter'. With this development the way has been opened for using three-phase traction motors in the new generation of motive power.

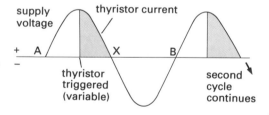

▶ A thyristor converts AC current into DC, like a rectifier, and at the same time controls the current supply, as a tap-changer. This diagram shows AC supply voltage and thyristor current (shaded area). A to B represents one cycle. The thyristor is shown triggered at the peak of the voltage wave, delivering full power. For starting a train the triggering point would be moved to the right towards X, to a lower point on the curve of supply voltage.

▶ Seen here in 1978 hauling an InterCity service out of London Euston for Birmingham New Street, Class 87/1 No 87101 *Stephenson* was the first to incorporate the new technology of full thyristor control. Its success strongly influenced the design specifications of the subsequent Class 90. Since then, thyristor control has become standard on BR's AC electric locomotive fleet, including Class 91.

# Tap-changers

The motors of an electric locomotive or motor coach are designed to work at a voltage within the range of approximately 600-900V. On direct current (DC) railways, the supply voltage and the motor voltage are the same. On alternating current (AC) systems, however, the supply voltage is much higher so that feeder points can be spaced further apart and light overhead wires instead of conductor rails are used to carry the current.

Every AC locomotive and motor coach carries a transformer in which the supply voltage is lowered to suit the motors. In a transformer, two coils of copper strip are wound on an iron core. There is no connection between them but when the supply voltage is switched on to the primary coil, a lower voltage appears in the secondary coil which has many fewer turns. The number of turns on both windings is calculated so that the input voltage is reduced to the motor voltage.

In many circumstances, such as in starting and when observing speed restrictions, the motors must operate at a voltage lower than the maximum for which they are designed. The number of turns in the windings cannot be changed, but different voltages can be 'tapped off' by connecting the motors to different points on the secondary winding. This process is called tap-changing. In BR motor coach stock, the connections are usually made through switches which are either operated electrically (contactors) or

by a motor-driven camshaft.

In a locomotive, tap-changing switches on the transformer's secondary coil would have to be big enough to break heavy currents. It is usual, therefore, to put the tap-changing system on a regulating transformer which carries the full supply voltage and to tap-off a variable voltage for the primary coil of the transformer feeding the power circuits.

Since the currents at high voltage are relatively low, they can be handled by finger-like contacts which slide over the row of tapping contacts. In BR Class 86 and 87 locomotives, the fingers are moved by a bicycle-type chain passing over a sprocket driven by a small electric motor.

Current to the motors must not be interrupted whilst moving from tap to tap. The tap-changers of BR's Class 87 locomotives make nine switching operations during each tap change to keep current flowing.

In a Class 87, there are 38 steps from starting to full power. The driver can notch up step by step or allow the pilot motor to run continuously, when it goes through the 38 steps in 25 seconds. In notching up by hand, the time taken to reach full power depends on the weight of the train and the gradient. Automatic notching is used to restore power quickly after running through a dead section of contact wire with the train still travelling at speed; or in accelerating after running

back to observe a speed restriction.

Present practice, both for locomotives and motor coaches, is to replace tap-changers with electronic control systems based on thyristors. Even in the mid-1960s some engineers were predicting the end of the tap-changer but it has survived to give good service over many years.

▲ As the tap-changer is tucked away inside an electric locomotive it is rarely seen. It consists of a bicycle-type chain, driven by a small electric motor, which passes over a sprocket. The chain moves 'fingers' over a row of tapping contacts which draw off voltage from a regulating transformer. It takes nine switching operations to ensure the current is tapped off smoothly.

◀ Tap-changers enable the traction motors of an AC electric locomotive to work from lower voltages up to the maximum for which they are designed. The voltage level supplied from the overhead wire is first reduced in a regulating transformer and different voltages are 'tapped off' by making connections from different points through the tap-changer.

power busbar

regulating transformer with tap-changer

to pantograph

rectifier     secondary windings     primary windings

fixed ratio traction transformer

return to feeder station

traction motor     axle bushes and wheel

# Dual-voltage trains

Electric trains normally use one of two basic methods of power supply, alternating current (AC) or direct current (DC), and these may be at a variety of voltages.

Collecting the current from a source outside the train can be done in several ways. In the UK, three basic methods are used: overhead wires (catenary), third-rail pick-up (as on the Southern Region), and third-rail pick-up and fourth-rail return (as on the London Underground).

Extra considerations arise when trains are to be run over parts of two or more different networks which use different power supplies and therefore require two methods of power collection. Dual-voltage trains are designed to adapt to different current supplies as necessary.

Examples in use on British Rail (BR) are the Class 313 trains introduced in 1976 for the Moorgate line, and the newer 1987 Class 319 for the north-south cross-London Thameslink connection. Both classes are able to collect current via a pantograph from BR's 25kV AC overhead lines, or 750V DC from the third rail via current collector shoes. However, both types can work from anything between 600 and 750V DC.

The traction motors on the wheels operate on a DC voltage and so, when collecting current from the **750V DC third rail** by **collector shoes**, the **power supply changeover switches** connect directly to this supply. Current is then fed via a **resistance bank** (to vary the power) to the **traction motors**.

## All change

To run on the **25kV AC overhead supply**, the **changeover switches** are set to connect to the supply from the **pantograph**. The higher AC current must first be reduced to a lower voltage, which is the function of the **main transformer**, and then converted from AC to DC, which is the job of the **rectifier**. When it is time to change back to a third-rail supply, the **vacuum circuit breaker** cuts off the current to the main transformer before the pantograph is lowered.

The circuits for achieving these tasks are of heavy duty construction but are fairly straightforward in concept (indeed, what is normally called a transformer to run a model railway actually consists of both transformer and rectifier). Once transformed and rectified, the resulting lower voltage DC current is fed to the traction motors via the resistance banks.

The actual current supply changeover is controlled by the driver when the train is stationary – at Drayton Park in the case of the Class 313 trains, and at Farringdon in the case of the Class 319s.

### Lancashire in the lead

Dual-voltage trains are not a new idea; in 1906, the Lancashire & Yorkshire Railway (LYR) introduced stock capable of working the 650V DC system of its own lines and the 500/525V DC system of the Liverpool Overhead Railway (the elevated line at Liverpool). Later a locomotive on its Aintree line was capable of overhead or third-rail collection.

▼▶ These dual-voltage Class 313s began life in 1976, hauling services from Moorgate and King's Cross to Hereford North and Welwyn Garden City. The units complete most of their journeys by using a 25kV AC overhead supply, but between Moorgate and Drayton Park the power comes from 750V DC supplied from the third rail. Previously this section had been in the hands of London Underground's Northern Line trains, using 660V DC. When the changeover came, the insulators under the centre rail were removed and the rail was dropped on to the sleepers and bonded to the running rails to ensure a good return.

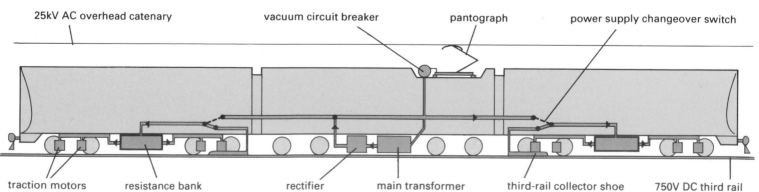

25kV AC overhead catenary    vacuum circuit breaker    pantograph    power supply changeover switch

traction motors    resistance bank    rectifier    main transformer    third-rail collector shoe    750V DC third rail

# Electric braking

Brake blocks acting on the wheel treads and brake pads acting on discs on the axles are subject to heavy wear. Electric braking slows a train from high speed to a level at which the mechanical brakes have less work to do in bringing it to a standstill.

The most widely used electric system is rheostatic braking. When operated, power to the motors is cut off but they continue to revolve, driven by the energy of the train. The control system connects resistances (rheostats) to the motor terminals but restores current to the motor field magnets. The motors now act as generators and send current through the resistances. As these warm up, the train loses energy and slows down, and the mechanical brake takes over.

The circuit changes to go from motoring to braking are made by a group of cam-operated switches. They include reversal of the direction of current flow in the motor magnet windings, without which the magnetism would be wiped out when the motors began generating.

Current is tapped off from the resistances to drive fans which help to disperse the heat. In EMU motor coaches, heat is sometimes diverted into the carriage heating system and in DC stock the resistances used during acceleration may also serve for braking.

Braking effort is controlled either by changing the value of resistance in the circuit or varying the current in the field magnets. Air braking takes over automatically when the generated voltage falls to a preset value. In early BR rheostatic systems the driver operated a power/brake changeover switch and controlled braking with the power handle. In later designs, the operation of the rheostatic brake has been linked with the driver's automatic air brake handle.

## Regenerative braking

The other form of electric braking is regenerative braking. It is based similarly on operating the traction motors as generators but current is returned to the supply (overhead wire or live rail) to be used by other trains. Problems may arise if there is no train nearby to absorb the power. This could cause a big build-up of voltage at the regenerating train and operate the protective relays. The train would then be isolated from the supply system and braking effort would stop abruptly. Usually back-up resistances are provided, and electronic switching changes between regenerative and rheostatic braking according to conditions at any moment.

Regeneration is used mostly on DC railways because on AC railways (where rectifiers convert AC into DC for the traction motors), current cannot flow in the reverse direction back to the supply. Recent developments in thyristors (controlled rectifiers) now offer ways of overcoming this difficulty.

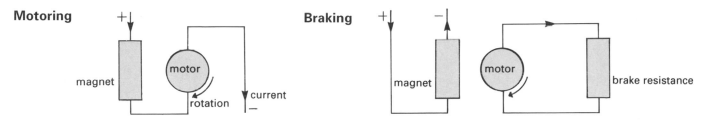

**Motoring**    magnet   motor   rotation   current

**Braking**    magnet   motor   brake resistance

▶ ▲ A representative of rheostatic braking in Britain is the Class 91. When power to the motors is cut off they continue to revolve, driven by energy from the train. The control system alters the connections in the motors so that instead of drawing current from the supply, from which they have been disconnected, they act as generators, sending current through the resistances. This produces heat in the same way as the bars of an electric fire, which drains the train of its energy and so it slows down until the mechanical brake comes into action to stop it.

# Wheel arrangements

## *Steam locomotives*

The wheel arrangement notation devised by the US engineer, Frederic Whyte, has been adopted in Britain and the United States for steam engines.

The Whyte system counts the wheels. Three numbers are separated by dashes – the first number gives the leading carrying wheels, the second is the driving wheels and the third the rear carrying wheels. T after the wheel arrangement denotes a tank engine. The two parts of articulated locomotives such as Garratts are described separately and joined by a +.

The continental system counts the number of axles. The French use a number for the driving axle, the Germans use a letter (see chart below).

On steam locomotives all power is transmitted through the driving wheels, which are connected by coupling rods. The leading carrying wheels may be in the form of a two axle bogie or a single one, either in a pivoted pony truck or in curved guides.

A heavy locomotive needs to be guided through curves and complicated trackwork when it is running at speed to protect the engine from derailment and the track from damage. Trailing carrying axles also have a guiding function but are usually provided to support the weight of a large firebox or, in the case of tank engines, the coal bunker.

## COMMON WHEEL ARRANGEMENTS FROM 1923

| Whyte / French / German | | Whyte / French / German | Name |
|---|---|---|---|
| 0–4–2 / 021 / B1 | | 4–6–2 / 231 / 2C1 | Pacific |
| 0–4–4 / 022 / B2 | | 4–6–4 / 232 / 2C2 | Hudson, Baltic |
| 2–4–0 / 120 / 1B | | 0–8–0 / 040 / D | |
| 2–4–2 / 121 / 1B1 | | 2–8–0 / 140 / 1D | Consolidation |
| 4–4–0 / 220 / 2B | American | 2–8–2 / 141 / 1D1 | Mikado |
| 4–4–2 / 221 / 2B1 | Atlantic | 2–8–4 / 142 / 1D2 | Berkshire |
| 4–4–4 / 222 / 2B2 | | 4–8–0 / 240 / 2D | |
| 0–6–0 / 030 / C | | 4–8–2 / 241 / 2D1 | Mountain |
| 2–6–0 / 130 / 1C | Mogul | 4–8–4 / 242 / 2D2 | Northern |
| 2–6–2 / 131 / 1C1 | Prairie | 2–10–0 / 250 / 2E | |
| 2–6–4 / 132 / 1C2 | | 4–6–6–4 / 2332 / 2CC2 | Challenger |
| 4–6–0 / 230 / 2C | Ten-wheeler | 4–6–2 + 2–6–4 / 231+132 / 2C1+1C2 | |

**KEY TO CODES:** 0–4–2 notation used in Britain and North America
021 notation used in France
B1 notation used in Germany

# Wheel arrangements

## *Diesel and electric locomotives*

A European notation system was developed for diesel and electric locomotive wheel arrangements. This has been adopted in Britain, although usually in a simplified form.

Each bogie is treated as a separate unit, and the number of driving axles is denoted by a letter: A means one driving axle, B two, C three and so on. Unpowered axles are denoted by a number: 1 for one axle, 2 for two axles.

In the original system two further distinctions are made. A bogie in which a motor powers two or more axles is distinguished by a plain letter. But in a bogie where each axle has its own traction motor a letter 'o' is added. A locomotive running on two 2-axle bogies, with one motor for each bogie, is classified as B-B, but if there is a motor for each axle it is Bo-Bo.

Secondly, in the Continental system, when two or more bogies are connected between themselves and to the couplings by an articulated drawbar running underneath the body of a locomotive, the notations for each bogie are joined by a plus sign. But when the tractive forces are transmitted through the body of the locomotive, the bogie notations are linked with a dash.

There is very little variety in British notations. Modern main line electrics and diesels are sometimes described simply as CC or BB. Rigid wheelbase diesel shunters are still described with the Whyte notation of 0-4-0 and 0-6-0, and the new generation of locomotives are confined to CC or BB configurations. However, preserved locomotives of the older BR generation sometimes have unusual wheel arrangements. The Class 45 diesels, for example, which under the Whyte notation could have been described as 2-6-0 – 0-6-2, are classified as 1C-C1.

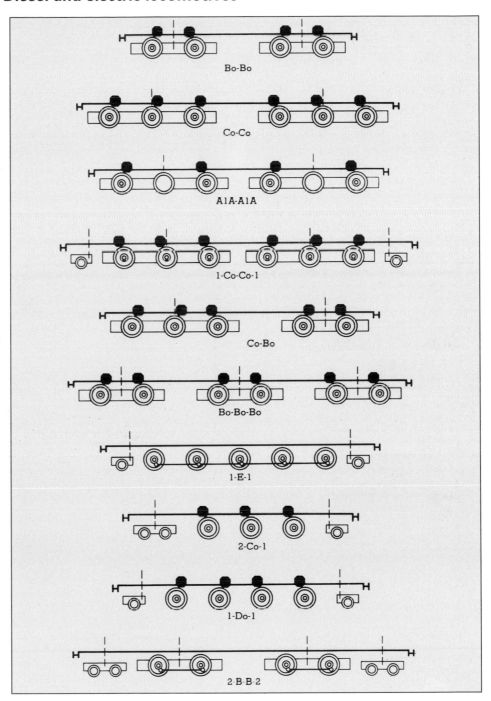

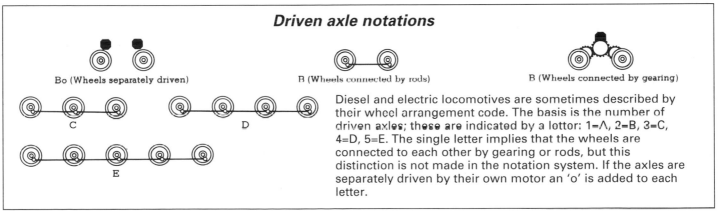

### Driven axle notations

Bo (Wheels separately driven)

B (Wheels connected by rods)

B (Wheels connected by gearing)

C

D

E

Diesel and electric locomotives are sometimes described by their wheel arrangement code. The basis is the number of driven axles; these are indicated by a letter: 1=A, 2=B, 3=C, 4=D, 5=E. The single letter implies that the wheels are connected to each other by gearing or rods, but this distinction is not made in the notation system. If the axles are separately driven by their own motor an 'o' is added to each letter.

# Unusual wheel arrangements

Any wheel arrangement, when it was first introduced, could be described as unusual, and was sometimes patented. The 4-4-0, a very widespread type in 19th century America and Britain, first appeared in 1837 and its builder, Henry Campbell, patented it, although other engineers soon found ways of avoiding royalty payments.

Whereas the 4-4-0 was unusual only in 1837, there have been some wheel arrangements that were never repeated. The clearest cut example is the 4-14-4 built in Stalin's Russia. Previously, 12-coupled wheels had been regarded as the absolute maximum, as exemplified by the 2-12-0 of the Union Pacific RR. But a revolutionary country deserved revolutionary locomotives, it was said. So the 4-14-4 was built and proved its revolutionary credentials by spending more time on the sleepers than on the rails.

Also qualifying as unusual arrangements are those that could not be fitted into Whyte's system of wheel notation. This system, which, for example, describes a Pacific as a 4-6-2, was thought to be all embracing when first introduced, but it was baffled by some designs, such as the locomotives with intermediate carrying axles built for Turkey early in this century. This design started as a conventional 2-6-0 but, because in that form the axle weight was too high, a pair of small carrying wheels was inserted between the central and rear driving axles.

The Fontaine locomotive of the 1880s would also have defied any wheel notation system. It had steeply inclined cylinders connecting to a pair of driving wheels whose axle was above the boiler, in front of the cab. These wheels had no contact with the rails, but instead had friction rims bearing on a pair of wheels directly below them which did rest on the rails. The claimed advantage of this arrangement was that the friction rims had the effect of gearing so that the carrying wheels, though only 4ft 8in, were the equivalent of 7ft 6in. Some US railroads accepted this locomotive for trials, but none saw any point in placing orders.

Equally imaginative were the few prototypes of the Holman roller-skate locomotive. Here again, the idea was to use upper driving wheels to multiply the speed of smaller wheels which actually carried the locomotive on the track. This concept had three tiers of wheels and, like the Fontaine locomotive, it represented a clever, but completely valueless idea. Its one advantage over the Fontaine design was that existing locomotives could be converted to the new system merely by mounting them on the skates. However, such locomotives could not clear many existing overbridges.

Whereas articulated locomotives such as Garratts were built in relatively large numbers, non-articulated double-engine wheel arrangements remained rare. An early example of these was Drummond's Double Single for the LSWR. This resembled a 4-4-0, except that the two driving axles, far from being coupled, were each driven by a separate pair of cylinders. Under the Whyte system, this was a 4-2-2-0.

In more modern times, several US railroads built locomotives with similar divided drive, so that coupling rods could be kept lighter, thereby reducing stress. The Baltimore & Ohio, for example, in the late 1930s introduced what was in effect a back-to-back 4-4-0, which under the Whyte system was a 4-4-4-4.

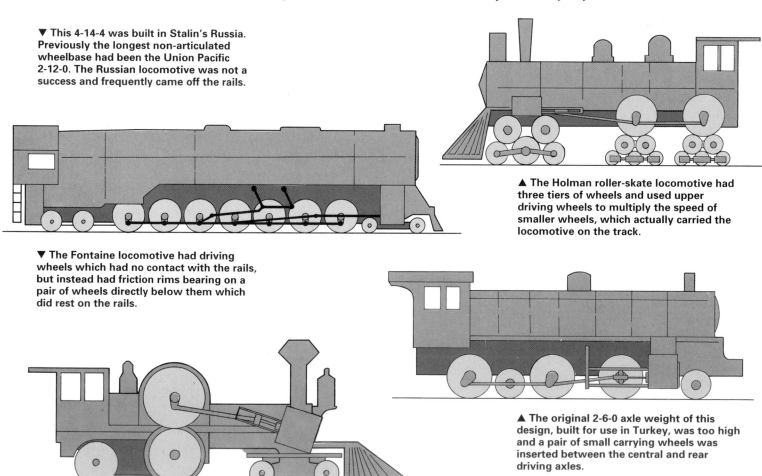

▼ This 4-14-4 was built in Stalin's Russia. Previously the longest non-articulated wheelbase had been the Union Pacific 2-12-0. The Russian locomotive was not a success and frequently came off the rails.

▲ The Holman roller-skate locomotive had three tiers of wheels and used upper driving wheels to multiply the speed of smaller wheels, which actually carried the locomotive on the track.

▼ The Fontaine locomotive had driving wheels which had no contact with the rails, but instead had friction rims bearing on a pair of wheels directly below them which did rest on the rails.

▲ The original 2-6-0 axle weight of this design, built for use in Turkey, was too high and a pair of small carrying wheels was inserted between the central and rear driving axles.

# Articulated locomotives

Articulated (jointed) locomotives are those on which the driving wheels are grouped into two, or occasionally three, sets with each set having its own drive. Articulation allows a locomotive with a high number of driving wheels to negotiate tighter curves than one on a rigid frame.

With conventional locomotives, 10 or 12 coupled wheels was the greatest number that could be accommodated without unacceptably hard grinding of the forward and rear coupled wheel flanges against the rail on curves. Articulated locomotives such as the Garratts were built with 16 driving wheels in 2-8-0+0-8-2 configuration for the London & North Eastern (LNER) railway and 4-8-4+4-8-4 configuration for use in Africa and Australia.

The need for articulation developed towards the end of the 19th century, with the quest for greater haulage power, spread so that light track did not suffer. The need was even greater on colonial and narrow gauge lines, where sharp curves and lightly built track were commonplace, once the lines attempted to increase their traffic.

There were several different approaches to articulation, each known by the name of its inventor. Two, the Garratt and the Mallet, grew into massive main line machines. A potential weakness was the steam and exhaust connections to the cylinders but this was overcome by using flexible pipe joints at the cylinders or the pivot centres.

▶ **An East African Railways Garratt builds up steam in Nairobi in September 1966. Garratts also saw service in Australia and some were bought by the LNER and LMS in the UK.**

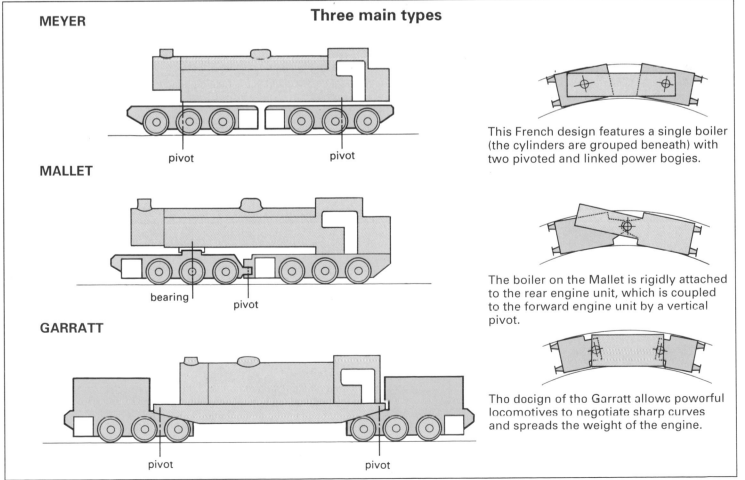

**Three main types**

**MEYER**

pivot    pivot

This French design features a single boiler (the cylinders are grouped beneath) with two pivoted and linked power bogies.

**MALLET**

bearing    pivot

The boiler on the Mallet is rigidly attached to the rear engine unit, which is coupled to the forward engine unit by a vertical pivot.

**GARRATT**

pivot    pivot

The design of the Garratt allows powerful locomotives to negotiate sharp curves and spreads the weight of the engine.

# Steam sanding

Since the 1840s, it has been normal to apply sand from the locomotive to the rail head to prevent wheels slipping and to improve their adhesion. Methods have developed over the years to ensure that the sand always gets under the driving wheels in all weather conditions.

Most systems required that the sand be dry, free from pebbles and with a low clay content to ensure it ran freely to the track. Drying and sieving was carried out in a furnace installation at the locomotive depot.

In the 19th century, there were some crude systems in use. In some cases sandboxes were fitted in the cab, from which the fireman was expected to scoop up sand by hand and pour it into a funnel-ended pipe leading to the rail. This was unsatisfactory, since he could only sand one rail at a time. As the wheels on one side of the locomotive only gripped, there was a high risk of twisting stresses in the axles.

The more usual arrangement placed the sandboxes in front of the wheels, at platform level. A disc valve in the bottom of each box, rotated by a linkage from the cab, allowed sand to run down the sandpipe and fall on to the rail. This was simple, but disc valves could jam in their gritty environment and the sand was necessarily delivered some distance in front of the wheel. Strong winds could blow the sand off the rail before the wheel could reach it and this was of no help at the moment of starting when adhesion was needed most.

The Midland Railway recognized these shortcomings and in 1886 it adopted a system, devised by the Derby works manager, in which the sand was blown under the wheels by compressed air bled from the Westinghouse air brake pump. When Westinghouse objected, the system was adapted by to be worked by steam, and has since been widely adopted. However, many railways using air brakes, particularly in the US, continued to use compressed air sanding until the end of steam.

## Operation

The successful operation of the sanding gear depended on the sand in the sandbox and sand trap remaining dry. Boxes on, or under, the side platforms were vulnerable to rain or condensation, and wet sand had to be cleared from the system before it would work. Some railways mounted sandboxes on the boiler top, where heat kept the sand dry and away from the motion. However, this raised the problem of access for sandbox filling, and sometimes this was not possible due to loading gauge restrictions.

When the BR Standard locomotives were designed in the early 1950s, they were fitted with a variation of steam sanding named after its inventor, Downs. There were no sand traps as the sand ejector sucked the sand directly through a coiled and slotted sandpipe in the box. Round this was wound a steam heating pipe (which also fed the sand ejector) to keep the sand dry. The Downs system was not a success and was soon replaced.

An alternative system was Lambert wet sanding. This method used a series of water nozzles in the sandbox to flush the sand through a trap on to the rail.

> ### 'Modern technology'
> In the 1980s, during a bout of particularly cold weather, many of BR's trains were experiencing difficulty in maintaining their grip on the icy rails. As a contingency plan, sand was kept in small sacks in the driver's compartment and in the case of severe wheelslip, the driver was to stop the train and shovel sand under the wheels. As one exasperated EMU driver made his way back to his cab he was heard to mutter 'In the days of steam I could do this without leaving my seat. So much for modern technology!'

▼To provide adhesion to an express passenger steam locomotive, sand was used and placed in a sandbox, usually positioned on the running plate. Underneath, a sandtrap prevented sand running out of the sandbox until it was drawn out by vacuum (suction) through a sandpipe; this led down to a sand ejector just above the rail. The sand was then blown at high speed by a small convergent steam jet (the cause of the vacuum) along the outlet pipe into the gap between the wheel and the rail.

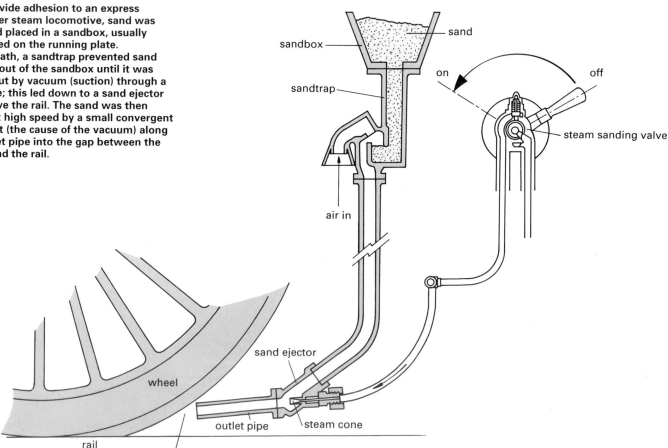

# Tyres and profiles

In the early days of railways, most vehicles had spoked wheels made of wood and surrounded by a flat profiled, plain metal rim or tyre, running on angled rail. These tyres would wear out quickly and, in an attempt to reduce wear, various cone shaped profiles (set at an angle to the rail) were tried by the different railway companies.

As railway technology progressed, experiments were undertaken to understand how the wheels moved on rails; the behaviour of wagon and bogie wheels on tracks was closely studied. In one case, British engineers were required to lie headlong in a cage beneath a wagon hauled behind various locomotives and trains at up to 60mph.

The various studies showed that bogies with wheels which had steep cone-shaped profiled tyres, wobbled fiercely as they tried to centre themselves on the rails after leaving a sweeping curve or a set of points.

If the movement is fierce enough to allow wheel flanges to graze repeatedly back and forth against the railheads, it is called **hunting**. This not only causes excess rail and wheel wear, but also gives a rough ride. These findings led to the use of cone shaped tyres of a less steep profile. By the time of the Grouping in 1923, the English and Scottish railway companies had agreed to standardize their wheel profiles.

## Tyre wear

The profile a tyre obtains in service is the result of a number of different factors: **fallen leaves on the line** can be ground into a pulp by wheels, causing wheel slip (when the wheels spin on the same spot and then grip, before spinning again). One of the results of wheel slip is called a flat – a flat spot on the round tyre tread. It can also be caused by **incorrect use of the brakes**. Flats cause hammering, vibration, damage the track and give a rough ride.

Fortunately, **clasp brakes** remove some of the leaves from the wheel. These grip the tread on the outside of the wheel to slow the train. But their application can distort the shape of the profile, eventually leading to rough riding. Modern trains fitted with disc brakes have reduced that wear, but as there is nothing to push leaves off the wheel tread, it makes the leaf slip problem worse.

Thin or worn flanges are potentially dangerous as wheels can pass on the wrong side of crossing angles, or derail trains on points. This is called splitting a point. The allowed wear varies from $^1/_{16}$in to $^3/_{16}$in (according to the vehicle type) before the flange is said to be in need of reprofiling.

## Correcting defects

To correct surface defects, such as worn tread or flats, wheels are turned (reprofiled) on a huge lathe. This can machine the tread, and sometimes the flange as well, into a new and correct shape. Some wheel lathes allow complete sets of wheels to be turned at the same time, without having to remove them from the locomotive.

The wheel rim gets smaller with wear and repeated turning until it is too thin for use. Some countries used to fit monobloc wheels (one piece castings without tyres) and when they were worn down to scrap thickness, new tyres would be fitted on the outside.

▼Because locomotive wheels are made of metal, it is not often realized that they need tyres to protect them. Metal tyres are expendable and when they lose their shape, are reprofiled a number of times until they are considered to be too thin to use; then they are scrapped and new ones fitted on to the wheel. To do this, the metal tyre is heated until it expands and then the wheel is lowered in. As the tyre cools it shrinks slightly to form a tight fit around the wheel.

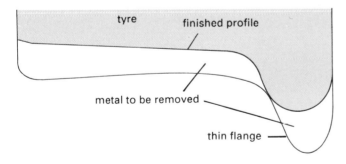

▲Thin flanges can cause derailments. The profile can be restored by removing some of the metal surface on a huge lathe.

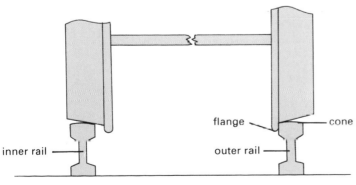

▲When the wheels go round curves, the flanges often grind against the railhead causing wear and a great deal of noise.

# Disc wheels

Railway wheels have been produced in such a wide variety of designs that the only common features are their flanges and their circular shape. For passenger and freight rolling stock, the transition from spoked to disc wheels was well underway at the turn of the century.

Disc wheels, easier to manufacture than spoked and also better in terms of strength and weight, were favoured for freight vehicles in the US in the 19th century; they were later adopted by some European railways. Until steel replaced iron, such wheels were often cast so that the outer edge cooled faster than the inside, producing a very hard running surface. Britain continued longer with the spoked wheel, but by the 1920s, British industry was producing both cast-steel and rolled-steel disc wheels.

The area of contact between wheel and rail is very small so the stress placed on the tyre and its support is very great,

especially at higher speeds and on bumpy track. With spoked wheels, any part of the tyre situated between the spokes is less well supported and this is one theoretical argument in favour of the unspoked wheel.

## US heavyweights

In most countries, locomotives continued to use spoked wheels, whose strength to weight ratio was adequate, until the end of steam. But in the US, where wheels carried far greater stresses, there was an earlier move towards disc wheels for steam locomotives.

Many of the heavier locomotives, built from the 1930s onwards, had the patented Scullin wheel. This consisted of two cast-steel discs back to back forming a hollow wheel centre and bound together by the rim and central boss. Apertures, cast in the disc, lightened the wheel and provided pockets in which lead weights could

be fixed for counterbalancing the wheel. This counterbalancing was done by the locomotive builder, not the wheel manufacturer.

These disc wheels were found to eliminate tyre failures resulting from distortion of the rim between spokes. Moreover, when hot tyres were shrunk on to these wheels there was less likelihood of heat warping.

The disc wheels of the Southern Railway's (SR) Merchant Navy Pacifics, which included not only the coupled wheels but also the carrying wheels of locomotive and tender, were wrongly described as Boxpok when they were introduced in 1941. Strictly speaking, they were BFB (Bulleid/Firth Brown) wheels, a joint creation of the SR's Chief Mechanical Engineer O V S Bulleid and a leading steel company. Bulleid's wheel was more complex than the Boxpok both in design and manufacture.

### Wooden wheels
Britain was unusual in that well into the 20th century its railways preferred a wooden wheel for coaching stock. The Maunsell wheel had a steel rim and boss but consisted mainly of a disc formed by wooden blocks which gave a beneficial cushioning effect. No doubt the increasing weight of coaches would have put an end to this type, but it was World War I, causing an enormous rise in the price of teak, that doomed it.

▲ In Britain, one of the greatest proponents of disc driving wheels was O V S Bulleid, the last Chief Mechanical Engineer of the Southern Railway. During the war, he made use of their ease of construction, great strength and relative lightness in all his designs, including Merchant Navy Pacifics like No 35008 *Orient Line*, seen here at Weymouth. Although this class was completely rebuilt in BR days, the disc wheels were retained.

▶ The disc wheel was designed to give greater strength than spoked types; there is support all the way round the tyre, not just where the spokes are. In the US, many of the heavier locomotives were fitted with a type called the Scullin wheel. In this, two cast steel discs were placed back to back to form a hollow wheel centre. Counterbalancing, carried out by the locomotive builder, was done by placing lead weights in apertures cast in the disc.

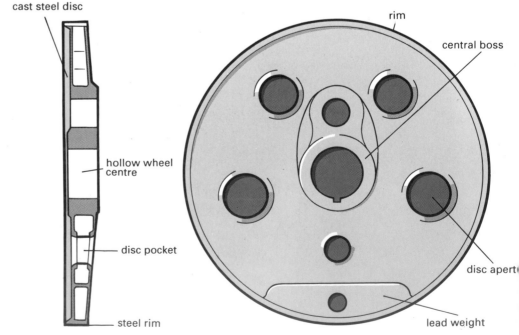

cast steel disc

hollow wheel centre

disc pocket

steel rim

rim

central boss

disc aperture

lead weight

# Suspension systems

The system of springs between the axles and the body of a railway vehicle forms the suspension. Springing between the axles and the bogie frame is the primary suspension. Secondary suspension supports the body on the bogie.

In the basic form of primary suspension, the axleboxes can move up and down under the control of springs in openings cut in the bogie side frames. These openings, or guides, have to take the thrust of traction and braking forces and are given a face of wear-resistant material, such as bronze, to reduce friction. Small bounces of the springs can build up into larger ones and are suppressed by dampers.

Coil springs have replaced the leaf springs used in earlier coaches and locomotives, and the guides are now tubular pillars extending downwards from the bogie frame inside the springs. Rods fitted to extensions of the axlebox casings are a sliding fit in the tubes.

When moving, a bogie takes a course which weaves from side to side. The secondary suspension – between the vehicle and bogie – must allow for this movement without transmitting it to the body, which rests on a bolster.

## Bolsters

In older stock, the bolster is held in position by guides on each side, with a small clearance to allow it to move sideways. Present practice is to fix the bolster in position by short traction bars at each end which transmit the traction and braking forces and have rubber-bushed mountings to give freedom of movement.

An alternative to the bolster system is the flexicoil suspension used in many locomotives. Here, the body is supported by groups of tall coil springs mounted on platforms outside the bogie frames. A fixed cross member in the bogie carries the pivot, which is free to float under the control of rubber buffers when the flexi-coil springs deflect.

Many passenger vehicles today have air suspension, the body resting on circular air bags supplied with compressed air from the braking system in the train. The air springs may be mounted on a swing bolster or directly on the bogie frame. When mounted on the bogie frame their flexibility allows for the side-to-side movements otherwise permitted by a swing bolster.

In the Advanced Passenger Train (APT), the coach bodies tilted on curves to allow these to be taken at higher speeds than had been planned when the track was laid. However, some passengers complained of discomfort. Since the APT was withdrawn, tilting systems have been improved and are used on several railways in Europe. Spain uses a passive system in its Talgo trains, the coach bodies being free to swing outwards under centrifugal force. However, while on straight track the suspension is locked.

---

### Primary suspension with radius rod

In older railway vehicles, the primary suspension – between the axlebox and bogie frame – used axlebox guides to retain the axlebox in the frame. In modern stock, some primary suspension systems have no axlebox guides, but the axleboxes are connected to the bogie frame by shortening arms (radius rods). The rods are mounted on rubber bushes which allow the axleboxes to move up and down and also provide some freedom of movement at right angles to the rail. In this example, the primary springs are mounted on an equalizing beam connecting the axleboxes to balance the weights on the two axles.

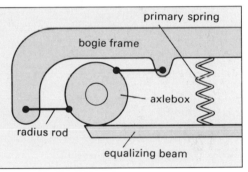

---

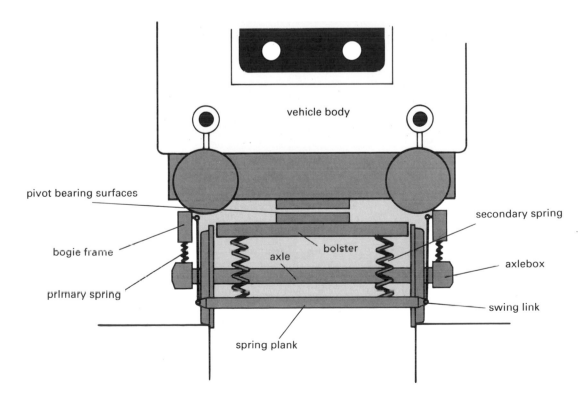

vehicle body

pivot bearing surfaces

bogie frame

primary spring

axle

bolster

secondary spring

axlebox

swing link

spring plank

◄ When moving, a bogie weaves from side to side and the secondary suspension – between the vehicle and bogie – must allow for this without transmitting it to the body. A spring plank, suspended from the bogie frame by swing links, moves from side to side and centralizes itself automatically. A transverse beam (the bolster) under the body sits on the spring plank through the secondary springs.

# Plain and roller bearings

The most vulnerable part of a moving train has always been the axlebox. This is where the fast rotating end of the axle, which carries the weight of the vehicle, is supported by a bearing surface. Enormous frictional forces, depending on the speed and weight of the train, are set up – without lubrication the close contact of the two surfaces will produce high temperatures, fire and melt-down.

Hot boxes were a daily occurrence on the railways. Even locomotives, which were always closely watched by their crews, could run hot bearings that necessitated a change of engine. With freight cars, less closely watched, hot boxes were quite common. Usually the first signs were a smell of burning oil, then smoke. Signalmen often spotted the fault and were able to stop the train in good time. If they did not, the brass bearing surfaces would start to melt and become distorted and the wheel would jam, possibly causing a derailment.

## Plain axlebox bearings

The plain, or friction, axlebox contained the bearing surface on which the axle end rotated. Its inner wall contained the hole through which the axle penetrated, and its outer wall, or often its roof, provided a flap through which lubricants could be loaded.

Brass was traditionally used for the bearing surface, but white metal linings came into favour later, because the pressures imparted by the rotating axle actually hardened brass. Hot boxes could only be avoided if there was always a microscopically thin film of oil separating the two metal surfaces. This film could be broken by tiny particles of extraneous matter, or a tiny irregularity of the bearing surface, starting a process that would end with a hot box.

## Roller axlebox bearings

An alternative to a plain bearing is the roller bearing – a cone that is pressed tightly on the axle and rotates with it, becoming the inner race. The outer race does not rotate and is mounted in the axlebox. Between the races are the rollers, which transmit the load from the inner (axle-mounted) to the outer (axle-box-mounted) race. The rollers run along a cone-shaped, tapered inner race, so they also bear side loads, as when the wheels are moving round a curve.

Roller bearings handle the load on rolling rather than sliding surfaces, so friction is very low. This reduces rolling resistance, so less horsepower is required to keep the train moving – although the difference in tractive force required actually to start the train is very small.

Some countries have now equipped all their stock with roller bearings, expense being the main obstacle. However, some engineers have had reservations about roller bearings, because, although they reduce the frequency of hot boxes, when they do run hot they give out little warning in the form of smoke and smell. Their hot-box incidents can therefore be catastrophic and cause much damage.

> ### Hot-box horror
> During World War II, US Army 2-8-0 locomotives operated on British railways. These, unlike British locomotives, had brass bearings and grease lubrication in which quite high running temperatures were normal – and indeed necessary if the grease was to flow. High failure rates were reported by depots for these locomotives until it was realized that warm bearings on these engines did not mean they were running hot.

▼ Bearings support the rotating axle which in turn carries the weight of the train. On steam locomotives with frames on the inside (*below left*), the bearings are behind the wheels. Generally they come in two types – the plain bearing axlebox (*below*) and the roller bearing axlebox (*bottom*). The bearing and axle are separated only by a thin film of oil, which in a plain bearing is distributed by cotton waste or wadding.

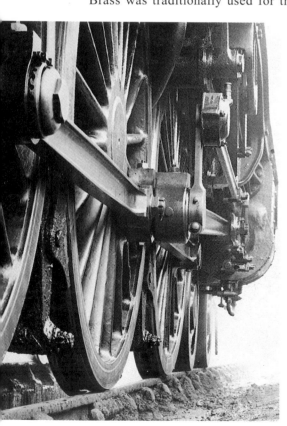

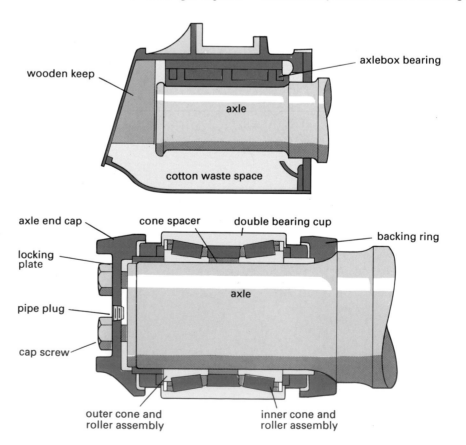

# Buffers

The purpose of buffers on railway vehicles is to absorb impact and maintain spacing. Originally they were dumb (wooden) without any springiness; the first spring buffers were primitive affairs stuffed with horsehair. Like the screw coupler, spring buffers seem to have originated on the Liverpool & Manchester Railway as a means of making first class passengers more comfortable.

In the USA the early move to central stress-bearing couplers – which ran under the frame of the vehicle – made buffers redundant. In this century they are generally found only on European railways or railways under European influence. The British companies soon standardized the height and spacing of the buffers to make rolling stock more compatible.

## Face shapes

The buffer face is traditionally round; its size is determined by the greatest degree of lateral swing that the vehicle is likely to produce, which depends on track curvature and vehicle length.

Dock and industrial shunting locomotives have very wide buffer faces to help eliminate the danger of buffer lock – on a bumpy ride over a sharp curve the buffer face passes behind the opposing buffer face and jams in that position, causing a derailment. To cope with this danger, the London Midland & Scottish preferred faces that were horizontally oval, and almost all BR coaches have similar faces.

## Buffer types

Until recently springs were the commonest method of impact absorption.

In the **spindle buffer**, the round buffer face is cast at the end of a long spindle, which passes through the buffer beam. Behind the buffer beam the spindle is flanged and surrounded by a coiled spring. It is this spring that absorbs impacts.

The **spindleless (self-contained) buffer** is shorter and fatter than the spindle buffer. The buffer face is cast on to a cylindrical plunger that slides inside the outer retaining barrel, with the coiled spring located inside the plunger itself. The floating spindle is a combination of the spindle and self-contained types.

Compound springs consist of two springs, one inside the other. The shorter spring, normally on the inside, does not come into play until the longer spring has been compressed a few inches. As the shorter spring acts only when the shock is severe, it can be made stiff to absorb heavy impacts.

In the Argentine, the front buffers of locomotives were hinged, and usually folded up and back. This was to avoid entanglement with wandering cattle.

## Modern buffers

Instead of using springs, the Oleo self-contained **hydraulic buffer** contains oil, which when compressed absorbs the impacts.

The **pneumatic** is a more complex form of buffer. When pressed, the oil acts to compress air, and this pocket of air provides the impact absorption.

## *Spring-worked buffers*

In the days of steam the spindle and spindleless types of buffer were used – these can still be seen in the UK. Buffer type usually depends on the operating conditions of rolling stock. As the weight of trains increased, new and stronger forms of buffers have gradually evolved.

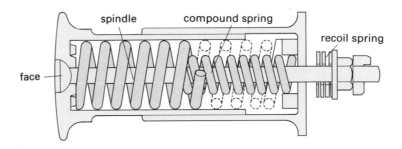

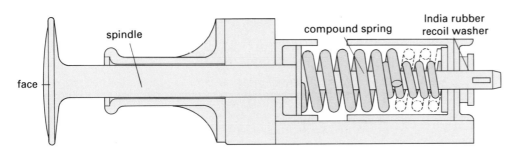

▲**Floating spindle:** A combination of the spindle and self-contained types – behind the compound spring is a strong recoil spring which pushes the buffer back into position. This type of buffer was often chosen for Indian railway stock where operating conditions were very primitive.

▲**Spindle:** These buffers were usually fitted to private owner wagons, particularly the 12-ton wooden bodied coal trucks built in huge numbers before World War II. The compound spring inside the plunger absorbs impacts, which can be very heavy during shunting operations.

▶**Spindleless (self-contained):** This type is less liable to break and can absorb heavier shocks than the spindle buffer and was therefore often fitted to locomotives. As there is no spindle or hole in the baseplate behind the spring these buffers were stronger than the spindle type.

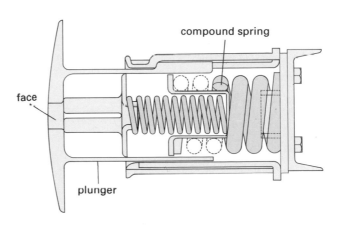

# Manual couplings

The manual coupling of wagons takes several forms, the most common being three-link, Instanter and screw coupling.

The **three-link coupling** is very simple and was used from earliest railway times. Until recently it remained the commonest form of freight train coupling in the UK, and it can still be seen on engineering trains. Long regarded as archaic on the Continent, its survival in the UK can be explained mainly by its cheapness and speed of operation.

Vehicles fitted with three-link couplings have a drawhook at each end connected by a drawbar which transmits the tractive power down the train. One end of the three-link chain is attached permanently at the rear of each hook. The chain hangs vertically when not in use, but when being coupled its outer link can be lifted and swung over the hook of the adjacent vehicle.

The three-link method sometimes allows the use of a shunting pole, which simply lifts the link and places it on a hook. Because it is not necessary for the shunter to stand between the vehicles to couple them up, he can couple or uncouple in comparative safety.

This loose coupling method is easy and fast to use. But because the train consists of loosely coupled vehicles which can bunch up or string out, driving and braking are difficult and speeds have to be restricted. Vehicles tend to bang against each other, which can lead to damage claims.

The characteristic drawn out clanging when a loose coupled train starts moving, with slack being taken up vehicle by vehicle, is reflected in wear and tear. However, this gradual taking up of slack can sometimes help the locomotive to start its train.

The **Instanter** coupling has a pear shaped central link, with irregularities that enable it to hold fast whether in a horizontal (long) or vertical (short) position and allow the shunter's pole to lever it into either position. The short form holds the vehicles closer together while running, whereas the long form makes coupling and uncoupling easier.

Because loose couplings were unsuitable for passenger vehicles, the British companies used the **screw coupling** – which holds vehicles closer, buffer to buffer – for passenger trains and later for fast freights.

The screw coupling has long been in use on Continental European railways for both passenger and freight trains. Fundamentally, it is the three-link coupling with the central link replaced by a threaded rod that screws into the outer links. This rod has a handle to assist turning, and the turning action draws the two outer links closer together, shortening the coupling and effecting a tight attachment.

Screw and three-link couplings are compatible and trains can contain vehicles of both types. Both require side buffers, unlike most automatic couplings.

There are some narrow gauge railways that still use the primitive **pin-coupling**, which is effective for small loads but requires careful manipulation.

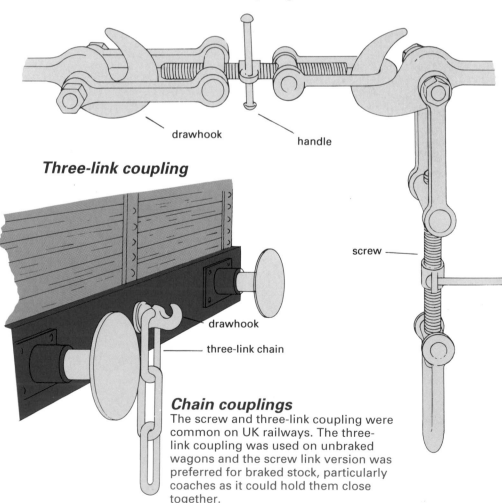

### Screw coupling

drawhook

handle

screw

### Three-link coupling

drawhook

three-link chain

### Chain couplings

The screw and three-link coupling were common on UK railways. The three-link coupling was used on unbraked wagons and the screw link version was preferred for braked stock, particularly coaches as it could hold them close together.

▲**Joining vehicles manually can involve ducking between buffers and hoisting a link over a drawhook and, for a screw coupling, turning a handle – a task that needs considerable strength and dexterity.**

# Automatic couplers

Though known as automatic couplers, the most widely used types are in fact semi-automatic. The couplers are strong and cope with both tension and impact, therefore permitting heavier trains and the elimination of buffers.

The **buckeye coupler**, sometimes known as the Janney, was developed for American railways. The coupler jaw is a clasped-hand arrangement with hinged knuckles. At least one of the knuckles must be opened before coupling. When the vehicles are pushed close together the open knuckle moves to the closed position, and a locking pin drops into place. To uncouple, the cars are pushed together to take the load off the coupler, and an uncoupling lever is hand turned to lift the locking pin so that the knuckles open as soon as the vehicles move apart.

This coupler was imposed on the US railroads in 1893 because of the large number of accidents with the existing couplers – fingers, hands and even lives were lost. Not only does the buckeye simplify coupling, but it also has the advantage of remaining coupled in derailments, so reducing damage. Passenger train versions of the coupler are slightly different, being locked against vertical movement.

Though the strength and convenience of the buckeye coupler were recognized, railways outside North America were reluctant to adopt it because it was incompatible with existing couplers. In Britain the buckeye was used for some passenger vehicles. Coaches fitted with it had a normal screw coupler as well, the buckeye swinging down when out of use.

The **Willison coupler** functions with an open jaw to which the link of an older non-automatic coupler can be attached. This coupler consists of an open head, which on one side has a locking piece that automatically falls into a recess of the approaching coupler. The locking takes place on both sides, whereas with the buckeye coupler all the strain is on the locking pin. Dividing the strain means that the Willison coupler can be lighter.

With all these couplers the train pipes have to be connected by hand, and the dream of designers was a truly automatic coupler. Nowadays such a coupler is used on many multiple unit trains. There are several variations, but the well tried **Scharfenberg** design, whose earlier versions were used in the 1930s, is still the most common.

This has a long nose that pushes up a horizontal rod on the approaching coupler head, so opening a revolving cover to expose the electric contacts, which connect as soon as the coupler jaws are engaging satisfactorily. Brake pipes also engage, with their cocks opened automatically by a spring release. Disengagement is by air pressure, typically initiated by a foot pedal in the cab. The automatic coupler used on modern multiple units works on the same principle.

Changing an entire wagon fleet to automatic couplers is a massive undertaking – a feat achieved only by Japan and Russia.

▲One of the main advantages of the buckeye coupler is its great strength. This form of semi-automatic coupler was developed by Janney in the USA, where trains over a mile long and weighing 10,000 tons exert great pressure on the coupling jaws. It has since been improved, but is still incompatible with non-automatic couplers.

▶ The operation of the buckeye coupler is simple. Coupler jaws are held in place by a locking pin; to couple one vehicle to another, one of the jaws must be open. When the vehicles are pushed close together the coupler jaw closes, and a locking pin drops into place. To uncouple, the locking pin is lifted by turning an uncoupling lever. As soon as the vehicles move apart the jaw opens.

*The buckeye coupler*

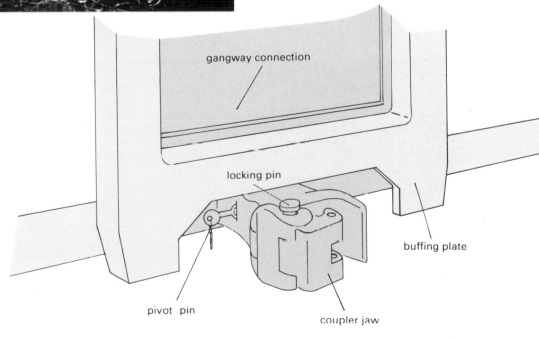

gangway connection

locking pin

buffing plate

pivot pin

coupler jaw

# BR coach bogies

British Rail (BR) Mark I coaches came into service in the early 1950s and were built in considerable quantities and types until 1963. They were fitted with the B1 bogie. This used leaf springs for its primary suspension and proved adequate for reliability and cost-effectiveness. Over time, however, its ride was increasingly criticized and from 1961 many Mark I coaches were fitted with the more expensive cast-steel, coil-sprung Commonwealth bogie.

The Commonwealth bogie was a stopgap measure until a new design could be introduced. In 1963, the B4 fabricated bogie appeared with coiled springs for primary and secondary suspension. It was fitted to all Mark II coaches and retrospectively to some Mark I vehicles.

The B1 bogie, still in use, has a maximum permitted running speed of 90mph (144km/h), although with special maintenance, some are allowed to run at 100mph (160km/h). The B4 bogie has a maximum permitted speed of 100mph (160km/h).

BR's Mark III coaches use a design of bogie known as the BT10, which is capable of running at 125mph (200km/h), although in some regions a lower speed is set as a maximum. It employs coil springs as the primary source of suspension, with a secondary air suspension system. The BT10 bogie accounts for the superior riding of Mark III coaches.

The Mark IV coaches use a Swiss SIG design – the BT41. This bogie has triple ventilated disc brakes on each axle, rubber mounted coil spring and swinging arm primary suspension, and secondary air suspension. This has airbags which incorporate their own rubber springs to absorb lateral deflection. As the coach body rests on these springs, in the event of the airbags deflating the springs maintain a degree of comfort. The air suspension contributes greatly to the smooth riding qualities of the Mark IV coach.

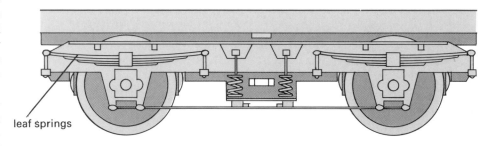

leaf springs

▲The B1 bogie was introduced in the early 1950s and was built until 1963. It was fitted with leaf springs for its primary suspension. Some are still in use and have a maximum running speed of 90mph (144km/h).

▼In 1963, the B4 fabricated bogie appeared with coil springs for primary and secondary suspension. It was fitted to all Mark II coaches and some Mark I vehicles. It has a maximum speed of 100mph (160km/h).

## Bogie history

Bogies were first used in Britain in 1873 on the narrow gauge Ffestiniog Railway, a year before the Midland Railway introduced a Pullman train on the London St Pancras – Bradford route. Pullmans had been developed in America specifically to upgrade comfort for passengers, who had previously had to put up with shorter four- or six-wheel rigid base carriages. The Pullmans were longer than any carriages seen on Britain's railways up to that time, and used bogies which gave superior riding to normal coaches. The next decade saw bogie coaches introduced on the Great Northern Railway, the London – Brighton line and the GWR.

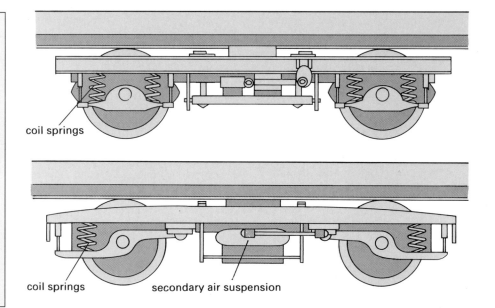

coil springs

coil springs          secondary air suspension

▲The BT10 bogie is fitted to Mark III coaches and is capable of running at 125mph (200km/h). It employs coil springs as the primary source of suspension, with a secondary air suspension system.

◀ Mark IV coaches use the Swiss SIG design BT41 bogie. This has disc brakes on each axle, rubber mounted coil spring and swinging arm primary suspension, and secondary air suspension.

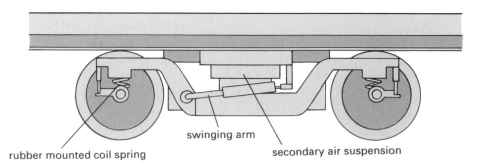

rubber mounted coil spring          swinging arm          secondary air suspension

# Air suspension

A simple axle will run quite smoothly on rails, but in order to absorb shocks, minimize wear on both vehicle and track and give passengers a smooth ride, a suspension system is fitted. Over the years, engineers have favoured many different approaches, but there is now wide acceptance that nature provides the best form of suspension – a cushion of air.

In fact, some luxury motor cars incorporated such systems decades ago and the idea of applying them to railways is not new. However, a successful system requires a fair degree of technology to meet the standard of ride demanded from today's trains.

## Two suspension systems

The precise design of a coach bogie varies according to requirements, particularly in respect of its maximum likely speed and loading, but the principle of air suspension is the same.

The bogies on which modern BR coaches run use a combination of springs and airbags. Springs act as primary suspension, to absorb the bulk of a shock, and airbags as secondary suspension.

The primary suspension is invariably one of coil springs, with dampers to reduce the effect of the spring's natural tendency to bounce up and down. The secondary suspension has an airbag (more properly called bellows) on which the coach body sits. It is the system's most distinctive visual feature and looks much like an inner tube of a lorry tyre.

The bag is inflated with compressed air, the amount being controlled by a levelling valve, which constantly monitors the amount of air according to the load as passengers board or alight. As the weight varies, so the coach body pushes further down on the airbag, tending to compress it, or lifts off it, letting it expand. A levelling valve admits or exhausts air accordingly to let the airbag return to its original shape. This process keeps the coach at a constant height above rail level.

Although air suspension is more complex than conventional springing and is more expensive to install and maintain, the system has many advantages. The cushion of air effectively de-couples the coach from the bogie, so it not only absorbs shock very well, but also considerably reduces the transmission of noise to the coach interior, making for a much smoother ride.

### Smoother braking

A by-product of air suspension is that variable load braking becomes relatively simple to achieve. Since the airbags monitor pressure in proportion to the number of passengers, this can be measured and linked to the braking system, which can adjust the braking force according to the load.

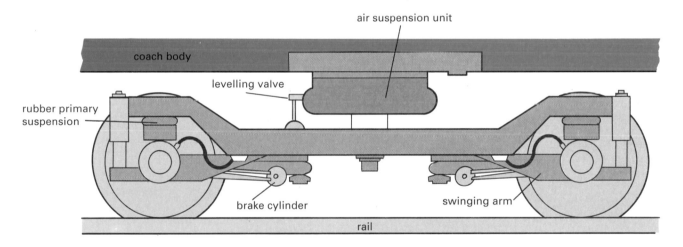

**Modern bogie with air suspension unit**

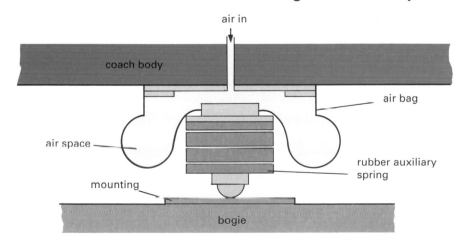

**Air suspension unit – cross section**

▲This type of bogie is seen on the trailing coaches of many of BR's latter-day multiple units. The primary suspension usually consists of coil springs, with dampers to reduce the effect of the spring's natural tendency to bounce up and down. The secondary suspension is made up of an airbag on which the coach body sits.

◄ The secondary suspension of the bogie is made up of an airbag filled with compressed air. Air into the bag is controlled by a levelling valve. As the weight of the coach varies – with people joining or leaving the train – the coach body moves up or down on the bag, which either compresses or expands with the action. By doing so, the coach body is kept at a constant height above rail level.

# Atmospheric railways

The appeal of atmospheric railways in the 1840s was due mainly to the notion that they would eliminate locomotives which carried no traffic, added considerably to the weight of the train, and threw sparks. So a railway that could manage without them would be more cost-effective.

With the atmospheric system, stationary power-houses along the route performed the function of the locomotive boiler, while one continuous cylinder, or tube, placed between the rails, replaced the two cylinders of the locomotive. Power was applied not by steam, but by a vacuum in front of the train, created by air being pumped out of the tube.

The piston was attached to the train through a slit in the tube. The slit was sealed by a continuous leather flap, one of the edges of which was fixed to the tube while the other edge, weighted down by an iron strip, was held tight by gravity and the suction beneath. A mixture of various greases was laid on the edge of the slit to ensure a snug fit of leather against metal.

Rollers attached to the piston rod pushed the leather aside as it passed. The slit could never be absolutely air-tight, but a partial vacuum would have been adequate.

To obtain the effect of the atmospheric pressure behind the piston, a vacuum was created ahead of it. This was done by the power-houses where steam engines drove pumps that sucked the air from the tube.

## First line

A short atmospheric line was built at Croydon, but the most ambitious project was that by Brunel in South Devon. Here there was an additional reason for using the atmospheric system. The South Devon Railway did not offer enough traffic to justify the expense of double track. But single track, with the signalling methods of that time, imposed a risk of head-on collisions. The atmospheric system made the chances of a head-on collision practically impossible.

The line was designed to run from Exeter to Plymouth, and it was ideally suited to the sharp curves and heavy gradients that could be expected. But it never progressed beyond Newton Abbot,

for after a few months, the South Devon management abandoned the system. Brunel had made several crucial mistakes.

He had underestimated the cost of building the line by four times. More importantly, he had not foreseen the difficulty of keeping air-tight the slit in the tube, through which passed the rod connecting the piston with the piston carriage at the head of the train.

The 15in diameter of Brunel's tube was too small, which meant that a higher degree of vacuum was needed, which in itself meant that leakage was more likely. The steam engines were too small to maintain this vacuum and had to be worked very hard, leading to breakdowns.

In addition, a cold winter and hot summer weakened the leather, so that it tended to be torn by passing trains. Replacing it was expensive and seemed likely to be frequent. The special formula grease included beeswax and tallow, and was loved by rats, who also enjoyed nibbling the leather. In 1848, the system was abandoned.

## Brunel's system

In Brunel's atmospheric railway, a single continuous air-tight pipe was placed between the rails. Air was pumped out of the pipe to create a vacuum in front of the train. A piston, attached to the forward vehicle through a slit in the pipe, pulled the train along. The slit was sealed by a continuous leather flap and held tight by gravity and the suction beneath. The leather flap was pushed aside by rollers attached to the piston rod as it passed. Numerous problems resulted in closure of the railway in 1848.

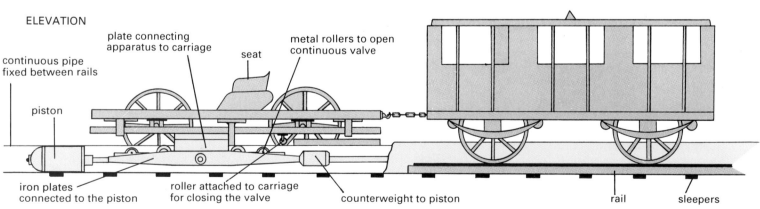

ELEVATION

continuous pipe fixed between rails

plate connecting apparatus to carriage

seat

metal rollers to open continuous valve

piston

iron plates connected to the piston

roller attached to carriage for closing the valve

counterweight to piston

rail

sleepers

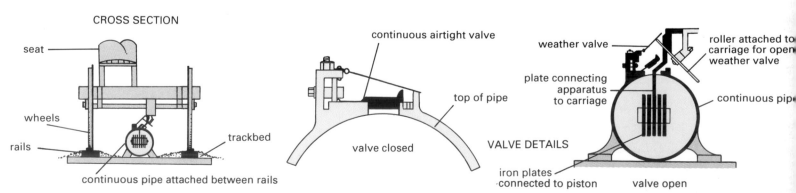

CROSS SECTION

seat

wheels

rails

trackbed

continuous pipe attached between rails

continuous airtight valve

top of pipe

valve closed

weather valve

plate connecting apparatus to carriage

roller attached to carriage for opening weather valve

continuous pipe

VALVE DETAILS

iron plates connected to piston

valve open

# Streamlining

The world's first streamlined train, the Windsplitter of the Baltimore & Ohio Railroad, appeared in 1900. Although the engine itself was not streamlined, the tender and the coaches were modified with the addition of side valances. However, the trial was soon judged to be a failure because it did not justify its initiators' belief that reducing wind resistance would result in very high speeds.

Wind resistance is very small compared to other components of train resistance – such as friction and gravity. But, small as it is, it increases with the speed of the train. British designers considered wind pressure negligible for speeds of up to at least 60mph.

However, the early 1930s saw streamlined racing cars and it was one of their designers, Bugatti, who produced a well publicized streamlined railcar in France. In 1934 two US railroads were operating long distance streamliners. To update their public images, railways of several other countries then introduced streamlined trains. The Hungarian railways even built a streamlined tank engine.

In Britain, after exhaustive air tunnel experiments, the LMS introduced 23 streamlined Coronation class engines, and the LNER built its A4 Silver Links – one of which, *Mallard*, was destined to win the world speed record for steam locomotives although it is questionable whether the streamlining of these locomotives produced much advantage apart from good publicity.

Streamlining of the Coronations – and particularly of the Coronation Scot train they were designed to haul – actually increased the surface area of the side of the train. Side winds are much more of a brake than head winds because they force the train sideways so that its wheel flanges grind against the rails. Streamlining was removed from the Coronation class locomotives after World War II and never replaced.

The LNER, however, retained streamlining after the war. The wedge shaped front end did at least have the merit of sweeping smoke and steam well clear of the driver's line of view. Two older LNER engines, B17 Sandringham class 4-6-0s, were also streamlined merely so that the inhabitants of Norwich and towns on the main line to the city of London could be flattered by their very own streamlined train, the East Anglian. The coaches, however, were not streamlined, the LNER explaining without a blush that this was because the speeds of the train did not justify it.

On the GWR the chief mechanical engineer, C B Collett, did not believe in streamlining but, urged to stay in the publicity race, gave two of his engines a few decorative extras which suggested that they too belonged to the streamline age.

At the highest speeds, especially when there was a headwind, streamlining did allow the same amount of energy to produce a slightly higher speed. *Mallard* would probably not have beaten the record without its streamlining, which was worth about four miles per hour in still air at 126mph.

But it was not until the substantial fuel savings of the era of the High Speed Train that the technique really justified itself. Even then care had to be taken during the design stage to ensure that the streamlining did not present a bigger area to side winds.

The application of streamlining did not always improve the performance of a locomotive – but it radically altered its shape. The difference is seen by comparing these two members of the B17 Sandringham class 4-6-0s.

# Dynamometer cars

During the days of steam the performance of a locomotive was recorded using a dynamometer car. Most importantly they measured the tractive effort and horsepower (work performed) with accuracy. These output figures could then be compared with input figures (fuel and water, or their product, steam) to see how efficiently the engine was working at different speeds and valve settings.

The dynamometer car was marshalled between the engine and train. One end of the coach, known as the live end, was coupled next to the locomotive. This live end contained a special drawbar, attached beneath the car by a spring. A buckle, fixed to the spring, moved in accordance with the tension or compression of the spring. The apparatus was linked to a pen that recorded the measurements on moving paper. The drawbar itself was supported by rollers so as to reduce friction to an insignificant quantity.

A GWR dynamometer car of 1879 had neither recording paper nor a special drawbar. But it was able to measure accurately the ground covered in fractions of a mile by means of a fifth wheel. By the 20th century some cars could also record oscillation of the car's body and the interaction of wheels and rail. Other dynamometer cars recorded the effectiveness of brakes, pressures on brake blocks and in the brake pipes, or took air speed readings and analyzed exhaust gases. There could be up to a dozen pens recording as the paper moved over the table.

The recording paper moved at a speed which matched the vehicle speed. Accuracy was obtained by connecting the paper through gears to an extra wheel running on one rail. In British practice, the paper could be set to move at either one or two feet per mile.

## Power readings

From these readings all kinds of calculations could be made. One of the simplest, and most basic, was the amount of horsepower exerted by the locomotive. This was calculated by multiplying the drawbar pull (measured in tons) by the speed (in mph) and by the factor of 5.97. The efficiency of an engine could be measured by comparing the weight of coal fed into the firebox with the horsepower-hours produced, rather than how many tons of coal were used per mile.

For the sake of accuracy, it was of the utmost importance that instruments were maintained in perfect order. This also applied to the devices that were used to measure the drawbar pull. Readings made by a dynamometer car of one British railway company have been questioned, as they seem improbable. It is possible that this car provided inaccurate measurements over a period of years.

## Well equipped

Most dynamometer cars also provided accommodation for their staff, and this could be quite elaborate in countries where long distances were involved, like India or Russia. A workshop inside the car, necessary for fixing minor defects, was quite common. All kinds of auxiliary apparatus was carried, sometimes for no apparent reason; some sympathy can be felt for the Russian policeman who tried to impound a dynamometer car, having persuaded himself that its calorimeter was really an illicit vodka still.

▼Dynamometer cars provided a variety of instruments and measurements. The special drawbar beneath the car measured the changing pull exerted by the engine. Recording paper moved over a recording table under pens, tracing data such as drawbar pull, speed, time and information taken from indicators at various points on the engine. Among the host of instruments in this vehicle, the builder's plate clearly states that it was built by the North Eastern Railway in 1906.

# Gas turbines

A gas turbine locomotive works by igniting a mixture of heated compressed air and injected fuel oil. The resulting gas expands and turns a set of turbine blades on a shaft. This, in turn, drives wheels through a set of gears. Gas turbines were pioneered on the railways by the Swiss Brown Boveri company and in the early 1940s a 2200hp unit worked on the Swiss Federal Railways.

The main advantages of gas turbines over other forms of traction are their high power/weight ratio, their acceptance of cheaper, heavier (residual) types of oil fuel and cheap maintenance and lubrication costs resulting from the absence of moving parts.

Gas turbines work best where the air is dense. This is a slight disadvantage in mountain operations, but a great advantage in cold weather. When turbines were later used in north eastern Canada, their power output was improved by up to 50% compared with use in mild conditions.

After the war, several railways experimented with gas forms of traction, although only the Union Pacific (UP) railroad in the USA, which already had a considerable fleet of powerful diesels, bought gas turbine locomotives in large numbers. In the 1950s, the company ordered 25 4500hp and later 45 8500hp turbine units.

## Efficiency drop

The gas turbine's greatest drawback is its sharp drop of efficiency when working at less than full power. Most railway locomotives work at full power for only part of their trip, usually when starting or climbing gradients. Several methods have been tried to solve this problem. The most common solution is to have a diesel and a gas turbine unit in the same locomotive. The diesel also boosts the turbine at peak requirements.

This method was employed in the UP gas turbine locomotives – which in any case needed a small diesel engine to start the main turbine. The diesel engine was big enough to generate sufficient power for the traction motors when the locomotive was moving by itself and, sometimes, when it was hauling a train downhill and full power was not required.

These units produced costs that were less per gross ton/mile than those of similar steam and diesel locomotives, but they have now been withdrawn as it meant the expense of maintaining two different forms of motive power. However, the high power/weight ratio of gas turbines has remained a constant advantage, only slightly compromised by the need to carry more of the heavier, lower grade – but cheaper fuel.

In the 1960s, the gas turbine locomotive was expected to enjoy a successful, if specialized, place on the railways. A series of train sets, known as turbotrains and built in France, have a gas turbine at one end and a diesel engine of about half the power at the other. These turbotrains were licensed for construction in the USA. But the rise in price of all oil fuels, with residual oils rising faster than light ones, have reduced their attraction in some countries.

On electrified railways, the turbine locomotive has little advantage in terms of power/weight, so its future remains with non-electrified railways carrying heavy traffic, which limits its long-term potential usefulness to North America and China.

## Improvements and problems

In several countries, there have been attempts to produce a gas turbine locomotive that can burn pulverized coal. This would have great attractions, especially for the coal industries that have financed much of the research. However, the problem of damage to the turbine blades by fly-ash has not been solved.

▼In Britain, the GWR ordered a 2500hp gas turbine from Switzerland, No 18000; BR had a similar but Improved version, No 18100 of 3000hp, built in Britain. The locomotives were found to be wasteful, since they consumed as much fuel when idling or running under low power as they did when hauling a heavy load. They had little chance of showing their capacity on a line where gradients were short and train loads not especially heavy. On 24 March 1953, a year after it was built, No 18100 hauls the London-bound Bristolian express over Goring troughs in Berkshire.

# Mixed freight trains

The most efficient transfer of rail freight is by **block train** going direct from source to receiver with one type of load. Certain commodities have traditionally been transported in this way: milk and fish trains travelling overnight, coal trains from pits to ports and ore trains supplying metal works. Yet, despite the financial merits of the block freight system, **mixed freight trains** were, until recently, far more common. This is because until 1957 the railways were defined as a common carrier and had to carry any load that was asked of them – unlike road freight hauliers who could pick and choose their customers.

The mixed train included different types of vehicles carrying diverse loads to a variety of destinations. Each vehicle would pass through freight yards and be attached to successive trains that would eventually deliver it to its destination.

In general, the composition of a mixed freight train depended simply on which vehicles destined for the same direction happened to converge on a sorting yard at a particular time. The open truck, the van and the tank wagon were the most common types of vehicles used in mixed freight trains.

There were a few rules governing the handling of such trains. Gunpowder vans, cattle wagons and long wheelbase vehicles required special shunting arrangements at yards. Most railways placed wagons containing easily combustible loads towards the rear, well away from locomotive sparks.

Until recently, wagons in the UK were fitted with one of three different types of brake: they were either **unbraked**, with manual side brakes only, **fitted**, with automatic vacuum brakes, or **piped**, with manual brakes fitted with a vacuum brake pipe but no vacuum brakes, enabling them to be placed among fitted vehicles.

If a train was composed of wagons with different types of brakes, special rules applied. The Military Railways Rulebook, issued by the War Office in 1938 stated: 'All trains must be marshalled so that all vehicles fitted with automatic brakes or pipes are together and next to the engine. Trains not composed entirely of fitted vehicles must have a hand-brake fitted vehicle marshalled in the rear and the guard must ride therein.' This meant that vacuum braked stock, whose brakes were controlled from the engine, would form an effective braking force. Manually braked vehicles would be restrained by the extra weight of the brake van, where the guard would operate his hand brake.

It was only with the advent of complete trains of air braked wagons that the brake van could be eliminated from freight working.

Fitted and piped vehicles were designed to move in fast freights. Their loads often included fish, fruit and vegetables. In the case of bananas, highly specialized vans, designed to maintain the right temperature for ripening, could be seen on fast freight trains originating from Liverpool, Bristol and Barry docks.

Empty wagons had to be returned to their owners, even if return loads could not be found for them. Before the railway and coal industries were nationalized in the late 1940s, wagons were prominently marked with their owner's name (one of the four railway companies or a private owner). Most private-owner wagons belonged to coal companies, whose trucks were often obsolete and badly maintained – a sore trial for the yard foreman who had to deal with any derailments in the yard.

▼Mixed freight trains were made up according to certain rules – particularly regarding the type of brakes fitted to the wagons. Usually the placing of wagons was determined by the order in which they were to be dropped off at their destinations.

# Brake vans

Railways in Britain were slow to fit all their goods wagons with automatic brakes, so freight trains had a brake van at their tail end. Although this van had several functions, the most important was to supplement the braking power of the locomotive.

Brake-blocks were fitted to all four wheels and these were controlled by the guard who turned a wheel inside the van, effectively screwing down the brakes. The guard could help control the train by making light applications of the brake on falling gradients and harder applications in emergencies, or when a fast heavy train had to be brought to a halt before the next red signal.

To maximize the braking power, the weight of the brake van was increased by using a heavy form of construction. Ballast was added – typically in the form of cast-iron blocks placed in pockets in the underframe. The British four-wheel brake van weighed about 20 tons.

## Guard's duties

The brake van also provided a working and resting place for the guard. Conditions inside were Spartan. The guard usually had a desk for his paperwork, where he kept a train journal and made entries in the train detail list. This gave the numbers of vehicles, nature of loads, and destinations.

At yards en route, the guard would look after shunting and a locker was provided for shunting poles. Other items were sand lockers and a stove that not only kept the van warm, but also served as a hot plate for the guard's meals.

A vital aspect of the guard's work was to watch over the train at all times. This requirement influenced brake van design and there were various arrangements of windows and open platforms. Most companies provided an open space at each end of the van, from where the guard could get a good view of the train and the line behind, and was within reach of a brake wheel. The Great Western Railway (GWR), however, preferred a platform at one end only, which was said to reduce draughts.

## Communication

Guards were equipped with whistles and red and green flags, but when in motion the engine whistle was used to coordinate the actions of driver and guard. Three short blasts signalled the driver's request for application of the guard's brake.

Good cooperation between guard and driver was essential, not only to eliminate sharp jerks that could break couplings, but also to give the guard a reasonable ride. Occasionally, because of mutual dislike or for no apparent reason, driver and guard could not work well together and each would give the other an uncomfortable ride.

Some express freights had automatically-braked vehicles coupled behind the engine, and unbraked at the rear. Parcels trains, however, usually had a passenger-train style of brake van. The Southern Railway (SR) introduced bogie (four-axle) brake vans for its express freights.

### Rough riders

Although in the 20th century some attempt was made to provide better springing on brake vans than on ordinary goods vehicles, the ride was extremely rough. With its rigid two-axle wheelbase, the van would swing violently from side to side and the guard might suffer cuts and bruises.

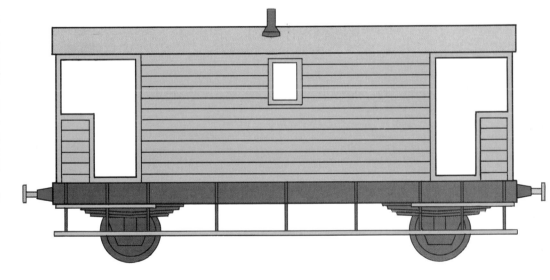

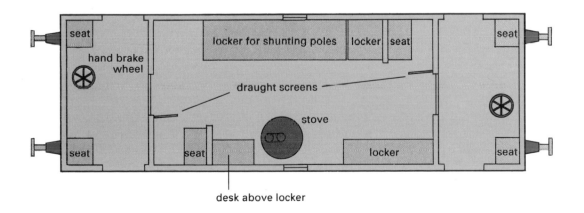

◀▲The style of brake vans varied from company to company. The GWR vans only had a guard's look-out position from one end. The LNER used a design of van which had a platform at either end. The SR inherited a design of brake van from the London Brighton & South Coast Railway (shown here) which had a veranda on each end. Brake vans could be extremely cold and draughty places, so the stove was much appreciated by the guard for cooking and heating.

seat · hand brake wheel · seat · locker for shunting poles · locker · seat · draught screens · stove · seat · locker · seat · seat · desk above locker

# British diesel railcars

Several railway companies were persuaded to introduce the railcar in the 1930s due to competition from thriving country bus services (and their low operating costs). They used mainly diesel propulsion, although the LNER also built a steam series.

In 1934 the LMS and GWR introduced two very different versions. The LMS tried a 260hp unit for its broad gauge lines in Northern Ireland that was virtually a coach with an elevated driving cab at either end and two Leyland diesel engines. It could be sandwiched between two trailer coaches to form a three-car train, carrying 278 passengers. Like many subsequent railcars it was intended for medium-distance stopping trains and was expected to have lower operating costs than a locomotive-hauled train.

The GWR railcar design was very different, although its horsepower was the same. A single unit, it took the GWR into the streamline era and was very much a high publicity venture. Far from lowering costs per passenger, however, it raised them; with a buffet at one end it could seat only 40 passengers paying third class fares plus a supplement of half-a-crown. With a top speed of 75mph, it was meant to develop cross-country intercity routes and made its debut with the Birmingham – Cardiff service.

The GWR version was more successful than that of the LMS, and more units were pressed into service until the company eventually ran a total of 38. They were built by bus manufacturers AEC rather than the GWR's Swindon works; some were twin-sets, two were for mail and parcels only, and some were intended for branch lines. They performed well and lasted into BR times. (Later models had angular rather than streamlined ends.) Ironically, on intercity services they became so popular that they had to be replaced by bigger, conventional trains.

Although the GWR railcar might be seen as an ancestor of the HST, in general terms subsequent railcar design took two different paths. The first was the multiple-unit railcar set for short- and medium-distance services. This offered low running costs, quick terminal turnaround and good acceleration from stops. These were built in large numbers in the 1950s and were immediately successful, later evolving into BR's Sprinter series.

The second path was towards the cheap, bus-like railcar for branch line use. In Germany, where the government made a determined effort to retain branch lines, the two-axle railbus was built in large numbers. BR bought a few but did not keep them for long, and they certainly did not save the British branch line. Some of their features reappeared in BR's modern Pacer series, however.

Even in Germany the railbuses rarely made a line profitable; they simply provided a better service at a reduced loss. In Britain, with conventional accounting, railcars were not even cheaper than locomotive-hauled trains. This was because branch services were usually entrusted with rolling stock that was well beyond its depreciation life – new railcars only added substantial capital charges to the balance sheet.

▲In 1933, the GWR introduced a single-unit railcar for cross-country and intercity routes. Though capable of 75mph, their streamlining was very much a publicity exercise. Far from cutting costs, these railcars carried few people and proved expensive to run.

▼This BR diesel multiple-unit railcar of the 1950s was designed to work on branch lines and feeder services for main line expresses. It could be multiplied up to a maximum of four twin-sets to suit peak and off-peak periods. Top speed of this railcar was 70mph.

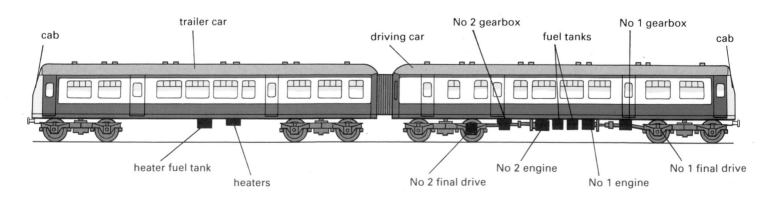

# Passenger train make-up

Photographs of the LNWR's Anglo-Scottish expresses show irregular carriage roof lines and six- eight- and twelve-wheel coaches in the same formation, with both old and new running next to one another. This untidy effect was heightened when non-passenger stock fitted to run in passenger trains were also present; such vehicles included parcels vans, horse boxes and ventilated wagons.

Trains were assembled to provide the best seating arrangements for the type of passenger traffic expected. Local passenger managers knew from experience what proportion of first class passengers to expect on each train and composed the train's accordingly. For example, weekday morning and early evening intercity trains would have more first class coaches than Saturday services because of the different types of passengers travelling at those times.

Long distance trains also had little uniformity. Coaches were added and detached at intermediate stations and often included carriages from other companies as part of a through service. This meant passengers did not have to change trains at a station; instead their coach was shunted from one train to another with the passengers still on board.

Trains were made up according to a printed roster and large coach depots had considerable remarshalling work, using shunting locomotives working full time. Passenger trains were usually marshalled in large carriage sidings, strategically placed near main line stations.

The use of different systems often complicated the work of passenger depots. Until grouping in 1923, the co-existence of two incompatible brake systems – air and vacuum – was a particularly irritating factor; the East Coast Anglo-Scottish trains could only be formed from coaches fitted with both brake systems.

After World War I it became increasingly common for suburban trains to be composed of fixed-formation sets, but longer distance trains were still made up from a variety of different carriages. With standardization, passenger trains on BR today are usually made up of coaches that are outwardly identical. For economic reasons the coaches are often in a fixed-formation where they are semi-permanently coupled together as complete trains.

## Coach types

There has always been a variety of different interior carriage layouts. Passenger carriages could be divided into corridor and non-corridor coaches, both of which could be compartmented and non-compartmented (saloon) stock. Saloon coaches were rare until the LMS standardized the centre aisle layout.

Some coaches provided only first or third class accommodation; others, called composites, had both. Composite coaches were especially useful for trains that had to provide first class accommodation but carried few first class passengers.

There was a wide selection of catering vehicles, ranging from a single buffet car to a three-coach dining set and the choice rarely satisfied all the passengers. Catering vehicles were hard to position in a train. They often ran for only a part of the journey, but placing them at the end of the train to make them easy to attach and remove meant that some passengers would have a long walk from one end of the train to the other to find refreshments.

▼Before coaches were formed into semi-permanent fixed formations, sprawling carriage sidings could be seen near many large stations. At Bristol on 28 March 1964, a mixture of BR standard, ex-LNER teak and ex-LMS coaches wait to be made up into trains for their next journey.

# Tavern cars

Possibly the UK's most unusual and controversial refreshment cars were the tavern twin sets designed by the equally controversial O V S Bulleid, Chief Mechanical Engineer of the Southern Railway at the time of Nationalization. One coach was a buffet kitchen (the tavern), the other a full restaurant car (tavern trailer).

Bulleid had previously designed some very comfortable buffet cars (the Bognor Buffets) which had led to some passengers spending most of the journey in them at the expense of others. The tavern sets were intended to discourage this through a less appealing interior, but Bulleid had apparently also become attracted to the 'olde worlde' style of many of the south-east of England's inns.

## Good health

The interiors of the tavern cars were of a mock Tudor style with real oak beams, patterned glass, imitation metal lanterns and floor tiling (all based, apparently, on the Chequers Inn at Pulborough). The Tavern car itself had a kitchen, laid out conventionally, a cocktail bar and lounge, with stainless steel and plastic laminate in marked contrast to the other fittings.

The restaurant car, with similar decor, had 24 seats with tables in the first class section and 40 seats in the third class area. First class seats were in old rose and turquoise brocade; third class seats had maroon upholstery. Luggage racks were of toughened glass so that passengers could see if they had left any luggage, and recessed fluorescent lights were fitted to the ceilings. But most conspicuous was the lack of windows, only narrow sliding toplights being provided to rob passengers of the passing view.

Externally, the coaches were liveried in the carmine and cream (blood and custard) colour scheme of the time. The kitchen half of the tavern car was conventional, but the other half of the same coach continued the pub theme. The lower carmine was painted as imitation brickwork, while the upper cream part had black mock-timbered lining plus a hand-painted inn sign. The restaurant car looked equally bizarre, with its lack of full-depth windows.

Eight sets were built, not simply for the Southern Region, and entered service in 1949. The restaurant cars immediately met with complaints from passengers who disliked the claustrophobic atmosphere and deserted the cars even at peak times. Business hit all-time lows and, before long, the cars were withdrawn and rebuilt in conventional form between early 1950 and June 1951.

## Likes and dislikes

The tavern cars were less disliked by passengers (after all, what better than a pub on wheels?) and they were commercially successful; in fact, beer sales reached record levels. But they were very heavily criticised on aesthetic grounds and gradually the brickwork and timber was replaced with standard carmine and cream. From 1957, green began to appear and from 1959 they were rebuilt conventionally, losing their inn signs at the same time. By December 1967, all coaches of the sets had been withdrawn.

▶ The interiors of the tavern cars resembled the style of an 'olde worlde' English pub with real oak beams. They proved very popular with their patrons and beer sales reached an all time record high.

▼ The buffet kitchen car of the two-car sets was laid out quite conventionally, much like any other kitchen car running on BR at the time. The meals were served in an adjoining 24 seat restaurant car.

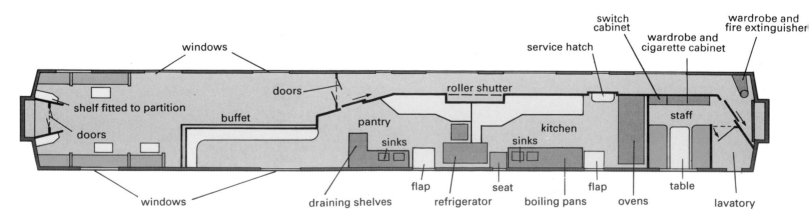

# Railway bottles

British railway companies made extensive use of bottles, particularly in their role as caterers to the travelling public. They provided restaurant and buffet cars in trains, refreshment rooms at stations, and bars and restaurants in railway hotels. Each of these establishments offered liquid refreshment of a type best transported in glass bottles.

Until quite recently, most bottles, rather than being discarded when empty, were returned to the manufacturers to be cleaned and re-filled. They were often used many times over, and were made thick and heavy to withstand so much handling.

## Missing labels

Although railway catering began at around the same time as the railways themselves, most of the surviving identifiable bottles date from this century. This is due to the fact that the majority of earlier examples were marked only by paper labels, most of which have long since disappeared.

The Great Western Railway produced bottled lager from the Wrexham Lager Brewery in North Wales, identified with labels reading, 'Specially bottled for the GWR'. One of these labels today would be a prize indeed.

The most numerous type to survive is the beer bottle. Most of the railways sold their beer in half-pint bottles, although occasionally a pint bottle is seen. Half-pint bottles are known to exist embossed with the names or initials of the Great Central, the Lancashire & Yorkshire and the Midland railways.

Of the post-Grouping companies, the London & North Eastern Railway and the London Midland & Scottish Railway (LMS) are the most common. Although there are a few examples in clear glass, most are in varying shades of dark green or dark brown, and are embossed with the company's name or initials.

The LMS bottles, for example, carry the company's initials in large capitals upright on the side. Some of the bottles used in the Midland Railway's hotels carry the words 'Midland Hotels', also in capitals, but ranged horizontally.

Popular on some lines were glass whisky flasks. These were small, pocket-sized containers with rounded bottoms. They could only be laid flat, which prevented them from being knocked over and broken by the motion of the train. They were sealed with a cork, on top of which was a small knob. With this, the cork could be pulled without the use of a corkscrew.

The biggest user of whisky flasks was the Midland Railway, although the Great Northern also had them. The Midland examples were again embossed 'Midland Hotels' in capital letters.

Mineral water was also purveyed in railway bottles. Perhaps the most sought after are the Codd type, with glass ball stoppers. These are rare, though, because all too often the stoppers were taken by children and used as marbles.

### Collecting bottles

As well as the usual railway auctions and swopmeets, good sources of railway bottles are the numerous fairs set up around the country by bottle collecting enthusiasts. The usual brown beer bottle from the London Midland & Scottish Railway should cost no more than a few pounds. Those from the London & North Eastern Railway are scarcer and therefore may cost fractionally more.

Pre-Grouping beer bottles from the Midland or Great Central railways will be more, but one from a smaller line could cost much more. For a Highland Railway bottle, for example, you could expect to pay several hundred pounds.

The Midland Railway whisky flasks should be well under a hundred pounds, while railway-marked mineral water bottles will be anything from £50 to a couple of hundred pounds.

◀ From left to right: Lancashire & Yorkshire Railway Liverpool; Great Central Railway; Great Western Railway Fishguard Harbour (very rare); Midland Hotels Cellars Derby; London & North Eastern Railway; LMS Hotels (London Midland & Scottish Railway).

# Restaurant cars

The first regular meal service on a train was provided in 1867 in a kitchen-fitted Pullman car by the Great Western Railway of Canada. In Britain, the first dining car train was introduced by the Great Northern Railway (GNR) in 1879.

In the steam era, some long distance trains were provided with three-coach dining sets, typically with one vehicle containing the kitchen and pantry, and the others serving first and third class passengers separately.

In Britain, first-class accommodation often provided two-seat tables on one side of the aisle and four-seat tables on the other, whereas third-class diners had the less spacious 4x4 seating.

## Kitchen conditions

In an effort to make eating on a train as comfortable as possible, most designers tried to limit cool draughts, sometimes by eliminating adjustable windows altogether and by providing extra internal doors at vehicle ends. Extra insulation, including thick carpeting, was provided to dampen sound and vibration.

Food preparation on a moving train was difficult. The kitchen car bounced over rail joints at 50mph and the difficulty was intensified by the necessarily cramped space. Vibration and intense working conditions took their toll of refrigerators and boilers, which sometimes failed in service.

Things are easier if meals are pre-cooked, airways-style, at stations and loaded on to the train just before departure. But BR abandoned this practice, believing that at least the main element (typically meat) of the dish should be cooked on the spot, even though some items might be partly prepared before loading on to the train. This gave a more appetising result and, it was hoped, better consumer-satisfaction.

Nowadays, restaurant cars are essentially a marketing attraction, aimed almost exclusively at travellers with expense accounts. Not only do the costs of providing a restaurant car exceed its income, but its inclusion in a train usually means that fewer seating coaches can be provided, reducing the number of fare-paying passengers. There is, therefore, a big advantage to be gained by concentrating all the functions – food preparation, storage and table service – in one vehicle, making further space available for more fare-paying passengers.

## Buffet cars

Although restaurant cars do not make a profit, their cheaper version, the self-service buffet car, is expected at least to cover its costs.

Buffet cars with seating areas were direct descendants of the cafeteria cars tried before the war. With self-service and a limited choice of items, the heavy losses associated with a full meal service could be avoided. However, because of the different trains in which a buffet might be included, it was difficult to achieve a good balance between the serving area and eating area. For example, a train with frequent stops might take on board passengers who planned to spend their entire trip in the buffet, whereas with longer trips passengers might make more frequent, but shorter visits. An excessively comfortable seating area encouraged clients to linger too long, denying access for others.

The problem of maximizing revenue-earning seats while retaining a buffet-style service has been solved by abandoning the buffet seating area; passengers return to their seats to consume their purchases. Alternatively, a train may have no buffet car and passengers are served from a self-contained on-board refreshment trolley passing through the coaches.

▼The kitchens of restaurant cars were designed very carefully. Those of the inter-war period, with their maximum use of flat surfaces and space, had much in common with today's domestic fitted kitchen. The first-class dining saloon and kitchen car of the Southern Railway (top) and café car of the GWR (below), were both introduced in 1932. The café car served refreshments similar to those obtained at stations, while the kitchen car could provide full meals.

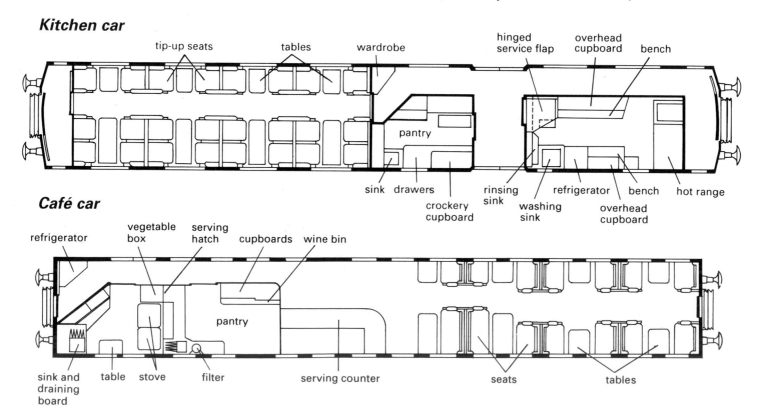

**Kitchen car**

tip-up seats · tables · wardrobe · hinged service flap · overhead cupboard · bench · pantry · sink · drawers · crockery cupboard · rinsing sink · washing sink · refrigerator · overhead cupboard · bench · hot range

**Café car**

refrigerator · vegetable box · serving hatch · cupboards · wine bin · pantry · sink and draining board · table · stove · filter · serving counter · seats · tables

# Observation cars

Arguably the most luxurious train ever seen in the UK was the London & North Eastern Railway's (LNER) Coronation express of 1937, introduced to commemorate the crowning of King George VI. Designed by Nigel Gresley, the train ran between London King's Cross and Edinburgh, setting new standards of speed and comfort.

## Special vehicles

Eight coaches, four articulated twin sets, always ran in a standard formation, but the most celebrated coach was an extra one used in the summer only – the observation car coupled to the rear of the train. Two cars, Nos 1719 and 1729, were built at Doncaster. They were 54ft 7in over buffers and ran on 8ft 6in Gresley bogies. The observation end was curved downwards and the shape was referred to as the beaver tail.

This shape was not only intended to reduce aerodynamic drag, but also to give passengers a spectacular view of the passing scenery. While the rest of the train ran in the same formation in both directions, the observation car had to be turned around and moved from end to end of the train at the two termini.

Externally, each car sported the two-tone livery of the rest of the train. Below the waist level the cars were Garter blue and the upper area around the windows was painted lighter Marlborough blue. The roof was lead white and the skirting black; the wheels had white tyres. Also, to match the rest of the train, the cars had stainless steel strips, raised numbers and letters, with the name Coronation displayed on both sides and the back below the rear windows which were made from large, curved perspex panels.

Internally, the cars had a luxurious decor, with limited, but spacious seating. Fourteen individual armchairs were provided, seven either side of the central aisle and one double armchair backed on to a mail compartment. The restricted area below the beaver-tail window featured a built in table. Naturally, for the period, the cars were all smoking.

Accommodation was intended to be temporary, a supplement of 1s (5p) being payable for an hour's use; tickets were issued by a lad attendant on the train. During the hours of darkness, the lights were dimmed to improve observation.

However, in truth, the view was not all that special; the side windows were no different from those on the rest of the train and the rear perspex panels gave a restricted view of the receding track, particularly when the train met Scottish mist, rain and tunnels.

## Small change

Initially, little alteration was made to the cars except for the addition of handrails in 1938. During World War II, the cars were put into storage with the other Coronation coaches ready for a post-war revival, but the Coronation never ran again as a train.

In 1959, the cars were rebuilt as full observation coaches, losing the distinctive beaver-tail shape in the process, but now provided armchairs for 28 passengers. The cars saw service in Scotland and both were bought from BR in 1968 for private preservation.

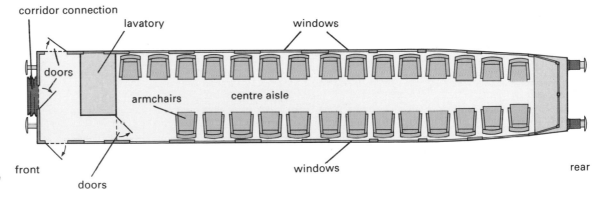

### Famous observations
Observation cars have been relatively few in the UK but the Coronation was not the only train to employ them. Such facilities had been provided before, although not always on a regular basis. Probably the most famous other observation cars were from the Pullman stable: *Maid of Morven*, built in 1914 for the Caledonian Railway, and the two vehicles built for the post-war Devon Belle, one of which has been preserved in Devon. Engineers' inspection saloons have also been used for such purposes from time to time, including the SR General Manager's saloon for the wedding of Prince Charles and Lady Diana.

▲ Few observation cars are in use today. One of them is the former Southern Railway Devon Belle car and is now run on the Torbay Steam Railway. This is particularly appropriate as this line runs over seven miles through Devon.

▶ The two Gresley Coronation observation cars were rebuilt in 1959 and in their later years operated over the Kyle line between Fort William and Mallaig. The viewing end of the cars was restructured and more seats were fitted.

corridor connection

lavatory

windows

doors

armchairs

centre aisle

front

windows

doors

rear

# Doubledeck trains

While doubledeck train designs have been seen in other countries, there has been only one revenue-earning design in the UK. This was the Southern Region's 4-DD (four-car doubledeck) electric multiple unit, the product of the imaginative O V S Bulleid, the last CME of the Southern Railway. The design was an attempt to solve the post-war problem of commuter overcrowding without costly lengthening of platforms to take longer trains.

## Loading gauge
A considerable obstacle to doubledeck trains (those with both lower and upper decks, just like buses) is the UK loading gauge. With numerous lines built at a time when carriages were shorter and narrower, many tunnels, bridges and other lineside structures do not have sufficient clearance to allow anything more than a conventional carriage to pass freely. This led many to discount the notion of dou-

bledeckers, but Bulleid had other ideas and he developed his new train just before Nationalization in 1948.

The design of the 4-DD was a remarkable feat of ingenuity. Top level seats were cleverly designed to interweave with those on the lower deck, so that those upstairs were sitting just above the heads of those downstairs. Individual compartments with side slam doors were retained with access steps to the upper level in each compartment. A trailer car had six such double compartments, each with 11 seats on both levels, with one 12-seat lower compartment in the middle of the coach. Additionally, 12 tip-up seats were provided on the upper level, so that each of the two trailers could seat 156 passengers; the motorcoaches could seat 120. Thus seating capacity of two four-car units was 1104, compared to around 772 in a conventional eight-car train.

Two sets were initially built and entered service in late 1949, numbered

4001 and 4002, and sporting the standard British Railways malachite green livery. There was some concern over possible accidents amongst operating staff, but public reaction was largely neutral except for some complaints about poor ventilation. However, experience soon revealed delays at stations while passengers alighted and some women were concerned at travelling alone, not knowing who might be on the other level.

## Final decision
Eventually, BR decided to make conventional trains longer and lengthen platforms, and no further 4-DD sets were built, ending this promising experiment. Nevertheless, the units proved they could accomplish their objective, carrying large numbers of commuters in modest comfort. The two sets ran in service for over 20 years, always on the same route and usually as a pair. They made their final run on 1 October 1971.

---

### More doubledeckers?
The 4-DDs may be regarded as a brave attempt at something largely precluded in the UK due to the restricted loading gauge. Other countries often have a more generous gauge which makes this less of an issue, although solid structures still prevent their use on certain lines. As to the looks of the 4-DDs, were they ugly or handsome – or perhaps just unusual? Interestingly, the proposals on privatizing the BR network revealed that at least one prospective lessee was seriously considering building further doubledeckers.

---

▼ Bulleid's two four-car doubledeck (4-DD) sets were introduced in 1949. Externally, the 4-DDs filled the Southern loading gauge to the maximum, and they were restricted to the Charing Cross/Cannon St – Gravesend lines. The flat sides were slab-like and extended down below the normal solebar level and high up to the roof. The guard's double doors were recessed to keep within the loading gauge, but in most ways they resembled the standard Bulleid 4-SUB steel multiple unit.

# Class 08 0-6-0

Classified 08 by BR, this type derived from an English Electric prototype of 1934 and totalled almost 1200 units. By the early 1990s, this number was declining because of the decrease in freight traffic and the dominance of block trains which meant much less shunting work than before.

Originally designed for 350hp, the class was soon uprated to 400hp. Unlike most diesel locomotives, they have a rigid frame, steam-locomotive type wheels and coupling rods. Although built in the 1950s, the design really dates back to the 1930s, when the London Midland & Scottish Railway (LMS) showed an interest in diesel shunters and ordered small batches from various manufacturers. Among them was an English Electric prototype similar to the present 08, but at that time it was inferior to other designs. In particular, its traction motors tended to overheat, but English Electric persevered, learned from its competitors and provided forced ventilation for them.

## Engine of war

At the beginning of World War II, the LMS ordered a hundred units of the improved design, but none was delivered until 1944, and went initially not to the LMS, but to the War Department. In the end, the LMS received only a handful, many of the WD engines never returning.

At the end of the war, the three other railway companies ordered a few similar locomotives for trial. What eventually became Class 08 was simply a post-war version of these locomotives, although it had 4ft 6in wheels (as had those ordered for the Southern Railway) instead of the 4ft 3in of the older type.

The SR preferred a larger wheel which meant a higher maximum speed could be obtained. The wartime locomotives could not exceed 20mph, which was quite adequate for yard work where good acceleration and easy reversing are the most useful qualities. But these locomotives were so convenient and cheap to run that many operators used them for trip freights between yards, where their limited speed was a handicap. This was especially true on the SR, where such freights had to run on lines used by intensive electric services. This was why some units (Class 09) were built for the Southern Region with different gearing, allowing a speed of almost 30mph.

No effort was made to style these engines, whose box shape derives from the 1934 prototype. Originally, vacuum brakes were provided for use when hauling transit freights, but with BR's change to air brakes, some 08s were fitted with both types and most of the surviving locomotives have air brakes only. There was a deliberate policy of fitting air brakes to the youngest members of the class, the vacuum-only units then being the first to be withdrawn. Some of these were later sold for industrial service particularly in the steel and coal industries.

### Export success

The 08 diesel-electric shunters were superb at their designated work and were ordered by industrial railways in Britain and some railways abroad. The Dutch railways had been impressed by these locomotives at the end of the war, and became the best overseas customer for them, but others were exported to Australia and West Africa. Netherlands Railways still use them, especially for shunting.

▼ On 15 November 1985, No 08556 *Chiltern Line*, painted in BR brunswick green, stands with a blue liveried member of the class beside the carriage shed at Marylebone station, London. Some of these shunters are the oldest locomotives on the BR network and many have been saved from the scrapyard by preservationists.

# 4-SUB roofs

Modern coaches have roofs which are almost spartan to look at – the latest styles having little more than a ribbed appearance. This is in stark contrast to some earlier designs where a variety of details could be seen, since designers regarded the roof as a convenient place to locate equipment without intruding into the passenger space below. Good examples of these early coaches can be found in Southern Railway-designed units, particularly in the vast range of electric multiple units (EMUs).

A popular type was the 4-SUB (four-coach suburban) introduced in 1946. In common with many coaches, the roof was used to house passenger ventilators. These units were of the Southern torpedo type and arranged centrally in a single row along the roof (one for each passenger compartment).

On either side of this row of ventilators ran two conduits or pipes. These carried the main electric cables to conduit boxes which connected to the adjoining coach. The conduits were, naturally, designed to be weather- and waterproof and were held in place by cleats spaced at intervals of 6ft.

### Extra features

A feature of Southern coaches was the roof-mounted naked electric light bulbs, placed in simple holders recessed into the roof. Two per compartment was typical and the cable supply was also mounted on the roof in two more sets of conduits. The cleats to hold these were fixed directly above the compartment partitions on the unit (at 6ft 1½in intervals). The conduits led to the end of the coach and down to a lighting fuse box mounted

directly beneath the jumper cable boxes. The driving cab and guard's van had their own ventilators and lights.

Another feature of the Southern's multiple unit was the periscope mounted above the guard's van. This avoided any need for side-mounted duckets which often restricted the width of the remainder of the coach to keep it within the loading gauge.

### Horns and lights

The 4-SUB units originally had a front-mounted whistle, but these were later replaced with roof mounted twin warning horns. Rain strips were placed towards the edges of the roofs.

Other SR units had similar roof layouts, but naturally there were some varia-

tions. Exact spacing of lights and ventilators varied according to the type of interior – such as whether a coach included a side corridor. Some longer distance units incorporated toilet areas and the pipes for these were clearly visible.

Roof designs of Southern multiple units continued in similar fashion into the BR era, although from the late 1950s, the lighting cables were placed elsewhere.

▼In 1946, the Southern Railway introduced the Bulleid-designed 4-SUB unit. After Nationalization, these units were built by the Southern Region until 1951 and operated successfully until 1982. A four-car train of this stock could seat 400 people. In 1974, one of the class waits at London Bridge.

▼The roofs of many post-war SR EMU designs were often the location for the coaches' ancillary functions – particularly the lighting, ventilation and main electric cables. The exact position of many of these features depended on the layout of the coach – whether it had compartments or a central gangway between the seats.

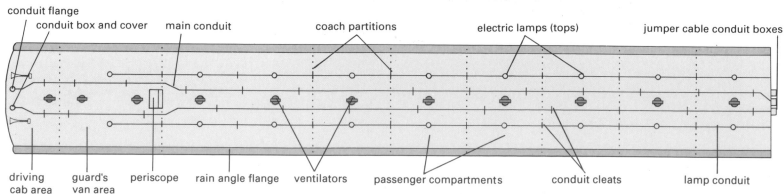

conduit flange
conduit box and cover    main conduit    coach partitions    electric lamps (tops)    jumper cable conduit boxes

driving cab area    guard's van area    periscope    rain angle flange    ventilators    passenger compartments    conduit cleats    lamp conduit

# EPB Class 415

EPB stands for Electro Pneumatic Brake, and the designation followed the familiar train classification system used on the Southern Region (SR). The original design of 4-EPB (the number 4 signifying four coaches) was conceived by the Southern Railway just before nationalization in 1948, but it was left to the newly formed British Railways (BR) to introduce it.

Basically, the 4-EPB was a more modern version of the earlier 4-SUB (suburban) units produced in large quantity by the Southern Railway. The EPBs were very similar in appearance and it is doubtful that their load of commuters were aware of any difference, as the basic style and carriage remained virtually the same. The front was perhaps a little tidier, but it still followed the shape of the 4-SUBs.

## Looks can be deceptive

On closer inspection, however, the cab fronts had been improved significantly. A buckeye coupling with Pullman style rubbing plate was fitted and waist level jumper cables and brake pipes enabled units to be coupled without the need for staff to work at track level. The headcode system was of the roller blind type and access to the cab was via the guard's van, eliminating the draughts from side doors which had led to complaints on the 4 SUBs. Inside the cab, the layout of controls was improved.

The EPB design also introduced some significant technical advances which were to influence electric multiple unit design for years to come. Of note was the inclusion of a 70V motor generator with battery backup which powered all control, lighting and braking. It was the braking which gave the units their EPB classification, as it included an electro-pneumatic brake along with the traditional Westinghouse braking system. This system became the standard for many years – until the Class 508 was introduced in 1979.

## Long service

Trials with the first unit began in December 1951, after which they appeared in quantity. At first, several experimental liveries in varying shades of green were tried, but soon the standard SR malachite green was adopted. Later, this changed to standard BR rail blue, and subsequently most units received blue and grey.

By this time, they had become BR Class 415, and a refurbishment programme from 1979 ensured a further period of service for remaining units (inevitably some had been withdrawn). Interior work included replacing the ordinary bulbs with fluorescent lighting and netted hat racks with metal ones.

There was considerable alteration to the original sets over the years including, from as early as the 1950s, incorporation of redundant 4-SUB trailers. In 1959, some two-car sets, designated 2-EPB, were introduced for general suburban duties. They were to the same design as their 4-EPB cousins and eventually became Class 416.

Serious withdrawals of the unrefurbished EPBs began in 1992 with the introduction of the Class 465 Networkers.

▼ In April 1966, a four-car EPB Class 415 No 5344 passes Wimbledon signalbox with a down service. This class was introduced in large numbers in the early 1950s and many had lives of over 40 years.

# Class 156

As part of the replacement of British Rail's first generation diesel multiple units (DMUs), the Class 156 Super Sprinters entered service in Scotland in 1988. Designed by Metro-Cammell and intended for long distance provincial services, the 75mph trains are formed from two virtually identical cars, each a Driving Motor Standard (DMS) vehicle of 23m length. The main difference internally is that one vehicle includes a disabled person's toilet and is therefore classified as a DMSL (L for lavatory) whereas the other has a luggage area

▼ On 14 January 1988, the first Class 156, No 156402, stands at Norwich. This was the first of the class to form part of a stud of 156s at Norwich Crown Point depot. In October 1993, one of these, No 156405, became the first Sprinter to cover over one million miles. This incredible mileage took less than six years and was made possible by intensive diagramming and good maintenance, ensuring that the unit stood still for the least possible time.

instead of a toilet.

Each car is powered in the same manner. BSI (British Standards Institution) automatic couplers enable the Super Sprinters to work in multiple if required; intermediate and flexible diaphragm end gangways enabling access throughout the train. Power operated sliding doors are worked by passenger-controlled push buttons (after conductor release), the doors being situated at the ends of the cars.

### Diesel drive
The single powered bogie on each car is located at the opposite end to the driving cab. It has a turbo-charged 285hp Cummins NT 855R5 diesel engine driving both axles of the bogie via a Voilth T211r hydraulic transmission system, effectively an automatic gear box and Gmeinder final drive units.

The BREL-manufactured bogies themselves are of similar design to many modern DMUs, featuring airbag

secondary suspension. This provides self-levelling for the coach body and adjusts automatically to changes in weight in the cars. The variable air suspension system also provides the loading information to the load-variable braking system which is fitted to the vehicles. Although of similar design to electric multiple units, the centre portion of the powered bogie is cranked to accommodate the drive shafts linking the two driven axles.

### Up-to-date
A combination of good insulation and air suspension helps to reduce transmission of noise to the interior, but the Super Sprinters nevertheless are diesel engined vehicles and therefore potentially noisy. Looking rather like a car exhaust system, a large exhaust silencer can be spotted beside the engine unit with the exhaust pipe itself being led up to one side of the intermediate corridor connection, exhaust therefore being dispersed above roof level.

### Cinderella
The Provincial Sector was long regarded as the Cinderella of the BR network, consistently losing money and seemingly being the last priority for new rolling stock and equipment. Many passengers saw the ageing first generation DMUs as unappealing and undesirable for travel; certainly, the comparison with InterCity services could hardly have shown greater contrast. The introduction of Sprinters, and their shorter-distance sisters the Pacers, aimed to alter the situation.

▶ The Class 156s are made up of two cars – a Driving Motor Standard (DMS) and a Driving Motor Standard (DMSL). The L stands for lavatory, although it refers to a disabled person's toilet. The arrangement of the drive mechanism on each of the Class 156 cars is located beneath floor level, as is the usual plethora of additional equipment, including battery box, fuel tank, air brake unit and heating equipment. The heating system itself is thermostatically controlled, utilising heat from the engine cooling system, supplemented by an auxiliary oil-fired heater. Heat reaches the interior via floor-level grilles.

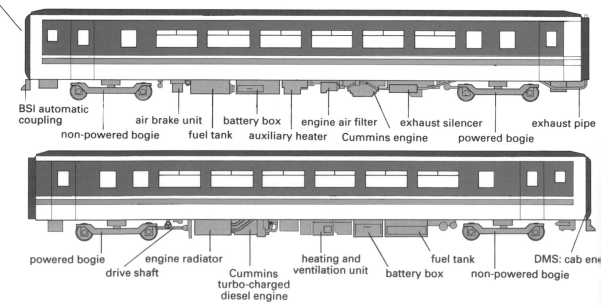

DMSL: cab end

BSI automatic coupling
non-powered bogie
air brake unit
fuel tank
battery box
auxiliary heater
engine air filter
Cummins engine
exhaust silencer
powered bogie
exhaust pipe

powered bogie
drive shaft
engine radiator
Cummins turbo-charged diesel engine
heating and ventilation unit
battery box
fuel tank
non-powered bogie
DMS: cab end

# BR coach seating

The evolution of the coach is a story almost as old and varied as that of the locomotive. The personal views of various designers have influenced not only body profile and style, but also the arrangement of the interiors, depending on whether comfort or high passenger loading was the main priority.

For this reason, a large variety of seating arrangements has been introduced in the UK over time, ranging from the spacious single-seat armchairs of the luxury streamlined trains in the 1930s to the post-war six-seat benches in the compartments of suburban commuter trains. Lately, however, there has been more of a move towards standardization of layout, although there are still differences in both type of seat used and precise layout according to the type of rolling stock.

The most spacious form of layout is known as the 2+1 seating arrangement. This type gives generous width and is usually combined with the seats being spaced relatively widely apart (normally according to the width of the window) giving extra legroom. This type of seating tends to be reserved for first class carriages and is most widely found on InterCity routes.

The 2+2 arrangement is sometimes known as the medium density or 'outer suburban' layout. As the latter implies, it is used for trains designed to travel over long and medium distances, and provides reasonable comfort and space. It is normally found in standard class coaches but may also be seen in first class compartments of trains used for medium distances. Legroom varies and some passengers have varying amounts of window to look through.

## Long distance suffering

The high density seating layout is intended for standard class local suburban travel, although it is often found on somewhat longer distances (Liverpool – Norwich, for example). This arrangement has been widely used in multiple unit formations since the early 1970s, and the intention is the provision of seats for adequate comfort for journeys of short duration.

In the early 1990s aircraft-style seating became increasingly specified by BR, not just on local or provincial services, but also on refurbished standard class InterCity trains. Usually, a few bays of facing seats are also incorporated into the arrangement, which has the benefit of ensuring that seats towards the ends are facing inwards into the coaches rather than towards the ends.

The actual arrangements may vary in precise location of seats from one coach type to another. There are also examples of other arrangements on later stock – the Class 442 Wessex Expresses, for instance, still include some corridor compartments for first-class passengers.

▼The design of many carriage interiors depends on whether comfort or high passenger numbers is the main priority. The 2+1 seating is spacious and often used in first-class areas. The 2+2 style is a medium density or 'outer suburban' layout. High density seating, used in multiple unit formations since the early 1970s, provides seats of adequate comfort for short journeys. In the early 1990s, aircraft-style seating was specified by BR.

### 2+1 low density

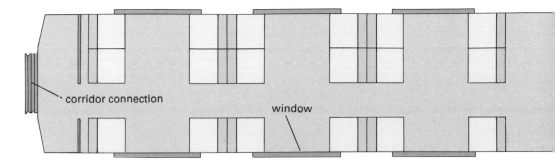

corridor connection
window

### 2+2 medium density

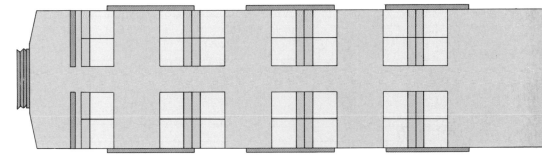

### 3+2 high density

doors
vestibule

### aircraft style

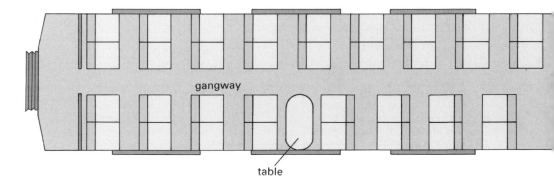

gangway
table

# BR coach air-conditioning

The first air-conditioned BR standard coaches – the Mark IId design – appeared in 1971. The original intention was to charge a supplement for luxury air-conditioned travel, but the decision was later taken to provide it as standard. Since then, air-conditioned vehicles have become the norm for principal services.

The system is designed to provide either heat or chilled air according to the external temperature, and is under continuous monitoring to ensure a constant climate for passengers.

## A breath of fresh air

A modern heating and cooling system is electric. Heating is by electric elements: a fan blows warmed air through ducts at floor level, while a set of shutters in the fresh air intake closes to recirculate the warm air. Thermostats ensure that the temperature is maintained at a constant level. To cool the carriage, in contrast, air cooled by an evaporator – much like a heat exchanger in a domestic refrigerator

– is blown into the passenger compartment through ceiling mounted ducts.

On Mark III coaches the cooling and heating mechanisms are situated together and blown out by a common fan. The direction is controlled by a gate (damper) which directs the flow as necessary – floor for heat, or ceiling for cool air.

Later designs of Mark IV coaches and those for the Class 442 Wessex units, and probably all others in the forseeable future, incorporate a heat pump which performs the same basic functions but extracts heat from the outside air, which can achieve energy savings of up to 40% under certain conditions.

## Shut that door!

The heating and cooling system itself is only one part of the equation. Proper functioning of a regulated temperature supply depends on good insulation in the body shells – all windows in the main passenger compartment are sealed double-glazed units. Efficient use also

depends on passengers keeping the compartment as much of a sealed unit as possible; this is why internal automatic closing doors are favoured.

Allowing interior doors and vestibule windows to remain open can affect the balance of the system. The classic example of this occurred on the Class 442 units, where individual first class compartments are provided. Passengers leaving open the doors to each compartment, as they had done since the steam age, caused such disruption to the air flow that the system had to be amended.

In extreme conditions, the air regulation system is much appreciated, but on normal days passengers may not notice the temperature control enough to comment. When the system fails, however, there is no back-up, not even opening windows, so the guard may suddenly receive numerous passenger complaints. This can be particularly uncomfortable should there be a long delay due to a failure with signals or locomotive.

▶ On 31 March 1992, a BR Mark IIe coach presents a smart appearance at Colchester station. The air-conditioning used in BR Mark IId/IIe coaches provides heated air on cold days and chilled air on hot ones. Thermostats regulate the balance between cold and hot to keep the passengers' environment constant at all times.

### Key

| | |
|---|---|
| ───── | air in |
| ➤ ➤ ➤ | warm air |
| ➤ ➤ ➤ | cool air |
| ➤ ➤ ➤ | recirculated air |

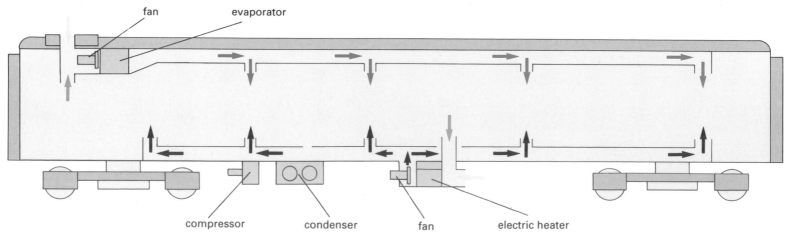

fan    evaporator

compressor    condenser    fan    electric heater

# Modern wagons

Goods trains for most of the steam era consisted of short-wheelbased trucks of all shapes and sizes containing many different loads bound, eventually, for myriad destinations. The modern railway freight scene, however, bears little resemblance to its forebears.

In the 1990s, most freights are block trains, carrying only one type of product and made up of the same type of vehicle. These wagons tend to be larger than their steam era counterparts and are designed for ease and speed of loading. A major advance has been widespread fitting of load-variable air operated disc brakes, enabling higher speeds to be achieved.

Some wagons have a specific purpose – for example container bogie wagons and articulated car transporters – but many are designed to be more versatile. This has resulted in some standardization of designs, but there is still a rich variety; a look at the types of four-wheel wagons confirms this.

Timber-sided open flat wagons are used for carrying steel, pallets and general goods. These have four drop sides, but another with three drop sides can also be seen. A steel-sided version, generally reserved for steel traffic, is of a similar design but with three, lower, drop sides.

## Hopper and tank wagons

The familiar hopper wagon comes in a variety of configurations depending on use, often ore or coal. The open wagon shown is widely used for mineral transport. Another type is the aggregate hopper wagon. Both these types have discharging doors at the bottom. Tank wagons, which are used for powders as well as liquids, also come in an assortment of types, including those which tip at one end.

## Vans

General purpose vans can be seen in a variety of types. Some have two centre sliding doors (for ease of loading with fork lift trucks) while others may have two full-width doors, centre sliding and hinged end doors, or curtain sides. These vans are used for transport of general goods. They all share a similar length of 33ft 6in (10.2m) and a wheelbase of 20ft 9in (6.32m). Vans originally built for Speedlink have a length of 42ft (12.8m) and a wheelbase of 29ft 6in (9.02m).

### Heavy weights

The exact weight and capacity of individual wagons naturally varies according to type, but generalizations can be made. Most open flat wagons weigh around 15 tonnes and can carry over 30 tonnes of cargo at 60mph (95km/h), or just over 25 tonnes at 75mph (120km/h). Both the shorter and longer general purpose vans weigh around 17 tonnes and can carry 29 tonnes at 60mph (95km/h) or approximately 24 tonnes at 75mph (120km/h), speed varying with the load.

**Timber-sided open flat wagon**

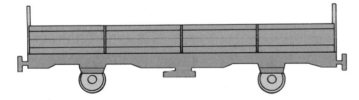

**Steel-sided open flat wagon**

**Hopper wagon**

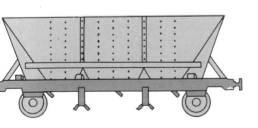

**Aggregate wagon**

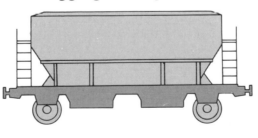

**Tank wagon**

**General purpose van**

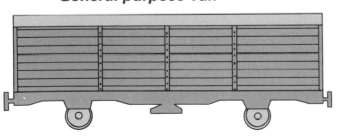

**Speedlink van**

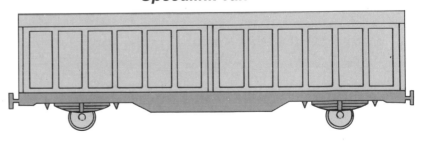

# Tank wagon design

Tank wagons are designed to transport liquids. Some wagons can handle a variety of substances – such as different kinds of light and medium oils – whereas others are designed for one particular commodity, such as milk, bitumen and specialized chemicals.

The loading of the wagons is normally done from the top, and the opening is fitted with a lockable cover. Access to the filling hole is usually by a side ladder. A gauge is provided on the outside of the wagon to ensure that heavier liquids do not rise to the same level in the tank as the lighter ones and therefore exceed the axleload.

In Britain, four-wheel tank wagons are still used but some oils are so heavy that they bring the axleload of laden vehicles to the maximum permitted. Eight-wheel bogie vehicles – which can carry a heavier payload – are favoured by oil companies for bulk hauls.

To reduce weight, a single central longitudinal beam is sometimes used as the main frame, without side beams. In Britain, the tank is often supported on the side beams for its whole length, being welded to wing plates. At one time baffle plates were fitted inside the tank to prevent fore-and-aft surges of the contents, but these are no longer regarded as essential.

Tank wagons must reach certain standards of strength, especially in the matter of puncture resistance. To this end, the tanks are welded and the lower plates are often thicker than the rest of the cylinder – this increases resistance to buffing stresses (for example, excessive shunting impacts) and also provides a stronger anchorage at the points where it is attached to the chassis – usually at both ends and in the centre.

## Shapes and sizes

The tanks do not need to be cylindrical – a closer fit to a railway's loading gauge can sometimes be obtained by elliptical tanks or by the cottage loaf (rounded top, flat sides and bottom), but such shapes do not have the strength of a perfect cylinder.

For some products, the tank is insulated, in which case conical ends are usually adopted. Steel is still the favourite material although aluminium is sometimes chosen, not so much because of its lightness as for its resistance to acids (including wines) and solvents, which quickly corrode unlined steel.

Linings are useful when a wagon is used to transport several different commodities. Epoxy resins are sometimes sprayed over the interiors, but these do not stand up well to steam cleaning. Metallized sprays are more resistant to this and also reduce the clinging of heavy oils on the inside surfaces when the tanks are discharged. Liquid bitumen vehicles need heating elements to keep the load fluid when discharging.

Tank wagons are either vented or sealed completely. Sealing prevents evaporation and is especially important for volatile loads. Safety valves are needed because the cooling of the load in transit can create a vacuum that would otherwise cause the tank to implode.

### Milk tanks
In Britain, before nationalization, the milk tanks used by several railways were considered to be remarkable vehicles. They were given six-wheel suspension, stainless steel tanks that were highly polished inside, and had a unique form of ownership – the dairies owned the tank and the railway company owned the chassis.

## Bogie tank wagon

▼ Tank wagons have evolved over the years and can be seen on most railways around the world. In countries where freight routes are electrified with overhead wire, the controls of the wagons are usually placed on the frame, near ground level. In other countries, such as the USA where overhead electrification is less common, most of the controls are placed on top of the tank.

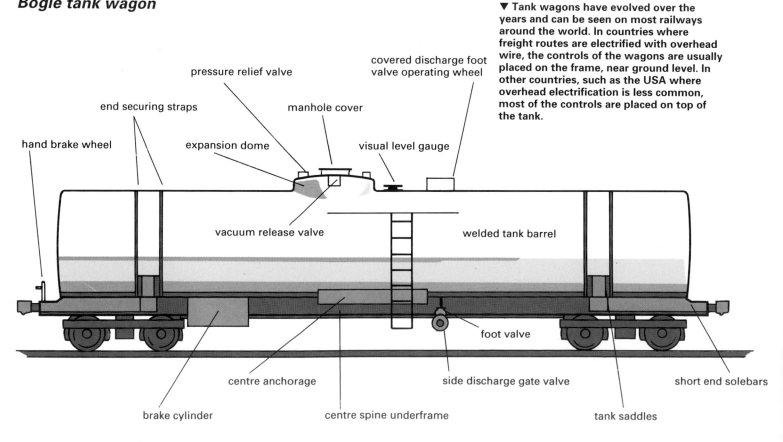

hand brake wheel · end securing straps · pressure relief valve · covered discharge foot valve operating wheel · manhole cover · expansion dome · visual level gauge · vacuum release valve · welded tank barrel · foot valve · centre anchorage · side discharge gate valve · short end solebars · brake cylinder · centre spine underframe · tank saddles

# Bulk powder wagons

Cement, flour and bulk chemicals at one time were conveyed by rail in 1cwt bags stacked in vans; this method can still be seen in Russia. But loading and unloading required much careful labour, so specialized vehicles were developed.

Powders, especially when they have been compacted by the vibration of their wagon, have a steep angle of repose. That is, when conveyed in a hopper they do not drop through the bottom doors unless the walls are steeply sloped. This presents design problems, not the least being that the greater the angle of slope, the smaller the usable space.

However, another characteristic of powders is that when they are perfectly dry they can be aerated, and will then behave like liquids. The unloading of bulk powders therefore uses one or both of two methods: aeration of the powder and discharge by compressed air.

Part of the aeration gear, the aeration plate, passes air (whose pressure can be as low as 1-5lb psi) upwards into the load, while preventing powder from moving downwards. However, for fine powders like cement, the prevention of this downward movement is difficult to achieve. Sometimes porous sponge rubber is sandwiched between perforated steel sheets, but various arrangements of steel mesh are also used.

Pressure-assisted unloading can be used, with or without aeration, in both hoppers and cylindrical tank designs, and is essential when unloading from the top. Considerable air pressure (up to 50lb psi) may be involved, especially if the load has to be lifted through pipes to tall storage structures. The use of such pressure requires strong walls; the cylindrical tank has an inherent advantage here, while hoppers need considerable strengthening. The Presflo hopper, of which thousands were built for BR and private owners in the 1960s, was made conspicuous by its heavy external ribs. The Prestwin was also built, for use with the larger grains that require high discharge pressures. This had two cylindrical silos, each with 2ft diameter aeration plates.

Pressurized containers have also been used. When these are horizontal they can be transferred to a special road vehicle that tilts them for unloading.

In the depressed-centre or chevron design, unloading is helped by a permanent tilt. The two ends of the cylindrical tank slope downwards towards the centre, aiding discharge from the base. Some four-axle units were also built, consisting essentially of two depressed-centre tanks on a single frame. However, cement companies often preferred the two-axle vehicles because so many of their consignments were small.

With their changed distribution system the cement companies are likely to send less of their production by rail in future. However, other bulk powders that are still carried by rail include flour, silica, alumina and soda ash.

The commodities carried by the railways all have different angles of repose, so ideally they should be carried in specifically designed vehicles.

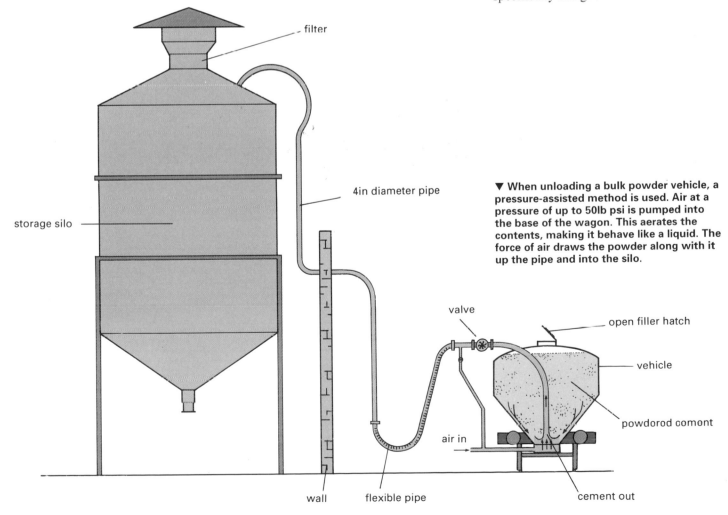

filter

4in diameter pipe

storage silo

▼ When unloading a bulk powder vehicle, a pressure-assisted method is used. Air at a pressure of up to 50lb psi is pumped into the base of the wagon. This aerates the contents, making it behave like a liquid. The force of air draws the powder along with it up the pipe and into the silo.

valve

open filler hatch

vehicle

powdered cement

air in

wall

flexible pipe

cement out

# Hopper wagons

Railways have always excelled as bulk carriers, but their low transport costs per ton can be lost if there are high loading and unloading expenses. Unloading coal wagons by shovel was, until recent decades, a common sight on BR, but nowadays bulk freights (such as coal, aggregates and ores) are carried in hopper wagons, in which the load is discharged through the bottom.

The essential features of hoppers are the **underside doors** and a body shape which ensures that the load will slide downward and out as soon as the doors are opened. This entails **inward sloping sides** and a floor which consists of internal **transverse ridges** that form the summits of sloping bottom sheets. Each set of **slope sheets** forms a vertical pocket leading to an underside door. The simplest hoppers consist of just one large pocket.

## Best possible shape
The task of the designer is to find the best contours for the particular load envisaged. In Britain, hoppers designed for coal can handle most other bulk commodities, although for some large-scale traffics like aggregates and ore, specialized wagons are usually built. This is also so for traffics requiring protection from moisture and covered hoppers are built for commodities such as grain and fertilizer.

## Density and capacity
In general, the heavier (denser) the commodity the gentler the necessary slope of walls and sheets, and the gentler the slope the greater the cubic capacity. Ore is very dense (needing only about 100cu ft to accommodate 10 tons), so ore wagons tend to be of smaller cubic capacity in order to keep the axleweight within limits. Coal is not so heavy, requiring about 400cu ft for each 10 tons and aggregates about 200cu ft for 10 tons.

Railway systems with only one type of hopper can handle denser traffic by partially loading coal hoppers, although at the expense of somewhat higher costs per ton. In North America, woodchips are a common traffic and are of very low density (700cu ft per 10 tons); specialized woodchip hoppers are as big as permissible and, because the load is reluctant to drop through the doors, the cars are often attached to mechanical vibrators when they are unloaded at the paper plant.

## Unloading
Most hoppers unload directly on to troughs or belts below rail level, although those used for track ballast may drop their stone directly on the sleepers for immediate use. Releasing the doors was originally done by operating a manual lever or wheel, and most hoppers still provide this, even though it is often difficult to operate, especially in freezing conditions. Other methods are now more common. The hoppers used by BR's merry-go-round trains had their doors actuated by lineside trips, and wagons have also been built with pneumatic devices actuated by compressed air from the train's braking system.

Dumper wagons are less useful, and hence less numerous, than hoppers. Their purpose is to unload the traffic well away from the track. The old tip-up wagon used to perform this function, but some railway systems have big dumper wagons in which a pneumatically operated pushing rod raises the wagon body at a sharp angle, allowing the contents to fall well away to the side. Such vehicles are useful for lineside dumping.

▲ Hopper wagons like this have been in use since 1964 and are designed to be loaded and unloaded quickly. Bulk loads such as coal, aggregates and ore are usually discharged through the bottom of the wagon. Some have canopies to stop small particles being blown away.

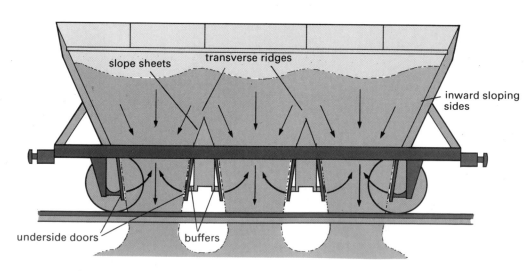

◀ To get the load to slide downward and out as soon as the doors are opened, the body shape of the wagon has inward sloping sides and a floor of internal transverse ridges forming the summits of sloping bottom sheets. Each set of slope sheets forms a vertical pocket leading to an underside door.

# MGR operation

Rail has traditionally been a major means of transporting coal between colliery and power station and the sight of long trains of short, often privately owned trucks became a familiar sight on Britain's railways for many decades. Speed was not considered a priority, and the wagons themselves often served as a convenient means of storing coal in sidings at the power stations. The practice persisted into the nationalized era with little change, except for more modern motive power.

During the 1960s however, it was realized that a more efficient method had to be found, both to provide a more economical service to the power stations and to shift increasing amounts of coal to meet a growing demand for electricity from both private consumers and industry. With co-operation between British Rail, the National Coal Board and the Central Electricity Generating Board, the key players at the time, the merry-go-round (MGR) system was devised as a more up-to-date and cost-efficient method of transporting coal between colliery and power station.

## Conveyor belt operation

The merry-go-round principle is effectively that of a conveyor belt. Trains of semi-permanently coupled wagons run from colliery to power station, then back again on a circuit, with all loading and unloading performed automatically. Special high capacity wagons – 32 tonnes compared with between 16 and 25 tonnes previously – are equipped with an automatic mechanism to discharge their load through bottom drop-down doors. They are also able to run faster due to the fitting of air brakes.

At the colliery, coal is loaded into the wagons through large overhead bunkers. As the train moves slowly through the wagons are filled, then it continues on its journey to the power station.

At the power station, the train pauses for the locomotive to engage slow speed control before the discharging mechanism on the wagons is triggered by special lineside equipment. The coal then falls straight into underground storage bunkers through the bottom doors. When the load has been emptied, the train returns to the colliery and the process begins again.

In this way, wagons are used far more efficiently and trains sometimes perform two or more round trips per day, depending on distance. This compares with as many as 10 days using the traditional handling method. By 1980, BR had built the ten-thousandth MGR wagon and it calculated that this number of such wagons could handle the same traffic as 200,000 conventional wagons. The savings in construction and maintenance alone were considerable, quite apart from efficiency of movement.

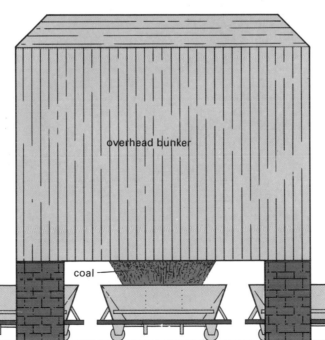

▶ Merry-go-round trains are designed to make loading and unloading of coal a highly efficient operation, having taken over from trains of short-wheelbased wagons. The key to the success of the scheme is the HAA hopper, which can hold up to 32 tonnes and are marshalled into semi-permanent trains of around 30 wagons. These trains make continuous circuits between the power station and the colliery. When loading, the train actually passes through the bunkers, which discharge around 1000 tonnes of coal directly into the wagons.

overhead bunker

coal

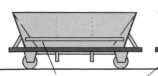

32-tonne MGR hopper wagons

▲Class 58, No 58041, hauls a merry-go-round working near Burton Salmon. The Class 58s are fitted with creep control enabling them to slow to $1/2$mph as they load and unload. Creep control exploits the fact that when a wheel starts to slip, the friction between wheel and rail increases momentarily, before decreasing rapidly. Instead of cutting back the power, the wheels are kept slipping in the area where adhesion increases. However, the condition of the rail head can vary over a short distance, and this requires changes in speed for maximum adhesion.

# Coaling locomotives

Before 1930, the coaling of steam engines at most motive power depots was done manually. At small sheds, coal was shovelled by hand from a wagon to a locomotive standing on an adjacent siding. In some cases the wagon siding was built a few feet higher than the engine road to make the work easier for the coalman.

Most medium and large depots had a coaling stage alongside the line of engines. Shunting engines pushed coal wagons up a ramp to a platform about 10ft high. Coalmen shovelled coal from the wagons into steel skips on wheels; each skip held about half a ton. The skips were then pushed across the platform and the coal was tipped into the tender, or bunker, of a locomotive waiting below. The work was heavy, dirty and labour intensive.

After World War I the process began to be mechanized and by 1923, four major depots were equipped with plants in which coal was tipped from wagons into an underground hopper, from where it was carried by bucket conveyor to an overhead bunker which in turn fed the locomotive.

Road competition made the railways look into ways of cutting their operating costs as much as possible and the LMS and the LNER and to a lesser extent the SR, began a modernization programme. The GWR was the exception, since it used mainly soft and powdery Welsh coal.

Three main types of mechanical coaling plant were installed. **Small plants**, in which coal was still unloaded manually from wagons into small tubs, but these were then hoisted up on a steel framework and tipped over into the tender. These plants suited small depots and servicing points. **Wagon hoist plants**, where a wagon loaded with coal was hoisted to the top of a large bunker and its contents tipped in. **Skip hoist plants**, where the wagon was tipped at ground level into a container which either fed

smaller skips for hoisting to the bunker top or was itself hoisted and tipped.

Both the last two types had coal capacities of 150-500 tons according to demand. Wagons were raised and lowered by electric motor or gravity. Because wet coal is corrosive, the plants were made from reinforced concrete. The storage bunkers were lined with steel plates to resist abrasion.

▼Wagon hoist plants raised a wagon, containing around 16 – 20 tons of coal, on a section of track to a height of 60ft. Here it was tipped over, emptying its contents into a large bunker inside the plant.

Coal was released from the bunker by the driver or fireman, operating controls in a cabin on a small platform. These controls set in motion the jigger or shuffler which regulated the outflow of coal from the bunker. Water sprays drenched the coal in the wagon to keep the dust down.

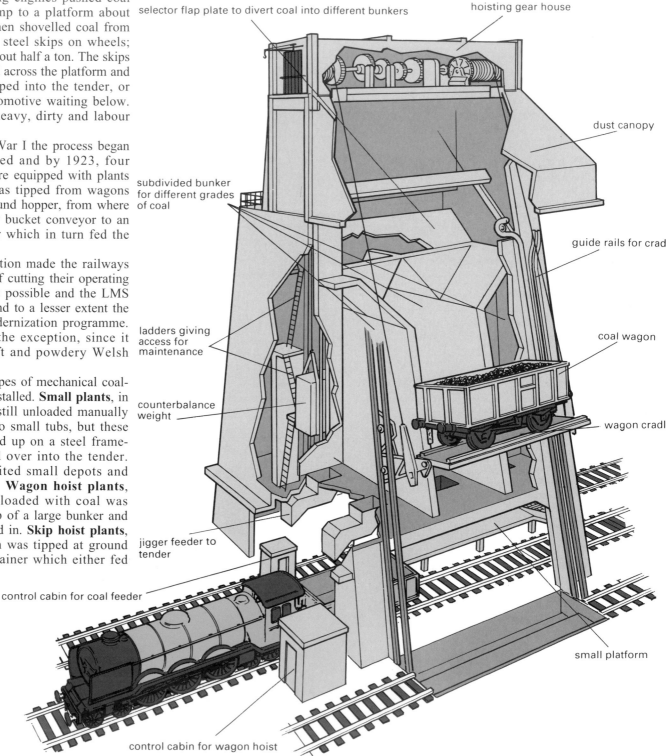

selector flap plate to divert coal into different bunkers

hoisting gear house

dust canopy

subdivided bunker for different grades of coal

guide rails for crad

ladders giving access for maintenance

coal wagon

counterbalance weight

wagon cradl

jigger feeder to tender

control cabin for coal feeder

small platform

control cabin for wagon hoist

# Low-loading wagons

With the growing international movement of freight traffic, height restrictions on rolling stock are no longer simply local inconveniences. The British rail network is especially affected because its lines were built to closer height restrictions than in other countries. Also, faced with uneconomic short hauls domestically, the rail companies derive proportionately more revenue from international container traffic, especially with the advent of the Channel Tunnel.

Most containers are of international standard dimensions originally adopted by shipping lines. To obtain its share of seaboard traffic, BR had to cope initially with containers 8ft 6in (2.6m) high, and then 9ft (2.74m) heights. Even taller 9ft 6in (2.9m) containers are now also coming into use internationally. Two methods have been used to accommodate such heights – raising over-line structures (or lowering track beneath them); and introducing flatcars with very low floors.

By reducing the wheel diameter it is possible to lower the floor sufficiently to gain those few precious inches. The Lowliner flatcars which BR acquired to permit container haulage on the height-restricted Isle of Grain have a wheel diameter of only 1ft 8in (51cm), which gives a floor height of 2ft 4in (71cm). On BR main lines such cars could allow the haulage of 9ft 6in (2.9m) containers.

## Continental solutions

Some railway administrations are opposed to small-wheel cars, fearing that small wheels are more likely to become derailed on points and crossings where there is a small gap to be jumped. Small wheels certainly place a more concentrated stress on the rails, as the axleweight is applied to a smaller surface. Also, small wheels may not have enough volume to absorb and dissipate the heat generated by braking; and, due to space limitations, the bogie bearings have to be inside the wheels – a position where hot-box detectors are unlikely to be able to sense hot running.

The small-wheel solution was not chosen for Channel Tunnel traffic, partly due to French inhibitions. Instead, flatcars very similar to the French Multifret design are used. These have 2ft 9in (84cm) wheels and their floor height of 3ft 1in (94cm) gives them a $3\frac{1}{2}$in (89mm) advantage over British standard Freightliner wagons.

Other European countries have opted for even smaller wheels than BR. The 'rolling highway' concept adopted in some Alpine countries, in which motor trucks and their drivers are taken by flatcars to reduce congestion on mountain roads, demands even lower heights than in parts of Britain. For these tunnel routes, flatcars have 1ft 2in (36cm) wheels, giving a floor height of 1ft 4in (41cm).

Some continental railway systems handle piggyback shipments, in which highway trailers rather than containers carry the payload. These trailers have wheels at one end, so they are higher than containers of the same capacity. The solution is the kangaroo flatcar, in which part of the floor slopes down to form an underslung pouch for the trailer wheels.

◄▼ A Leeds – Southampton container train makes its way south of Oxford in June 1980. As containers have increased in size, large loads are often transported by low-loading wagons to avoid fouling loading gauge restrictions. Low-loaders are often used in piggyback operations for transporting lorries, with their loads, long distances. Of the two types, the kangaroo flatcar carries a lorry trailer, while the small-wheel transporter carries a trailer or a truck.

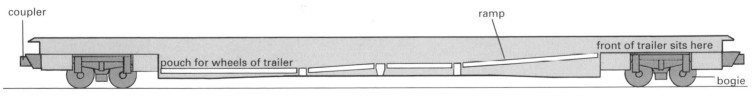

*Kangaroo flatcar*

*Small-wheel transporter*

# Open wagons

Open wagons are traditionally divided into those intended for merchandise and those for minerals. The decline of general merchandise traffic has meant these wagons have virtually disappeared.

Merchandise wagons were intended to carry all kinds of manufactured products, apart from those that required the greater protection provided by a van. They could be covered by a tarpaulin and many had a central longitudinal bar that could be swung up to form the ridge for a tarpaulin pitch roof.

## Drop-sided

Many British open wagons had hinged sides made out of a low single plank and would have been classified as flatwagons in other countries. Such wagons, with drop-sides, were ideal for big products like agricultural machinery. In Britain, open wagons were classified according to the number of planks forming their sides as a measure of capacity.

The London Midland & Scottish Railway (LMS), and later British Railways (BR), were big builders of three-plankers, which were regarded as medium-sized vehicles, capable of carrying 13 tons of freight.

Higher capacity open wagons, still limited to about 13 tons but with higher, five-plank sides, were also built, especially by the Great Western Railway (GWR). With its habitual originality, the GWR also contrived to build large numbers of 5½-plankers.

Most of these merchandise wagons had central side doors, usually hinged at the bottom, so the door could be lowered to form a platform over which trolleys could be wheeled. Some open wagons had corrugated-steel, rather than planked, end walls; later designs were all steel.

## Mineral wagons

From 1948, with the nationalization of the coal mines and railways, many wooden-bodied wagons were replaced by all-steel wagons of 16 ton capacity. Some of these had small flap doors on each side, big enough for shovelling, but others had end doors as well, while a few had trap doors in the floor. However, with the shrinkage of coal traffic and the greater convenience of hopper wagons they have been virtually eliminated.

Other countries use open wagons riding on bogies – these four-axle mineral wagons are known as gondolas in the US. In Britain, several private owners have introduced four-axle open wagons. Steel scrap is one traffic for which the higher capacity of four-axle opens is highly suited; such vehicles carry 73 tons for a gross laden weight of 102 tons. Four-axle open wagons with drop sides have also been built for pallet traffic, while high-sided opens have been constructed for aggregates.

---

### Never too old

When 253,000 wagons previously owned by the coal companies came into BR ownership it was decided to replace them as soon as possible, as their poor condition, grease lubrication and other defects made them uneconomic. But despite frenetic building of new 16-ton wagons there never seemed to be enough. So over 9000 of the standard 16-ton mineral wagons that had been supplied by British works for the French railways at the end of World War II were brought back in 1950. The French were glad to get rid of them, considering them small and obsolete, but they worked on BR for another two decades.

---

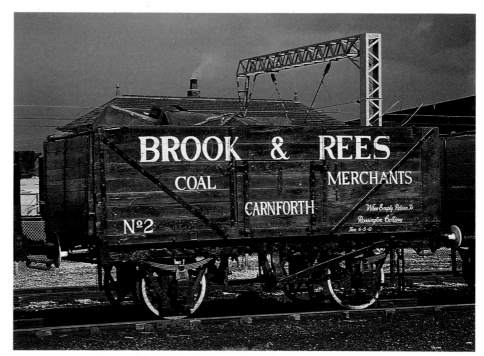

▶ Until World War II, most of the coal traffic on Britain's railways was conveyed in wooden-sided open wagons. A quarter of a million wooden vehicles were owned by colliery companies and their names were often boldly emblazoned on the sides. They were very basic – many did not even have brakes that could be controlled by the driver from the locomotive – and ran in long loose-coupled formations.

▶ After nationalization, the older wooden-bodied wagons were replaced by all-steel wagons of higher, 16 ton capacity. Some of the bigger ones could carry 21 and later 24½ tons, with a wheelbase of 12ft rather than 9ft. These had two small flap doors on each side for shovelling and end doors as well. A diagonal white stripe was painted on each side of the wagon to indicate which end was flapped.

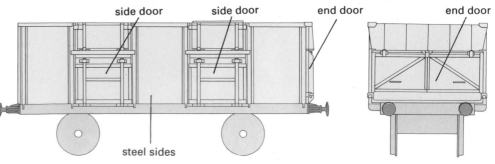

side door  side door  end door  end door

steel sides

# Service wagons

Railways have always reserved a large number of freight wagons for their own needs. In steam days, whole train-loads of coal were despatched in open wagons marked 'Loco' for the use of locomotive depots. The mechanical departments also had their own spare-parts vehicles. These spent their time shuttling between the depot and works, attached to fast freight trains.

On BR, the mechanical departments still operated their own vehicles, but on a much reduced scale. Two other departments, Track Maintenance and Signals & Telegraph, however, needed large fleets of their own rolling stock. These had their own liveries, the track maintenance vehicles being grey and yellow, while the signals' vehicles, appropriately, were painted in 'stop' red and 'caution' yellow and were hauled by the department's own locomotives.

This stock was often made up of old vehicles withdrawn from commercial service and perhaps modified. Old open wagons could be used for ballast and sleepers, for example, and standard bogie flatwagons could be modified to take rotating cable drums for wire laying. Old passenger coaches were converted for staff use – engineering personnel were not allowed to ride on moving wagons.

Standard commercial wagons could also be acquired new. The 'Wetrol' high-capacity well wagon, for example, can be seen carrying heavy machinery, or sometimes temporary buildings. But the track engineers increasingly prefer specially designed wagons.

## Ballast wagons

By far the most numerous service wagons are those used for track ballasting. Hopper wagons are commonly used, in a variety of sizes and designs, including a 50-ton bogie design called the 'Whale'. Some hoppers have three bottom doors, each with its own hand-wheel, and these enable the ballast to be dropped selectively to one of the sides or centre of the track.

The heaps of ballast deposited on the track can be flattened by scraper blades, with shovels finishing the job. Ballast train brake vans may have their own built-in scrapers or ploughs for spreading the heaps dropped ahead of them.

For moving old ballast and other waste materials, the low-sided tipping wagons are useful. The low drop-sides ease shovel-loading from track level, a laborious practice that is frequently inescapable. The loaded wagons are hauled away and their tipping enables the load to be dumped at a chosen location.

Rails are carried on standard bogie bolster wagons. These are bogie flat-wagons with transverse baulks on which the rails are laid, with side stanchions preventing any sideways movement of the load.

There are many other varieties, each with its own name, and long lines of these can be seen on weekdays at the many track maintenance depots; such wagons tend to lie idle when regular trains are running, emerging for bursts of frenetic activity at night and on Sundays.

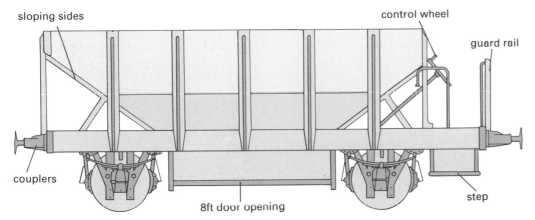

sloping sides · control wheel · guard rail · couplers · 8ft door opening · step

### Old methods

The just-in-time technique of material supply, which enables factories and retailers to dispense with their own stockpiles and which came to prominence in the 1980s, was long practised by the railway companies. The GWR's mechanical department, for example, had its 'Enparts' vehicle attached to a fast freight train. Thus, it was only necessary to hold stocks at the main works.

▲ ▶ Casual observers of the railway scene may have noticed that BR's permanent way wagons have aquatic names – the tope is the name of a small shark. It was a continuation of a GWR practice to use telegraphic code names for these vehicles, and BR's permanent way wagons continued with this tradition. Thus, 12 ton tippers were called mermaids, 25 ton hoppers were trout, and bogie hoppers included some known as walruses. When these vehicles had their vacuum brakes replaced by air brakes the names changed also. The air-braked versions of the walruses were known as sea lions. These wagons have sloping sides with doors at the bottom, making it easy to distribute the ballast.

# High capacity wagons

Wagons which have a high capacity are usually adopted for economic reasons, but sometimes special high load vehicles are built to carry exceptionally heavy loads. Before World War II, British railway companies not only carried heavy items, like battleship propellers, but even more massive loads like turbines for power stations, girders for big bridges and enormous stationary boilers.

A 550 ton reactor was once handled on a multi-axle car in the US, but the British record is a 275 ton boiler that was moved a few miles from Immingham Docks in 1968. The Weltrol 4-axle wagon, which can still be seen on the rail network, is not in this league, but a small number were built with 12 or six axles. As in Britain the maximum permissible main line axleload is $25^{1}/_{2}$ tons, that Weltrol type can be loaded to a gross weight of 156 tons.

## Small minds

The economies that could be won from using high capacity vehicles for regular traffic were long ignored by railway managements, and their introduction was delayed. Conservatism, or rather the realization that progress has its inconveniences, was another obstacle.

In Britain, the North Eastern Railway, at a time when coal was carried in 10-ton capacity wagons, tried to persuade mining companies to change to 20-tonners,

but met strong resistance. The companies said that their loading facilities were designed for the smaller wagons and claimed that the change would therefore simply benefit the railway at their expense.

In the USA, until quite recently, railroads that wished to introduce high capacity grain wagons were forbidden to do so by the government's Interstate Commerce Commission, on the grounds that the lower costs would constitute 'unfair competition' against the river barge lines.

Using fewer wagons for the same tonnage of freight means that trains can be heavier without the need to lengthen loops and sidings. The proportionate reduction in heavy items like buffers and couplings allows more payload per train, while train assembly costs and wage costs per ton load are reduced.

## Small loads

On BR, once the step to higher (32 ton) capacity four-wheel, mineral wagons had been taken, the next move was a wider adoption of bogie suspension in place of the traditional two-axle configuration. Privately owned vehicles set the pace, and bogie tank wagons with a gross loaded weight of 102 tons were among the leaders. The cement industry preferred to stay with four-wheel wagons.

---

### *Not such a good idea*
In the Soviet Union, where there was an obsessional quest for minimum railway investment and maximum railway traffic, the State Planning Commission came up with a collective brainwave in the 1970s. The problem of passing rising traffic on existing track could be solved, it said, by building wider freightcars. This idea passed through several commissions and committees, but was eventually dropped, possibly because one of its consequences would have been the decapitation of any railwayman who happened to stand between two passing trains on a curve.

---

▶ The well wagon was a favourite of many railways for particularly large and heavy loads. This vehicle had a flat or low-sided deck, carried at each end by a bogie, and was depressed in the centre almost to rail level to form a well in which the load could be placed. This well provided extra headroom. In 1939, what was described as a 'giant piece of machinery' destined for a new steelworks in South Wales was moved from Cardiff Docks to Blaenavon. A special well wagon was brought from Swindon particularly for the task. This had 24 wheels to spread the weight over a greater number of axles.

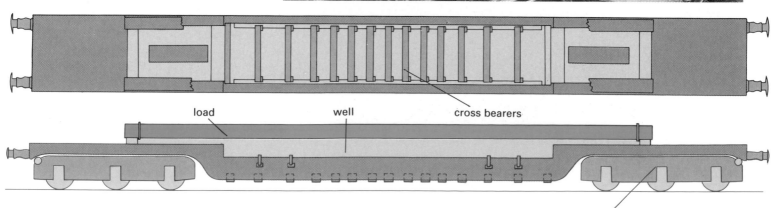

load    well    cross bearers

bogie

# Covered vans

The weatherproof van has always been a standby of railway freight departments. In Britain, its main use was to carry moisture sensitive manufactured goods – the alternative, the tarpaulined open wagon, was far less convenient. But, partly because there were so many of them, vans were rarely used efficiently, often carrying one small shipment that was far below the maximum capacity. In this situation there was little incentive to advance beyond the small van of about 12 tons capacity and 10ft wheelbase. British Rail (BR) in its first decades was still building such vehicles.

## Different varieties

The four-wheelers came in several variants. The ventilated van was perhaps the most common, having a vent just below roof level at each end (the Great Western Railway, always different, preferred two vents at each end). The body was typically made of planks, although plywood was also used – in BR days it became customary to use pressed steel ends.

Specialized fruit vans had much more ventilation, together with an insulated roof for protection against the sun, and racks for the fruit. Meat vans were similar but had hooks and hangers instead of racks, and were sometimes insulated all round. Banana vans had steam heating, because shippers wanted the fruit to ripen at this last stage of its journey – when the industry decided that ripening should take place elsewhere the railways lost their competitive advantage, and the traffic went to the roads.

Some all metal vans were also produced. Gunpowder vans were among these – they had lined interiors and at some periods were equipped with pairs of soft overshoes to be used by those going inside. But the most important feature of such vehicles was the gunpowder notation painted on the outside, guaranteeing that they would be carefully handled. However, it was not so much gunpowder as intricate manufactured goods that were most at risk from shunting impacts, and many vans were designed to be shock-absorbing. These, labelled as 'shock-vans', had bodies that could slide a few inches longitudinally under the control of springs.

Vans had central doors on each side, sometimes hinged and sometimes sliding. The growth of palletized traffic meant that doorways needed to be widened to give access to loading equipment, and this resulted in vehicles the sides of which seemed to consist of little more than door.

In some vehicles, used for cross-Channel services, both roof and side could be opened.

▶▼ The growth of palletized traffic meant that doorways needed to be as wide as possible to give access to loading equipment. This led to an abandoning of the traditional small van in place of the long-wheelbase van which, although still only four-wheeled, provides a much longer body. Typically, these have a 20ft 9in (6.32m) wheelbase and can carry 26.6 tonnes on the rare occasions when they are fully loaded. More importantly, there is space for a wide sliding door at the centre and hinged doors at the end.

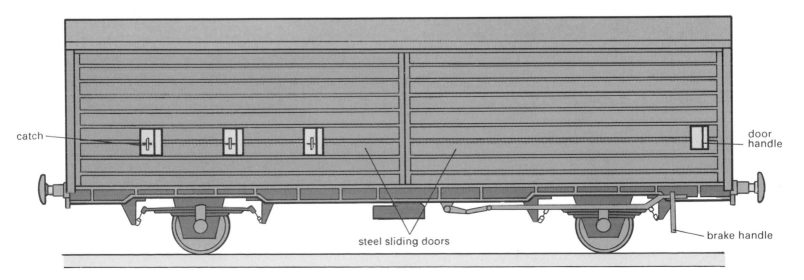

catch    door handle

steel sliding doors    brake handle

# Flat wagons

The traditional British general-duty flat wagon was a four-wheeler with a flush wooden floor of easily replaceable planks. This floor provided a base for nailing in the wooden blocks that held loads in place. There were also iron rings or other anchoring points for restraining ropes or chains. In the USA, flatcars have four axles and along the sides are rectangular pockets that can accommodate upright stakes when needed.

Wagons with short sides only a few inches high are also classed as flat wagons by some railways. In Britain, these semi-flats were used for very heavy items like pig-iron ingots where the high sides of a conventional open wagon would have hindered loading and unloading.

Traffic for which flat wagons were suited included heavy, bulky items like farm equipment and crated machinery. Later, the flat wagon was needed for container traffic. The inter-war companies and BR, using the old type of 16ft wooden container, built thousands of 'Conflat' wagons of from 11 to 13 ton capacity. Some of these had a shallow lip around the floor edges, while others had low plank or steel baulks at the ends to restrain any fore and aft slippage of the container. Securing chains were stored in pockets the lids of which were inset in the floor. With the growth of container traffic using large international standard containers, new designs of flat wagons were needed. Initially, some long wheelbased four-wheelers were used, but soon completely new designs were introduced for the Freightliners, in which wagons were permanently coupled in sets.

## Cars and steels

Specialized flat wagons were built for conveying automobiles. These, coded as 'Carfits', were originally four-wheelers, but later old passenger carriages were stripped down to the underframe to serve as bogie car carriers.

Other specialized flat wagons are used for metals traffic. Some of these were built in very small numbers, including armourplate vehicles which were quite short (33ft) but rode on two bogies. Ordinary steel plates also travel on special flat wagons.

Armour plate is no longer carried to the shipyards, cars are now carried in doubledeck wagons, and when BR was freed of its common carrier obligations, it no longer needed to provide flat wagons for awkward and unremunerative loads. So the variety of flat wagons is smaller nowadays. But the container flat is multiplying, and the steel industry still needs its specialist wagons.

### Rail carriers
One bogie bolster wagon that survived on BR into the 1990s is the Salmon rail wagon. About 800 were built in the 1960s and many have survived to find employment by the maintenance department in service stock, as they are useful for track relaying. At their two extremities the floor is hinged so that it can rotate in a vertical plane, so easing the unloading of the rail lengths. Such wagons can carry 50 tons of rail.

▶▼ **Long steel items, including girders and rails, are typically moved on bolster wagons. These are essentially flat wagons with transverse baulks (bolsters) and side stakes. It was once common to use a pair of four-wheel bolster wagons, each with its own central baulk. As the two were too far apart to be coupled, that function was performed by the load itself, with one end secured to each wagon. However, for most such traffic, and especially rails, the bogie bolster (right and below) proved most suitable. This was a flat wagon riding on bogies with two or more cross baulks to support the load. It was used especially by the GWR and LNER, which had heavy steel traffic, and the GWR bolster design was also built for BR.**

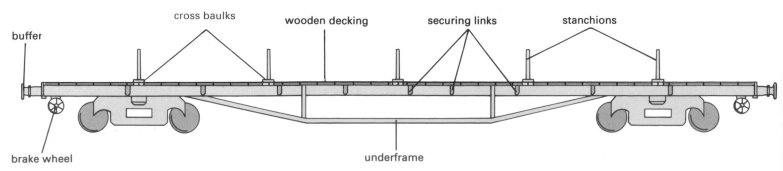

# Rail

The most important qualities of a length of rail are safety and long life. Durability not only limits the number of rails that a railway needs to buy, but also avoids frequent relaying and the consequent disruption to train schedules. The strength and reliability of a rail depend upon the properties of the metal used, its size – expressed in lb/yd or kg/m – and how firmly supported it is.

**Materials** Before the turn of the century rails used to be made from iron – on busy sections of track they were renewed every three months. As the weight of traffic increased, breakages were frequent. Rail ends, which take repeated hard knocks, were most vulnerable, and the introduction of steel rail which replaced iron did not solve the problem.

In Britain, every mile of track was patrolled by a lengthman, and most cracks were spotted in the daily inspections. But an internal fissure – a split or opening inside the rail itself – could suddenly become critical under a passing train. Controlled cooling of newly rolled rails helped to reduce this tendency to weakness. Ultrasonic examination is now used to detect invisible faults and the track is checked every two to three days.

**Rail choice** In 19th century Britain the bullhead rail was standard, but in the 1950s the flat-bottom type came back into use. Bullhead rail is held firm in chairs by wedges (keys), and the chairs are bolted to the sleepers. Flat-bottom rail provides better support and is simpler. It was originally spiked directly to the sleepers, but on British Rail it was supported on a base plate and attached to the sleeper by a patented clip. In Britain, rails are slightly inclined inwards, except through certain switches and crossings where they are laid vertically.

**Wear** The standard British rail is 60ft (18m) long; in America it is 39ft (12m). At the joints a gap is left to accommodate expansion in warm weather. The pounding of steel wheels on these joints causes the greatest wear, both of rails and wheels, but welding rails together in long lengths to form continuous welded rail (CWR) reduces this.

When CWR is laid, extra deep stone ballast and the avoidance of tracklaying in cold weather are two precautions to prevent lengthwise expansion that would cause buckling. The expansion that takes place in hot weather is absorbed not by lengthening but by a slight deepening and widening of the rail.

**Usage** In Britain, several old types of bullhead and flat-bottom rail remain in service, but main lines are laid with 113lb/yd (56.1kg/m) flat-bottom rails. For a further spell of use, worn main line rails may be relaid on secondary lines. At the end of their lives rails may be over 50 years old with their weight reduced by 10lb/yd (4.5kg/m) or more by wear.

In the USA, where axle weights are heavier, rails of 145lb/ft (72kg/m) are common. On straight flat track these rails are expected to last seven or eight years on the busiest lines. However, rail wear on curves, gradients and especially crossovers is faster – for crossovers, the more expensive but longer lasting manganese steel is often specified.

## Rail profiles

The head provides a low friction, long lasting running surface while the foot must be wide enough to guarantee stability and accommodate the clips, spikes or keys that hold it. The web gives rigidity, countering the tendency of the head to bend when under load. Because flat-bottom rail is better supported than bullhead it is far stronger weight for weight.

HEAD — WEB — FOOT

BULLHEAD

FLAT BOTTOM (STEEL)

**REVERSIBLE BULLHEAD**
Reversible bullhead rail was designed to be turned when the head was worn. The practice was stopped because damage from the chairs caused rough riding.

**BRIDGE**
The GWR used bridge rail for its broad gauge main line. It was fixed to longitudinal timber baulks rather than the usual transversal sleepers.

**FLAT-BOTTOM (IRON)**
Flat-bottom iron rail was used in the early 19th century before bullhead rail became standard. Some UK rail systems continued to use it until the 1920s.

# Gauge

A railway's gauge is the width between the inner faces of the rails on straight track. On curves it's usual to add a few millimetres to the gauge to ease the passage of wheels.

Broad gauges are better and cheaper for movement of heavy traffic, but the narrow gauges are less expensive to build – in India the cost of a metre gauge – 3ft 3³/₈in – line per mile was half that of a 5ft 6in gauge line.

While it is true that the broader the gauge the greater the stability of trains, design is also an important factor. Moreover, narrow gauge trains are not necessarily narrower than broad gauge ones – they usually are, but train width is determined not only by the width of the tracks but also by the choice of loading gauge. Trains of the 3ft 6in gauge South African Railways, for example, are as wide as those of British Rail with its 4ft 8¹/₂in gauge.

**Standardization** of a gauge within a country is desirable since it means that every vehicle can reach every railway station. The commercial disadvantages of having a variety of gauges have been keenly felt in a number of countries, especially Australia, where re-gauging of some lines is in progress.

However, in many countries, including Britain, different gauges co-exist for sound reasons. In most cases, a standard gauge accounts for most of the mileage, while a few narrow gauge railways – 3ft or smaller – survive for particular purposes.

British Rail's standard gauge of 4ft 8¹/₂in is in the process of disappearing because a tighter fit of wheel to rail gives greater stability. On mainline track 4ft 8¹/₈in is now standard. A similar cut of a few millimetres has been undertaken in the USSR.

Narrow gauge railways in Britain tend to be in private ownership. For example, the Snowdon Mountain Railway uses a 2ft 7¹/₂in gauge and Ffestiniog Railway has a 1ft 11¹/₂in gauge.

The standard gauge for most of Europe and North America is 4ft 8¹/₂in, but Russia and Finland have a 5ft standard, Ireland 5ft 3in and Spain and Portugal 5ft 6in. Spain is hoping to introduce the standard gauge to integrate itself in Europe. The 3ft 6in gauge is used in New Zealand, Japan, Indonesia and many parts of Africa. Metre gauge – 3ft 3³/₈in – is the standard gauge in East Africa and much of south-east Asia.

**Multi-gauge** countries include India and Australia. In India, shortage of money led the government to approve a second network of metre gauge lines once the main lines had been built to 5ft 6in gauge.

Later 2ft 6in and 2ft gauge lines (but not networks) were also approved. This was partly because narrow gauge lines are easier to lay in mountainous country. The multi-gauge system has now become a serious handicap, and some metre gauge lines have been converted to 5ft 6in gauge.

Despite being aware of the problems Britain experienced with the Great Western Railway's 7ft ¹/₄in gauge, the various states in Australia went their own way. New South Wales and the government-built Trans-Australian chose 4ft 8¹/₂in, Victoria and South Australia preferred the Irish gauge, and the others standardized on 3ft 6in. Argentina and Brazil were also plagued by the existence of two main gauges.

**Gauge choice** has often had far reaching effects. The inconvenience of the gauge battles lasted for half a century in Britain and brought home to the public the disadvantage of non-standard gauges. Brunel's broad gauge used on the Great Western Railway is often regarded as superior to Stephenson's 4ft 8¹/₂in gauge favoured by other railway companies. But it did have the disadvantage that passengers and freight moving between the GWR and other lines had to change vehicle. Passengers complained, but it was the freight industry that suffered most from this inconvenience.

Eventually, in 1846, Parliament had to force the GWR to conform, though it was not until 1892 that the last broad gauge train ran. This was followed by a week-end conversion of hundreds of miles of track in an operation that was carried out with military precision and not a few barrels of beer.

In Australia, some new 4ft 8¹/₂in lines have been built in states not normally using that gauge. Trains from New South Wales can now run to the capitals of Queensland, Victoria and Western Australia.

In Japan the 4ft 8¹/₂in gauge was chosen for the new high speed lines rather than their standard 3ft 6in gauge. This deliberate introduction of a new gauge seems largely dictated by the need for the greater stability of a wider gauge and by the planners' determination that the new lines, designed for high speed passenger trains, should never be used by ordinary trains as well.

## World railway gauges

Shown below are six of the world's principal rail gauges. Listed beneath each gauge are the countries and regions that use it.

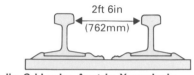

**India, Sri Lanka, Austria, Yugoslavia, Poland, Czechoslovakia, eastern Germany, Romania**

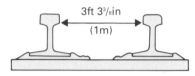

**East Africa, south-east Asia, India, Pakistan, Bangladesh, Burma, Bolivia, Brazil, Chile, Iraq, Portugal, Greece, Switzerland, Argentina**

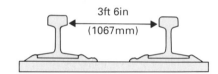

**Australia, New Zealand, Southern Africa, Ghana, Nigeria, Sudan, Indonesia, Japan, Newfoundland, Ecuador**

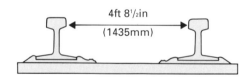

**Most of Europe, Australia, North Africa, Israel, Iraq, Iran, China, South Korea, Japan, Peru, Venezuela, Argentina, Uruguay, Paraguay, Mexico, USA, Canada**

**Ireland, Australia, Brazil**

**Spain, Portugal, India, Pakistan, Sri Lanka, Bangladesh, Argentina, Chile**

# Sleepers

Sleepers – known as cross-ties in the US – have two basic functions: holding the rails at the correct distance apart and transferring the pressures of passing trains from the rails to the ballast. Laying the rails not on cross timbers but on continuous beams beneath the rails was tried by Brunel, but proved a costly mistake, although a similar arrangement is still used on overbridges. Continuous concrete slabs work quite well but are too expensive for general use. Ideally the rails should be held firm but not rigidly – some give helps the ride to be smoother and reduces wear.

**Wooden sleepers** still predominate in most countries. Softwood, usually cheaper and lighter, does not last as long as hardwood; a softwood sleeper usually rots within 25 years, and may well need replacing after 12 years. Hardwood, such as the jarrah found on BR, lasts for at least 30 years. Both types are carefully prepared from seasoned timber, which is impregnated under pressure with wood preserver.

Creosote is the favoured treatment, although zinc chloride was used in the early decades of the railway age. In the USSR a shortage of creosoting plants often means the laying of untreated sleepers – these crack and the rotting process is speeded up by water seeping into the sleepers.

**Dimensions of sleepers** may vary. Their length depends on the track gauge, and third-rail electrification demands a greater length. The British Rail standard cross section is 10x5in (254x127mm) which is wider but less deep than those used in many other countries – in the US the spike itself may be 6in (15cm).

Flexibility and strength offered by timber was one reason why concrete sleepers were not at first highly regarded by most railway administrators. The steel sleeper seemed to have a better future in the interwar years and one company, the Great Western Railway, used it quite extensively.

**Pre-stressed concrete sleepers**, introduced in the 1950s, led to concrete being accepted as preferable to wood – the reinforced concrete sleepers previously installed found little favour. With the rising cost of hardwood, pre-stressed concrete sleepers became cheaper than wood. Also, it became possible to cast sleepers with channels on which to lay the rails, so dispensing with thick rigid baseplates. The weight of concrete sleepers is also an advantage, especially with continuous welded track, where the sleeper and ballast combination resists rail buckling because of expansion.

One of the problems of BR lengthmen is that sleepers are placed so that stepping on each one requires a very short pace, while stepping on alternate sleepers is uncomfortable even for the long-legged. Sleepers may be placed at varying distances apart, the decision being the responsibility of the civil engineer and enshrined in working regulations. A high density of sleepers raises costs but provides better support for the rail. Most railways have different densities for different categories of route – having the same density for high speed lines and sidings is pointless.

Often, sleeper density is increased on curved track, where lateral forces are higher. Some railways reduce density when concrete sleepers replace wooden ones.

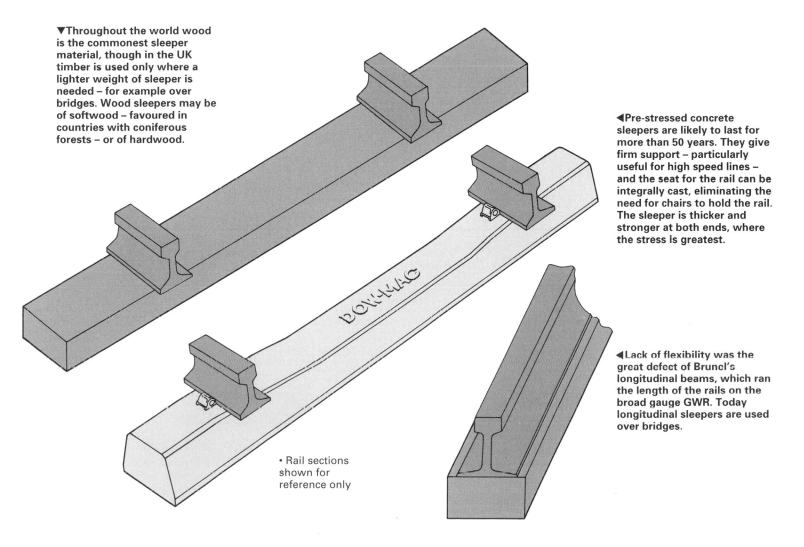

▼Throughout the world wood is the commonest sleeper material, though in the UK timber is used only where a lighter weight of sleeper is needed – for example over bridges. Wood sleepers may be of softwood – favoured in countries with coniferous forests – or of hardwood.

◄Pre-stressed concrete sleepers are likely to last for more than 50 years. They give firm support – particularly useful for high speed lines – and the seat for the rail can be integrally cast, eliminating the need for chairs to hold the rail. The sleeper is thicker and stronger at both ends, where the stress is greatest.

◄Lack of flexibility was the great defect of Brunel's longitudinal beams, which ran the length of the rails on the broad gauge GWR. Today longitudinal sleepers are used over bridges.

• Rail sections shown for reference only

# Rail fasteners

When a train travels over a section of track the pressure could push the rails out of position if they were not fixed in place. To prevent this the individual sections of rails are fastened together by fishplates held firmly in position by baseplates bolted to the sleepers. Baseplates are occasionally used on concrete sleepers, but more commonly the rail is held in place by a patented spring clip which fits into an integrally cast rail seat.

**Fishplates** have hardly changed since the mid 19th century. Essentially they are instruments in a losing battle. Because the rail joint is the weakest part of the track, however good the fishplate may be it cannot hold two separate rails rigidly together without some movement under the weight of a train. When a train passes, each oncoming wheel depresses a rail end and then hits the end of the next rail – causing considerable punishment to both rail and wheel. It is this action which causes the clickety-clack noise as a train passes over the rail joints.

Although a fishplate is designed to fit closely between the foot and the head of the rail – inside the depression provided by the thinner cross-section of the web – the continual hammering from passing trains means that it can never remain close enough for long. Moreover, the fishplate itself can bend.

Railways use different methods to deal with this situation. Some favour a long fishplate with six bolts, but British Rail uses a four-bolt fishplate. Placing the rail joint directly over two sleepers might be expected to reduce the depression caused by passing wheels. In fact, this fully supported arrangement seems little better than the fully suspended arrangement, where the joint is midway between two sleepers.

The Great Western Railway laid track with a partly supported joint, in which sleepers were brought close together by means of a shorter, two-bolt fishplate – but this made little improvement.

There are a number of methods used to fasten the rail to the sleeper – **spikes, baseplates** and **clips.**

**Spikes** are the simplest instrument for attaching the rail to the sleeper. The spike is driven into the wood so that its head overlaps the edge of the rail's foot. This method is still used in some countries, including the US.

**Baseplates** (soleplate) are now used in most countries to spread the weight between rail and sleeper. The plate is bolted to the sleeper and is channelled to provide a bed for the rail, with a variety of methods used to hold the rail in place on it. In the US a spike driven into the sleeper through a hole in the baseplate is common.

**Patented clips** are used in Britain and continental Europe on flat-bottom rail. These have an element of springiness, ensuring that the grip remains tight over a long period. As trains pass over, most of the shock waves are absorbed by the springiness in the clips instead of loosening the grip.

BR's decision to lay rails vertically in switches and crossings, instead of inclining them inwards slightly, reduced the size of the baseplates. This led to the adoption of the Pandrol clip in preference to screw and clip fasteners. A flexible pad between rail and sleeper can replace the steel baseplate when concrete sleepers are used.

With bullhead rail the arrangement is more complex. Cast jaws – known as **chairs** – are bolted to the sleepers to provide a channel for the rail. To hold the rail steady a **key** (wedge) is hammered in. Usually such keys are made of hardwood, but flexible metal ones are sometimes used.

These keys tend to loosen with the passage of trains, and permanent way lengthmen need to make frequent inspections, hammering back any loose keys. This is one of the reasons why flat-bottom track is cheaper to maintain than bullhead.

The development of continuous welded rail (CWR) means that fishplates are disappearing from main lines.

Special joints known as adjustment switches are used between the lengths, providing a small expansion gap to cope with fluctuating temperatures.

## Attachments

**Below:** bullhead rail showing standard BR four-bolt fishplate. **Right:** cross-section of rail joint shows flat-bottom rail held at an angle of 1 in 20. **Below right:** Pandrol clip used by BR holds the rail to the concrete sleeper.

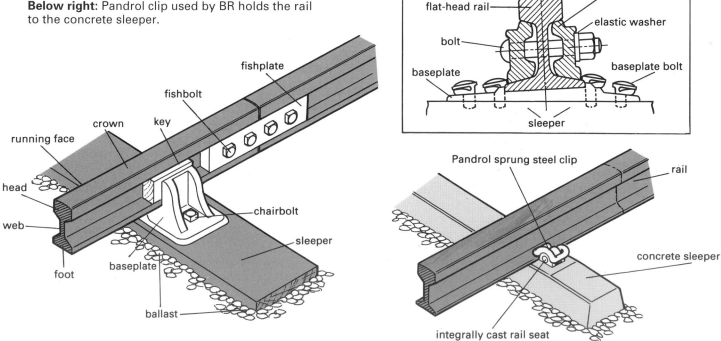

# Ballast

The pressure underneath a sleeper may approach 100lb per square inch when a train travels over it and because even a firm gravelly soil can withstand only about 50lb psi some sort of support system is needed.

Ballast holds the track in place and provides effective drainage. It also spreads the pressure under a sleeper so that the soft sub-structure is not damaged by the weight of passing trains.

**Materials** Crushed limestone was the usual material used on British railways because it was plentiful, but in recent years harder rocks such as granite and gritstone have been favoured. These stones are less likely to suffer from wet attrition. This occurs when rain washes off the surface layer of the stones and the combination of water and dirt forms a solution. This mixture acts as a grinding paste when the stones rub together under the weight of passing trains, slowly degrading the ballast.

Other materials can be used: crushed furnace slag and washed gravel are sometimes used in America, and in countries where rock ballast is scarce or expensive all kinds of materials are used, including crushed lava and sand. The USSR uses asbestos waste extensively – although possibly superior to rock ballast, this may pose serious health problems.

The favoured size of stone used for ballast is 1-2 ¼in (2.5-6cm). Under pressure these stones grip together tightly to form a lattice structure distributing the load outwards as well as downwards. This stone size also allows rapid drainage of rainwater and permits evaporation of moisture from the sub-formation.

The depth of the ballast depends on the type of trains which will run over the track. For high speed trains, ballast is usually laid to a depth of 12in (30cm). On less demanding stretches the depth is about 9in (22cm). Where track has been laid over a weak formation – soft clay, for example – a layer of sand is put down before the ballast is deposited.

Ballast extends beyond the ends of the sleepers, and on curves this shoulder is often extended and deepened to resist lateral pressures from trains that otherwise would progressively shift the track outwards. With continuous welded rail (CWR) such generous shoulders are also necessary on straight track to resist buckling in hot weather. Also, by extending ballast towards the drains, water is carried away from the trackbed.

**Maintenance** Ballast tends to become clogged up over time because of particle attrition and tamping and even with wind-blown dirt from the environment. Therefore, ballast has to be cleaned from

time to time to preserve it. Cleaning machines take up the ballast, screen it – remove the surface oil and grease – and return the stone to the track after shedding the dirt, adding fresh ballast to make up the loss.

Impaired drainage is cumulative, a small obstruction encouraging others until a situation is reached when the weight of passing vehicles produces momentary fountains of muddy water around the sleepers. This isn't dangerous when speeds are low, but main line track has to be kept scrupulously clean. Weedkilling is sometimes needed. Ballast cleaning helps but this is not usually done frequently enough to deter plant growth.

Freezing temperatures aggravate drainage problems, because frozen water can cause minor heaves of the track when it thaws. Railways in cold climates are badly affected by this, and face the additional problem that track maintenance is difficult, if not impossible, during the winter months.

**Spread** Modern technology has hardly affected the principles of ballasting. There have been experiments aimed at replacing ballast and sleepers with a continuous concrete slab but, except in a few particular places such as tunnels, this innovation seems unlikely to replace conventional practice.

## Trackbed structure

Ballast distributes the load under a passing train – its depth depends on the frequency and type of rail traffic. Ballast is also important for effective drainage. A layer of sand beneath the ballast helps drainage in areas of poor sub-formation.

When the ballast is laid by hand – known as shovel packing – the result is an open texture. A layer of granite chips is spread on top to fill in the gaps. More often today tamping machines pound the ballast down, forming a close mesh of rocks.

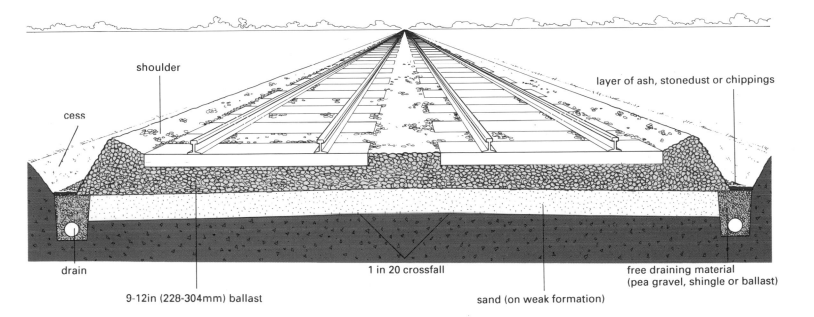

shoulder

cess

layer of ash, stonedust or chippings

drain

9-12in (228-304mm) ballast

1 in 20 crossfall

sand (on weak formation)

free draining material
(pea gravel, shingle or ballast)

# Water troughs

Although the LNWR installed the first water troughs in 1860 at Aber, it was not until the early 20th century that the idea of locomotives scooping up water at speed began to take hold. Even so, the few minutes and fleeting publicity gained by eliminating water stops and running long distance non-stop services rarely justified the expense of troughs. Outside Britain only a handful of railways in the USA and France installed them. Even in Britain, where they reached a total of 141, they were not used by the Southern Railway.

Initially water troughs were about a quarter of a mile long, but longer troughs gave the possibility of scooping worthwhile quantities of water. A typical length was 600 yards, and there were some half-mile troughs.

Finding suitable locations was often a problem. Ideally water troughs were sited on level track midway between stopping points. The LNWR's Standedge troughs had to be placed in a tunnel because that was the only suitable level stretch between Manchester and Huddersfield. Gently curved track could be used, but embankments were avoided because the drenching would have weakened them.

To contain the water, the troughs had to rise at each end, and to compensate for this the rails were high at the ends and then dropped a few inches over the troughs. This also made it easier for the fireman to lower the tender scoop into the water.

While adopting the same general dimensions, different companies used different designs of trough. Most eventually used a design with a lip along the sides to reduce spillage. Even so, water wastage was great – and the waste was enormous on those occasions when the fireman failed to raise the scoop before the tender overflowed. At the optimum speed of 40-50mph a locomotive could pick up about 2000 gallons of water.

Troughs were liable to freeze and so be unusable on frosty nights when few trains passed. Some heating devices were tried; the Great Central had a steampipe the whole length of the trough.

Troughs had to be strongly constructed. They were cradled in brackets bolted to the sleepers which were more closely spaced and larger than on normal lengths of track. The ballast was well drained, and ideally of heavy, large lumps that would not be thrown up into the trough. The trough sections were of mild steel and about 14ft long, 18in wide, and designed for a water depth of five inches.

A large water tank was the usual method of feeding the troughs, with a float valve opening and closing the outlet. So that a closely following train would not be left high and dry, refill pipes were of wide bore.

▶ As it speeds north to Carlisle in 1967, No 70013 *Oliver Cromwell* picks up water from the troughs at Dillicar, Westmorland. There was always considerable spray when trains took water; when two trains passed over troughs the effect was spectacular – and drenching for the unwary. No train was allowed to pass a royal train over troughs.

## *Water supply*

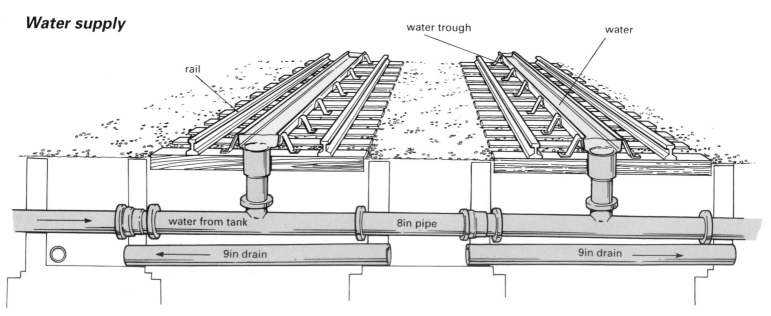

rail

water trough

water

water from tank

8in pipe

9in drain

9in drain

# Rail lubrication

The wheels of railway vehicles not only touch the top of the rails, but also the sides. On curves, centrifugal force presses the vehicles against the outer rail, causing the wheel flanges to grind. Apart from increasing the drag of the train, this grinding wears away both the wheel and rail. A solution is to apply a lubricant between the wheel flange and rail.

The seriousness of the problem depends on the sharpness of the curve and the speed and weight of the trains that use it. In exceptional circumstances, where heavy traffic passes over a sharp curve, the outside rail may need replacement within months rather than years. The wear on the wheel flange can also be serious. The thin, knife-edge flanges that are produced by constant grinding are unacceptable because, among other things, they can split points and cause derailments. Fast flange wear, therefore, means a short life for wheel sets before reprofiling becomes necessary.

## Lubricator types

One solution is to mount a rail lubricator on to the locomotive. Although this has certain attractions, one of which is that it can be conveniently refilled at locomotive depots, designs for such an apparatus have tended to spread oil on the top of the rail. This not only leads to wheel slip, but also reduces the effectiveness of the brakes.

Appliances mounted on the ground, by the track, have proved to be more successful. These are placed, typically, at the start of a curve and are designed to deposit a small drop of oil on the flanges of each of the outside wheels. The flanges then spread the oil on the part of the inner side of the rail that they press against. Keeping the oil reservoirs filled is the responsibility of track maintenance workers. With ground-mounted appliances, rails can last three or four times longer than if no lubrication was applied at all.

On the track, lubricators can be seen near the outer rail at the beginning of curves. The container holding the lubricant is the most conspicuous part. It is usually black, and the most common variety is circular, about 9in in diameter and usually placed between the rails.

### Williams all enclosed rail oiler

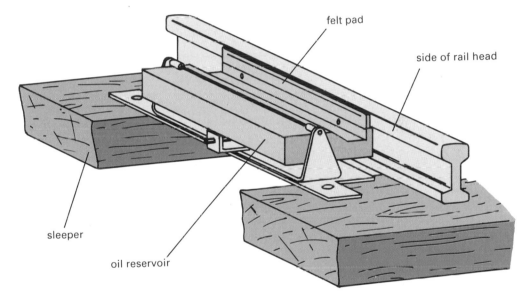

### Mills Hurcol rail and flange lubricator

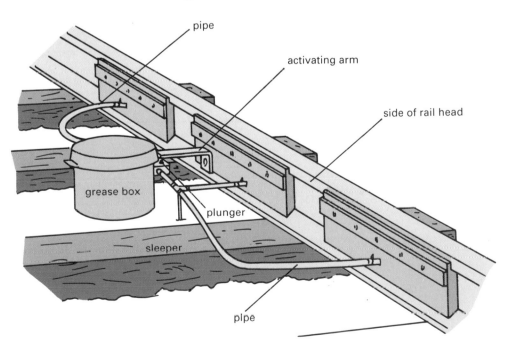

▲To show clearly the workings of the two rail lubricators, some of the detail has been omitted from both these diagrammatic illustrations. The Williams all enclosed rail oiler uses a felt pad to transfer the oil from the reservoir to the inside of the wheel flange.

◄Other devices rely on the train itself to activate a pump that forces lubricant on to the flange. The pump is usually beneath the rail and is operated by the pressure of the wheel passing over it. The Mills Hurcol rail and flange lubricator operates under the pressure of the flange of the passing wheel pushing down a plunger, squeezing some lubricant on to the side of the rail and this is then picked up and spread by the flange.

# Track circuits

The track circuit was invented in 1870 by an American, Dr William Robinson, as a way of indicating the presence of a train on a given section of line. Unlike previous methods, it did not depend on the fallible human brain.

With relay-operated signals, the extent of the circuit typically corresponds to a signalling block section. The source of current, traditionally a dry battery, is at one end of the section and the outward current travels down one rail to the end of the section, where it passes through a relay and is then fed to the other rail, along which it returns to the battery to complete the circuit. But if there is a train in the section, the current takes a short-cut through the wheels and axles, jumping into the other rail and returning to the battery without reaching the relay.

### Relay working
The voltage is safe and originally low (2-10 volts) but is sufficient to power the electromagnet in the relay, which in turn

holds up an arm. If the relay loses the electric current the arm drops and it completes another, independent, circuit.

In Dr Robinson's original scheme, the dropping of the arm switched on an electric circuit that operated a semaphore signal, and this is still the basis of automatic block signalling, where a train changes the signal behind it to red as it enters a section. But a common application is for the secondary circuit to power a small light or series of lights in an illuminated track diagram inside a signalbox. The several different track circuits fed to the box enable a signalman to see at a glance which sections of his lines are occupied.

For the system to work reliably, rail joints have to be electrically bonded with a wire connecting the two rail ends. At each end of the section, the circuit has to be kept in isolation – insulation is inserted between the rail ends, and fishplate, baseplate and bolts are also given a layer of insulation. It is not necessary to insulate the rail/sleeper fastening.

With the low voltage used, really good contact must be made between wheel and rail. The introduction of railcars, with less weight on their wheel rims, has sometimes caused problems because in certain conditions they fail to create the necessary short circuit.

Stray currents set up by the higher voltage conductor rails or wires can cripple track circuits if remedial measures are neglected. Initially, this problem was tackled by using a different type of current (DC or AC) for the track circuit and the traction power.

With modern continuous welded rail it is more difficult and less desirable to fit insulated joints. Although joints are sometimes put in, it is also possible to replace the simple battery-supplied current with coded electrical impulse track circuits. These rails are not insulated, but the coded impulse circuits allow a fade beyond their designed limits. Different codes for adjacent track circuits allow a specific relay to identify its own code.

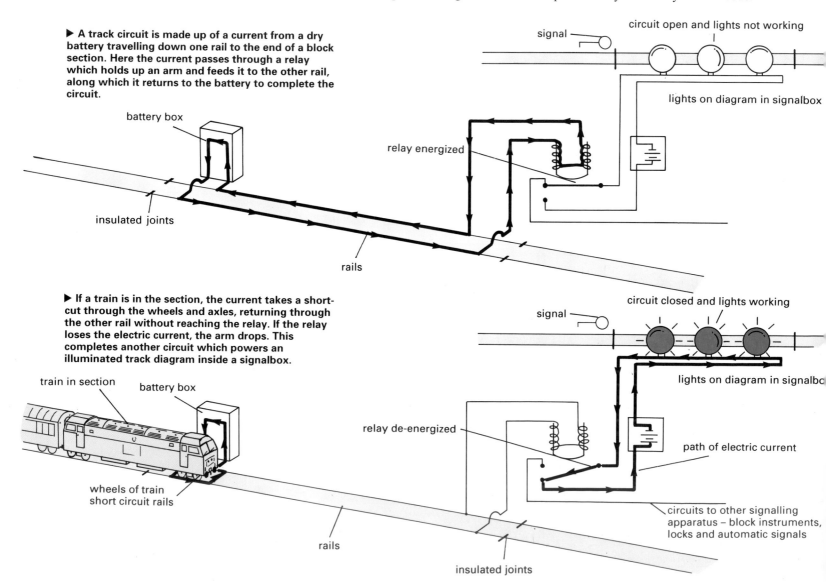

▶ A track circuit is made up of a current from a dry battery travelling down one rail to the end of a block section. Here the current passes through a relay which holds up an arm and feeds it to the other rail, along which it returns to the battery to complete the circuit.

battery box

relay energized

insulated joints

rails

signal

circuit open and lights not working

lights on diagram in signalbox

▶ If a train is in the section, the current takes a short-cut through the wheels and axles, returning through the other rail without reaching the relay. If the relay loses the electric current, the arm drops. This completes another circuit which powers an illuminated track diagram inside a signalbox.

train in section

battery box

wheels of train short circuit rails

rails

signal

circuit closed and lights working

lights on diagram in signalbox

relay de-energized

path of electric current

circuits to other signalling apparatus – block instruments, locks and automatic signals

insulated joints

# Third-rail pick-up

Overhead wires and pantographs are visible signs of how an AC train draws its power. By contrast, the third rail of the DC system and its method of current collection are hardly noticeable. Current is supplied to a train through collector shoes sliding on top of the third, or live, rail which is mounted on insulators at the ends of the sleepers, outside the running rails at one side of the track.

Shoes are mounted on the motor bogies. In older types of rolling stock, the shoegear consists of a shoebeam, usually of teak or oak, and the cast-iron collector shoes themselves which are suspended from the beam by slotted links. The beam is mounted on brackets on the axleboxes so that it is always at a constant height above the rail irrespective of the movements of the springs.

When not in contact with the live rail, the shoes hang slightly below its top surface. When they are on the rail, therefore, their weight (some 50lb) maintains contact pressure. A flexible cable leads from the shoe to a terminal on the shoebeam. No further insulation is needed because the wooden beam is itself an insulator.

## Current return

On third-rail systems the circuit is completed back to the substation through the wheels and rails. There is some leakage through the earth, which on underground lines in densely populated areas could cause trouble with telephone cables and gas and electricity mains. London Transport, therefore, uses an insulated fourth rail between the running rails as a return conductor. The return current shoes on its locomotives are attached to the underside of the traction motor frames or to a cross-member of the bogie frame.

In recent designs of third-rail stock, the shoe is carried at the end of a beam at right angles to the bogie frame and pivoted to the frame near the centre line. The pivot is a rubber bushing, and when the shoe is in its running position the rubber is trying to untwist. In doing so, the bushing acts like a spring, increasing the pressure of the shoe on the rail. As in the older arrangement, a beam is carried by brackets on the axleboxes, but its purpose is to limit up and down movements of the shoe.

Shoegear is fitted to both bogies of a motor coach and to driving trailers. A connection (power bus-line) runs through each coach of a unit, and jumper cables plugged in between coaches complete a continuous circuit between all shoes in a unit so that there is still a source of supply if one shoe is on a gap in the live rail — such as over points. On trains formed of two or more units, each collects its supply through its own shoegear.

Power bus-lines are not permitted on tube railways. Therefore, the motors and shoes in a London Transport tube train are spaced so that in passing over a gap in the live rail some motors will still pick up current. This prevents arcing and flashovers from damaging the train.

▼On a third-rail system, current is supplied to a train through collector shoes mounted on the motor bogies and sliding on top of the live rail. In both older types of rolling stock (left), and in later designs of BR third-rail stock (right), the shoes are suspended from a shoebeam. In modern stock the beam is pivoted underneath the bogie. A power bus-line runs through each coach of a unit to the traction motors.

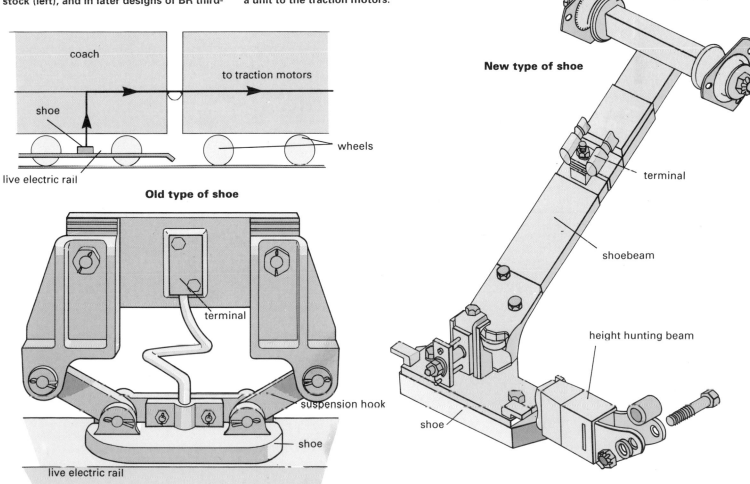

# Early rail types

During the 1990s, the traditional solid looking bullhead type rail became a rarity. With the adoption of the simpler flat-bottom rails and the phasing out of the bullhead type, a long drawn-out competition between different rail concepts on British railways was finally coming to an end.

In the early days of the railways there were many types of rail and it was only towards the end of the 19th century that the debate settled down to a competition between flat-bottom versus bullhead. In the pre-steam years, the main division in rail types was between plateway and edgeway types.

Edgeway was the forerunner of modern rail, with flanged wheels running over its upper edge. Plateway had an L-shaped cross-section, with guidance provided by the vertical half of the plate bearing against the flangeless wheels and the horizontal part bearing the weight.

At the beginning of the 19th century, plateways seemed the most promising as they had the advantage that vehicles could work over both plateways and ordinary roads. In South Wales, where edgeway was popular, some existing lines were provided with extra pieces so that there could be through running from plateways. But plateways had two problems that eventually doomed them – good points and crossings were difficult to

design and rocks and stones tended to lodge in the corner of the L cross-section.

## Material choice

Both the edgeway and plateway were made from either rolled or cast iron. Cast iron was much cheaper but rolled was more rust-resistant. In 1820, the engineer Birkinshaw invented a process for rolling I-section rails – this made them cheaper and better just as steam locomotives were about to demonstrate the brittleness of cast rails. The Birkinshaw rail also lengthened the odds against the survival of plateways.

The first rectangular edge rails had been only about four feet long. Plateway pieces had been even shorter, so that only one axle would bear on them at any one time. But Birkinshaw eventually managed to produce 20ft rails; this was important because it reduced the wear and tear on rolling stock caused by frequent rail joints.

The need to limit the load on the rail was especially important in the pre-steel era. Despite precautions, rail breakages were common and many methods were tried. An early attempt involved resting the rails on stone blocks, but this made things worse and it was then realized that the suppleness of the wooden sleeper could help reduce breakages.

Another more successful expedient

was the **fish-belly** rail in which the centre section (where breakages tended to occur) was deeper than the ends. The Stephenson & Losh rail had a **horizontal stiffener**, and also attempted to relieve the impact at rail ends by having **lap joints**.

Of the early steam railways, the different companies used the type of rail that they felt best suited their needs. The Stockton & Darlington used Birkinshaw rails on stone blocks. It also used some cast-iron Stephenson & Losh rails for loops. The Liverpool & Manchester used short fish-belly rails, while the later London & Birmingham used fish-belly types laid on wooden sleepers.

In the 1840s, Barlow's bridge rail made a short-lived appearance in Britain.

---

### Rejected success
Nowadays, railways around the world use flat-bottom rail as it has proved to be the strongest of all the rail types tried so far. In Britain, it is usually associated with permanently welded rail – the hallmark of the modern railway. In fact, in the 1840s, the prototype for flat-bottom rail, Vignoles rail, was rejected by several British companies. They preferred Locke's cheaper doubleheaded rail. Eventually this became known as the bullhead-type and was replaced by the flat-bottom type which was found to be stronger, many European countries having always preferred the Vignoles type. In the US, this type has always been favoured.

---

▼In the early days of the railways, even before the first steam engine, there were two main types of rail – plateways and edgeways. Edgeways were designed so that the flanged wheel of a vehicle ran over the upper edge. The plateway type, with its L-shaped cross-section, provided guidance to the wheel as the vertical half of the plate bore against the flangeless wheels and the horizontal part bore the weight.

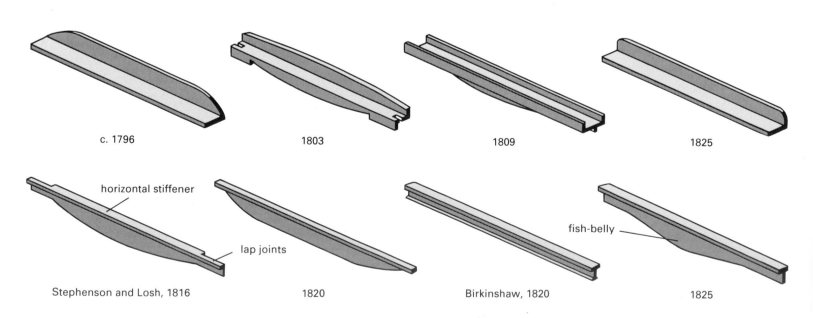

c. 1796          1803          1809          1825

horizontal stiffener

lap joints

Stephenson and Losh, 1816          1820          Birkinshaw, 1820          1825

fish-belly

# Points and crossings

What are commonly called points comprise two elements – the **switch** and the **crossing**. This combination, forming a turnout, was an important invention, because its predecessor, the turntable, could be used only by one vehicle at a time, and that vehicle had to remain stationary while it was turned from one track to another. The switch is the movable, tapered rail that can be slid laterally to divert the wheel flange of a moving vehicle. Whichever direction is taken, there is one running rail that has to be crossed by the flange and its wheel, and this intersection is the crossing.

## Different types

From the switch and crossing more complex configurations can be created. Two sets, placed face to face, enable a train to cross from one line to the other on double track – this is known as a **crossover**. Four sets make a **scissors crossover**.

Crossovers at right angles – rare in Britain – are rigid with no switch, as the angle of intersection does not permit a change of direction. However, where the angle is smaller, the **double slip** configuration combines the functions of crossover and turnout, offering four routings. In Germany this double slip is known as the English switch. It is expensive both to build and maintain, but can be a solution when four routes have to be offered in a confined space.

## Wear and tear

The crossings were traditionally fabricated from rail, but many are now monobloc (one-piece) castings. They endure considerable hammering from passing wheels and to resist this wear are often made of high-manganese steel. But even so, switches and crossings demand expensive maintenance.

An express switch made for high speed track can be expected to last only a year before replacement if it is placed on a very busy junction. Most of these units last around 25 years. There are something in the region of 25,000-30,000 on the British system.

Because of their high maintenance cost, there has been a tendency to reduce points and crossings to a bare minimum. On BR this policy has been helped by the closing of stations and especially of small freight yards – which on double track lines need a crossover for access from both running tracks.

## Speed limitations

On main running tracks the **angle of divergence** is very important because it determines the speeds at which trains can take the diverging route. In Britain, there is a range of standard divergences from one in seven – the angle of intersection at the crossing – which requires a maximum speed of 20mph (32km/h) to one in 28 (70mph). The wide angle means slower speed but allows for a shorter installation.

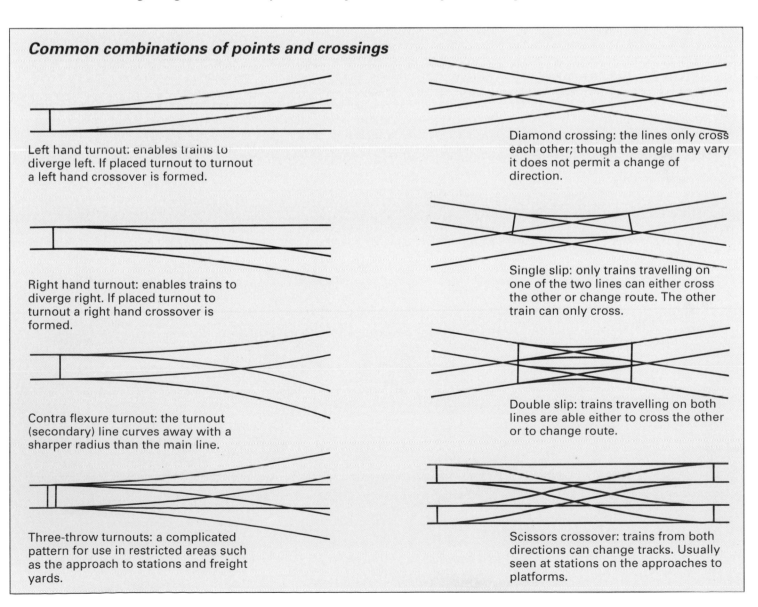

### Common combinations of points and crossings

Left hand turnout: enables trains to diverge left. If placed turnout to turnout a left hand crossover is formed.

Right hand turnout: enables trains to diverge right. If placed turnout to turnout a right hand crossover is formed.

Contra flexure turnout: the turnout (secondary) line curves away with a sharper radius than the main line.

Three-throw turnouts: a complicated pattern for use in restricted areas such as the approach to stations and freight yards.

Diamond crossing: the lines only cross each other; though the angle may vary it does not permit a change of direction.

Single slip: only trains travelling on one of the two lines can either cross the other or change route. The other train can only cross.

Double slip: trains travelling on both lines are able either to cross the other or to change route.

Scissors crossover: trains from both directions can change tracks. Usually seen at stations on the approaches to platforms.

# Changing tracks

The point enables trains to change tracks while in motion. Having only two moving parts, it consists basically of the movable **points**, which change the direction of travel of a vehicle's wheels, and the **crossing** (frog) which enables the flanged wheel to cross the intervening rail.

## Components

**Check rails** are placed alongside the outer rails to restrain the flanges of the outer wheels – this prevents the inner wheels shaking themselves out of the correct flangeway in the crossing.

The two **point rails** (switches) move in unison to change the route. Each inner end (blade) is tapered to fit closely alongside the rail when in the engaged position. Only one is held close to the rail, the other being positioned four to five inches from its running rail. The outer ends of the point rails are attached to the fixed **closure rails**, which provide the rail link with the crossing.

For most of their length the point rails rest on planed steel plates which, ideally, are well lubricated because the points are set by swinging the switch rails from one side to the other. To prevent distortion caused by the lateral forces produced when the point is changed, the two blades of the switch rails are held at their fixed distance apart by metal **stretcher bars**.

In Britain, with facing points – points at which trains diverge rather than converge – it became mandatory to provide in one of the stretcher bars two holes, into one of which a metal tongue was inserted when the point was set. This was the **facing point lock**, ensuring that the point was tightly closed and would not shift under a passing train.

## Operation

One of the switch rods makes an end-on connection with the **operating rod**, whose lateral motion changes the position of the points. Originally, the operating rod was actuated by a large lever in the hands of a pointman. In Britain, operating rods were usually extended to the nearest signalbox, where the signalman handled levers for the points of his area as well as the signals controlling movement over them. This saved time and labour and, additionally, facilitated mechanical interlocking devices to ensure that signals for a given route could not be cleared until the corresponding points were correctly set.

The rodding between signalbox and point was quite heavy. Despite frequent lubrication point operation was a highly muscular activity. Points could not be located at more than 350 yards from the signalbox, often necessitating the provision and manning of an extra box.

A solution to this problem, appearing in the late 19th century, was the electric or electro-pneumatic point, operated by electric power and actuated not by a lever attached to yards of rodding but by an electric switch. Electric operation of points made possible their setting by an operator many miles distant, and also permitted new – electric – forms of interlocking.

## Construction and durability

Points can be made complete on site at the manufacturer's and split up into separate components, or the rails can be taken off, short slave rails put on and the point assembled in small sections. The various segments are craned into position, the slave rails removed and the metal rails laid in their place.

Wooden sleepers are often a more common form of support than concrete ones because of the accuracy involved when laying new points. If the holes for the base plates on the sleepers are more than $\frac{1}{8}$in (3mm) out the rails cannot be fitted correctly.

An express point made for high speed track can be expected to last only a year before replacement if it is placed on a very busy junction. Most of these points last around 25 years. There are something in the region of 20,000 points on the British system.

## *How points work*

The key component of a set of points is the switch rail. Tapered at its leading end, it engages the wheel flanges to transfer the path of locomotive and its train. At one time switched mechanically, many points are now electronically controlled.

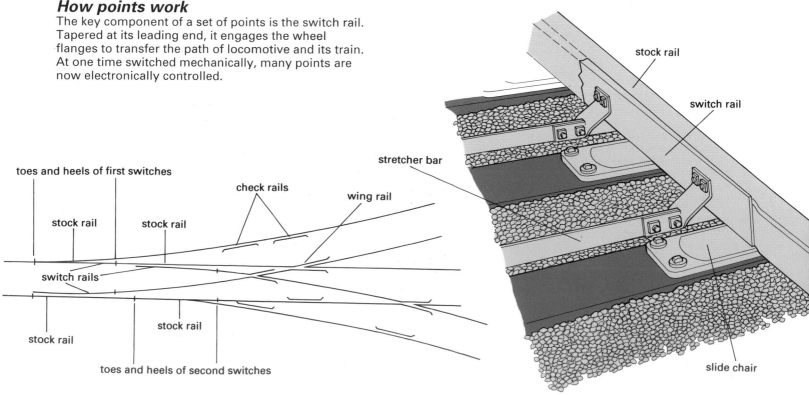

stock rail

switch rail

stretcher bar

slide chair

toes and heels of first switches

check rails

wing rail

stock rail

stock rail

switch rails

stock rail

stock rail

toes and heels of second switches

# Rack railways

Locomotives have a limit to the gradient they can climb before the wheels start to slip. Over the years, a number of methods have been used to get trains up severe inclines. A cog, or rack and pinion system is used for the steepest lines.

Rack railways became exceptionally popular at the end of the 19th century, and several still exist, especially in the Alps. The system works by meshing cog wheels on the underside of a locomotive with a cogged rail (the rack), laid between the normal running rails. This arrangement also provides a reliable method of braking. There are some lines which retain the rack simply for braking purposes.

There are several types of rack railway. These are classified by the particular rack system in use and whether the rack is used for the whole length of the line, or for steep parts of the route only.

The first tourist rack railway running up a mountain was the Mount Washington Railway in the USA, opened in 1868. It uses the **Marsh** system, whereby a rack that resembles a ladder is engaged by a steam-driven cog wheel on the locomotive. This enables the locomotive and its single carriage to tackle gradients as steep as 1 in 5.

About the same time, the **Riggenbach** system was developed for the Rigi Railway in Switzerland. This is similar to the US system, but with the cross-pieces of the rack designed to fit more snugly in the locomotive's cogs. Another Swiss line, the Pilatus Railway, uses the **Locher** rack in which the rail is laid horizontally and has teeth machined along both edges.

Perhaps the most successful system is the **Abt**. This has an upright plate, or blade, with slots machined into it. The locomotive cog, or pinion, wheels are machined accurately, so that there is a close fit, less vibration, and less wear and tear than other systems.

Sometimes the Abt system provides two blades side by side, with the rack teeth staggered between the two. With locomotives fitted with a pair of matching cog wheels, this means that there is a fresh tooth on which to engage every 60cm. The Snowdon Railway in Wales uses this system.

The **Strub** system is a version of the Abt, but is simpler to lay and maintain as it is bolted directly to the sleepers.

Locomotives used for railways that are partly conventional, partly rack, may have separate machinery for each function. With steam locomotives this can mean a four-cylinder design, with one pair of cylinders driving the wheels through conventional connecting rods, and another pair for the cog wheels.

▶ **The Mount Washington Railway in the USA was the first tourist rack railway to be built up a mountain. Opened in 1868 it is still open today and uses the Marsh rack system. A steam-driven cog wheel on the locomotive engages a ladder-like rack. This allows the locomotive and its carriage to climb gradients as steep as 1 in 5.**

## *Four types of rack system*

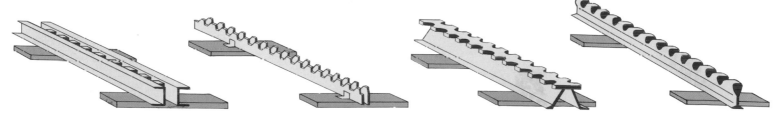

Riggenbach          Abt          Locher          Strub

# Track rationalization

The term rationalization suggests changing working methods to increase efficiency and cut costs. This has led to abuse of the word, and today, rationalization is sometimes used to mean simply a reduction in services. This certainly leads to a cutting of costs but not necessarily an improvement in efficiency.

Track rationalization may result from changing circumstances and all too often this change is a reduction of traffic. But sometimes, rationalization is brought about by new devices or methods, which enable the same tasks to be performed with less labour and less drain on other resources.

**Advanced signalling** methods can fit more trains into a given length of line and can arrange for trains to pass or overtake with more precision than was previously possible. This allows the number of tracks to be reduced, sometimes to a single track.

Bi-directional signalling, permitting trains to run in either direction along a single track, means that extra tracks may no longer be necessary. If traffic remains the same, or diminishes, this provides a chance to reduce four tracks to three or two. Steel rail can be salvaged and track maintenance reduced.

**Concentration schemes** involve the transfer of business from several lightly loaded facilities, typically freight stations, to one centre which can be provided with modern, cost-cutting equipment – such as containerization. One of the largest of these rationalization projects was BR's coal concentration scheme. This removed domestic coal traffic from the hundreds of stations that once dealt with one or two wagons a week, and sent it by the trainload to a few specialized, efficient facilities.

Several rationalization schemes have come out of major **modernization projects**. Electrification and resignalling generally take the form of joint studies, during which existing methods and facilities are examined to see if they are really needed.

This was not always the case. When the first major post-war electrification project, the West Coast main line, was undertaken, many miles of track were expensively electrified, only to find they were no longer needed. Three decades later, the lesson learned, the East Coast main line was electrified only after surplus tracks had been identified. In most cases this approach made the electrification easier, because it gave more space to the engineers. For example, removing a loop on curved track releases space which enables the running lines to be curved more gently, permitting higher speeds.

**Land sales** at times of high property prices become a highly attractive form of rationalization. The closure, or shrinkage, of large marshalling yards on the outskirts of cities has allowed money to be made from land sales. The closure of local freight stations releases land that can be sold for redevelopment.

◀▼Rationalization is chiefly concerned with cutting costs. Great savings can be made by reducing the number of points and crossings, sometimes by changing track layouts. The famous but high-cost diamond crossovers at the east end of Newcastle Central (below) were replaced by simpler layouts.

# Learning the road

Before a railway driver is allowed to take a train along a particular line, it is necessary for him or her to be completely familiar with all the physical features of the route. Even an express passenger driver has to know whether the train can be diverted into a particular siding or loop and, if so, under what conditions.

## Methods

Traditionally, route learning has been carried out by drivers travelling in the cabs of trains going over the line, but in recent years more use has been made of **inspection saloons** and single unit rail cars. These are specially fitted coaches with large glass windows at the front, which are propelled over the line by a locomotive. Various vital points along the route are indicated by an instructor. This method means that more than one driver can be instructed at a time.

**Simulators** are also used. These are videos giving a view of the track from the cab, whose speed is controlled by a driver sitting in a studio. Simulators are costly to build and operate and are used mainly when a new type of train is being introduced. But they are also employed when a major alteration of a section of line occurs and it is necessary to teach a number of drivers how to operate over it immediately after reopening.

## Restrictions

The most vital part of route learning involves getting to know the various **maximum speeds** allowed on every section of track. Until well into the 20th century, it was not customary for railways to provide *any* speed restriction signs. Later, it was only speeds that were lower than the overall maximum line speed which were marked, such as at junctions. It is now usual to indicate particular places where the speed is allowed to rise again.

In spite of all these signs, at most places where there is a reduction in the permitted speed, the driver will have to start braking before it is possible to see the sign. So it is important for the driver to know exactly where the train is relative to each restriction, especially at night and in fog or snow. Only in a few important places, when there is a particularly severe speed restriction, is it customary to provide additional triangular warning signs in advance of the restriction.

The Big Four used different ways of marking some of the more important restrictions. After the formation of BR, the London & North Eastern Railway's (LNER) system of large cut-out figures beside the track was adopted nationally. More recently, there has been a change to circular, road-type signs which are reflective and easier to see at night.

It is also important for the driver to learn the **gradients** along the route. Although it is no longer necessary to watch the water level in the boiler of a steam locomotive as it goes over a steep summit, it is still possible to damage the electrical equipment of a modern train by taking too heavy a load up a long, steep bank. Knowing when to brake for temporary speed restrictions is also affected by the gradients before them.

Another vital aspect of route learning is to understand the **signalling** system. With modern coloured lights, drivers no longer have to interpret the complications of large signal gantries. But there are still many places where several complex movements are controlled from a single set of signals, and the driver has to know exactly what each indication means.

There are many **weight or loading gauge restrictions** to be learnt. Sometimes a special authorization is required from the signalbox before a particular movement can be carried out, and the driver has to know how to obtain it. This includes any diversions from those lines normally used by a particular type of train.

◄Drivers must be thoroughly familiar with any route before they are allowed to take a train over it; the rail companies employ several methods to familiarize drivers with new or changed track layouts. The speed of many of today's trains means that drivers must anticipate any speed restriction well in advance. Even with coloured light signalling, junctions and the approaches to large stations can be quite complicated and mistakes interpreting the various signs can lead to disaster.

# Clearing House maps and diagrams

With the rapid expansion of the railway system during the 1830s and '40s there arose serious concern about the accounting arrangements used by the individual companies. This led to the Chairman of the London & Birmingham Railway, the famous George Carr Glyn, proposing the formation of the Railway Clearing House (RCH).

The main reason behind the establishment of this novel organization in January 1842 was to allocate the relative proportions of through fares and charges between the companies, and then to supervise the division of these through fares. To calculate these, it was vital that the precise distances between every station and junction was readily to hand.

In the 1840s and '50s, a number of companies published railway maps. The RCH standardized on Macauley's *Station Maps of the Railways of Great Britain*, published by Zachary Macauley – a clerk who worked in the RCH. The maps were printed on sheets 52x36in (132x91cm) on which each railway appeared in a different colour. The first issue of the new maps appeared in January 1851.

The RCH maps were developed over a period of 20 years and were divided into districts, using a scale of 10 miles to the inch. Typical districts were South Wales, Yorkshire and London.

The maps were regularly revised, as new lines were always being built. On Macauley's death in 1860 production was taken over by RCH staff, and by 1893 they had reached their 22nd edition.

Though the maps were good for routes they did not show distances. However, from 1871 an RCH map was produced which included full details of the distances (in miles and chains) between stations.

**Junction diagrams** were first recorded in 1855. From 1867 to 1894, John Airey – who worked for the RCH – published these diagrams privately. The RCH took over publication from then on.

These junction diagrams were meticulously drawn and coloured, and contained all the distances required by the RCH. The standardized form was in loose-leaf format with a map 6x10in (15x25.5cm).

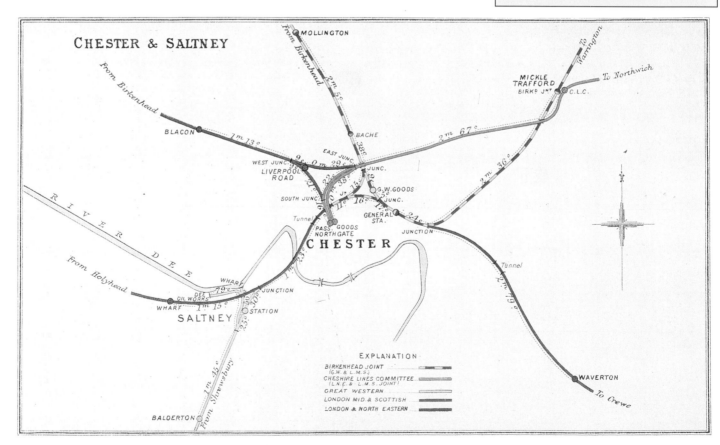

▲This Railway Clearing House (RCH) junction diagram was printed in 1928. It gives a detailed view of the three companies that served Chester after Grouping and their jointly owned lines.

The last map produced was of Scotland, published by the British Transport Commission – a successor to part of the role of the RCH – in 1960. The need for the RCH ended with nationalization.

# Single-lead junctions

**D**ouble-track junctions are made up from a double-tracked route (one up line and one down line). When the route diverges into two paths, one of the two diverging tracks has to cross over one of the main tracks. This is usually done with a diamond crossing. Such crossings demand little space, but suffer wear and inflict wear on the wheels of rail vehicles. These crossings need careful maintenance and are expensive to replace. In general, and largely for reasons of maintenance costs, it is preferable to have as few points and crossings as possible on the main line.

In the **single-lead junction**, the diverging route is reduced to a single track with a single turnout from one of the main (non-divergent) tracks. Instead of using a diamond crossing, diverging trains cross to the other main line and run the wrong way for a short distance before turning off. The single divergent track becomes double track some distance past the junction, wherever space is available.

In modern times, as part of rationalization schemes, many single-lead junctions have been installed, despite their inclusion of a length of track where trains move in both directions. With modern signalling, which elsewhere had coped successfully with bi-directional running, this should have been no problem, and the single-lead junction was regarded as a good layout where traffic on the divergent route was light.

## Accidents

There have been a number of accidents, or near accidents, at single-lead junctions. In 1989, a head-on collision occurred at Bellgrove Junction, Strathclyde, which raised initial doubts about single-lead junctions. This lethal mishap, which occurred on the single track bi-directional throat of the junction, was attributed to one train passing a signal at danger, bad siting of the signal and carelessness of the train crew.

Although the accident was not attributable directly to the layout of the junction, it was true that with a conventional layout the mistakes made would not have resulted in a collision; the diverging train would not have had to travel the wrong way over one of the main lines for any distance. Following this accident, it was decided that further conversions of double- to single-lead junctions would each have to be approved by the Secretary of State for Transport before implementation.

After the accident, the layout at Bellgrove remained as it was, but it was decided to double-block approaching trains. When the junction was not clear, approaching trains were halted a section in advance – not one, but two successive signals were held at danger, giving a safety margin in case a train ran past the first one.

An application of single-lead junctions was in the 1992 reconstruction of the layout at Ely, Cambridgeshire. Here, the replacement of double junctions by single-lead layouts eliminated diamond crossings and provided space for a better alignment, resulting in higher permissible speeds.

### Safety margin

The prime cause of accidents at single-lead junctions has not been the layout itself, but there is an argument that such layouts can convert a minor infringement of regulations, or even an obscurely written regulation, into a disaster. The belief that conventional double junctions provide an excessive safety margin is no longer acceptable.

## Ely rationalization

In 1992, many single-lead junctions were used in the rebuilding of the layout at Ely. Double junctions were replaced by single-lead layouts, removing most of the diamond crossings.

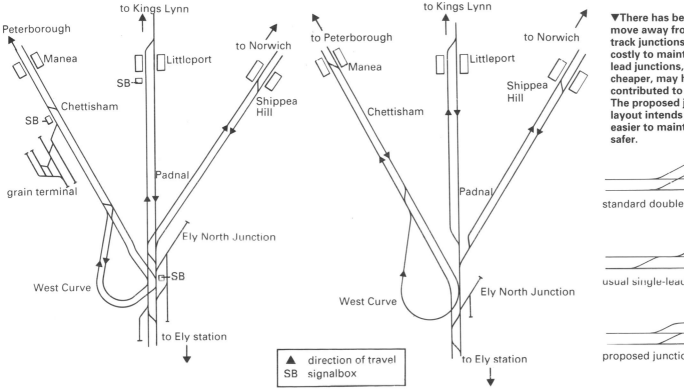

▼There has been a gradual move away from double-track junctions as these are costly to maintain. Single-lead junctions, though cheaper, may have contributed to accidents. The proposed junction layout intends to be both easier to maintain and safer.

standard double track junction

usual single-lead junction

proposed junction layout

▲ direction of travel
SB signalbox

# Single line tokens

Tokens authorized safe single line running – a driver could proceed along a single line only when he was in possession of a token for that stretch of line. Each end of the single line section had an instrument containing a token, the two being connected so that only one token could be obtained at a time. Though the instruments that contained the tokens are quite collectable they are very large and heavy. The tokens are the most popular collectors' items.

Three different types – tablets, staffs and key tokens – were used in the UK:

**Tablets** The first to appear was Tyer's Electric Train Tablet, patented in 1878. The tablets for this first design – 4³/₄in diameter – were larger than later patterns. Tablets for the later Nos 2, 3, 4 and 6 instruments were 4¹/₄in diameter and tablet Nos 5 and 7 were even smaller at 3³/₄in.

All forms of electric token needed to be configured so that a token for one

section could not be placed in an instrument for a different section. In the No 1 tablet instrument this configuration was made by the relationship between the notch in the edge of the tablet and the hole in its face, but in all the other patterns the configuration was made by the shape of the notch alone.

The earliest tablets were made of steel, but they had the names of the stations at either end of the single line engraved on a brass plate set into the front. Later tablets were made entirely of brass, then aluminium; eventually a red-brown fibre was used.

**Staffs** In 1888 Webb & Thompson patented a new kind of token, the Electric Train Staff (ETS). Early staffs were made of steel with brass rings, the configuration being made by the position of the fifth ring in relation to the other four. The Railway Signal Co was licensed to make the ETS, which was later produced in two miniature forms.

**Key tokens** In 1914, the GWR patented the Electric Key Token, which was licensed to Tyer and Co. The simplicity of this design made it cheaper to manufacture and maintain than rival apparatus, and it came to dominate the market. In the Tyer's KT, the configuration was made by the position of a groove on the operating segment of the token, which was attached by a short shaft to the handle by which the key was turned in the instrument. Today, keys are the most common tokens available.

---

## Collecting tokens

Tablets, staffs and key tokens are all in great demand by collectors. Most of Britain's single lines have been axed; on surviving lines many signalboxes have been closed and some branches converted to radio signalling. This means few collectable tokens of any type are now coming on to the market, but look for them in railwayana auctions, small ads in the railway press and collectors' newsletters.

---

## The staff system

First introduced in 1888, early staffs (such as this L type) were made of steel tube with five brass rings, with the section names at one end. The staffs were frequently fitted with an Annett's key which unlocked a ground frame to work points in the section.

The full length L type staff was 23in, and was contained in a very heavy, handsome instrument that was nearly five feet tall. Later, smaller types of instrument were produced, with miniature staffs; the M type staff was 10³/₄in long and the S type 9in.

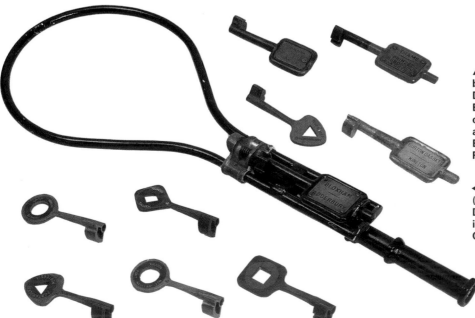

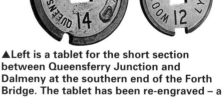

▲Left is a tablet for the short section between Queensferry Junction and Dalmeny at the southern end of the Forth Bridge. The tablet has been re-engraved – a common saving when block sections were altered; right, a tablet for Wooda (Woody) Bay to Lynton on the Lynton & Barnstable Railway.

◄ A selection of key tokens from the GWR (Thame – Princes Risborough and Burton Dassett – Kineton) and Scottish companies include (centre) the apparatus in which GWR keys were placed for handing over.

# Grade separation

The term grade crossing, still used in North America, means the crossing of a railway by a road or another railway line on the same level, or grade. In Britain, the term for an intersection of a road and a railway line is 'level crossing'. When two railway lines cross, it is known as a flat crossing.

Crossings of this nature cause problems. It is cheaper and easier to intersect on the level, rather than carrying one route over the other by means of a bridge or tunnel. But whereas crossing at the same level suits the builders, it makes life complicated for the transport operators. Rebuilding to place one route above the other is known as grade separation and can be particularly expensive.

## Road crossings

When a line ran through undulating terrain, with the railway constantly moving between cuttings and embankments, it was fairly easy to arrange for one route to pass above the other. In flat country, however, there was no such opportunity and, because of the absence of cuttings, there was no easy source of spoil for building embankments long enough to raise one route above the other.

In Britain, therefore, level crossings are most prevalent in the east, where flat landscapes faced railway companies such as the South Eastern and the Great Eastern which were too poor to afford extensive earthworks. That is why even today cities like Canterbury have busy main roads crossed by railways on the level.

Busy level crossings are expensive to operate and are unpopular among road-users. But because they are surrounded by buildings, replacing them with tunnels or bridges is impossibly expensive. In most cases, the only relief has been the replacement of hand-operated gates by the faster automatic barriers.

## Railway crossings

The intersection of one railway route by another railway route is quite unusual in Britain. Such crossings have always been regarded as inherently dangerous and advisable only when the traffic on one line was sparse.

However, when traffic on the minor route increases to such an extent that trains are habitually held up while the crossing clears, it is sometimes necessary to rebuild such crossings on separate levels – even though the expense is considerable.

In a declining economy, this situation rarely arises. However, in the 1960s new, big coal mines were developed on the west side of the East Coast main line to supply power stations on the east – leading to an enormous increase in east-west traffic. One result of this was the classic example of grade separation at Retford, where the former Great Central Railway's Lincoln to Sheffield route crossed the old Great Northern line on the level.

Already, before the coal developments, passenger trains on both routes were frequently held up by long, slow-moving goods trains crossing in front of them. With more than 20 daily merry-go-round trains planned for the east-west line it was clear that grade separation was essential. A flyover was rejected, partly on grounds of expense, so a dive-under was built.

### Flat out
In the US during the 1930s, where crossings were made on the level, speeds were restricted to 50 or 60mph. In the city of Syracuse in New York state, the New York Central main line ran up the main street for a mile before reaching the station. During this part of their journey, the great American trains would slow to 15mph, with their bells tolling to keep the streets clear.

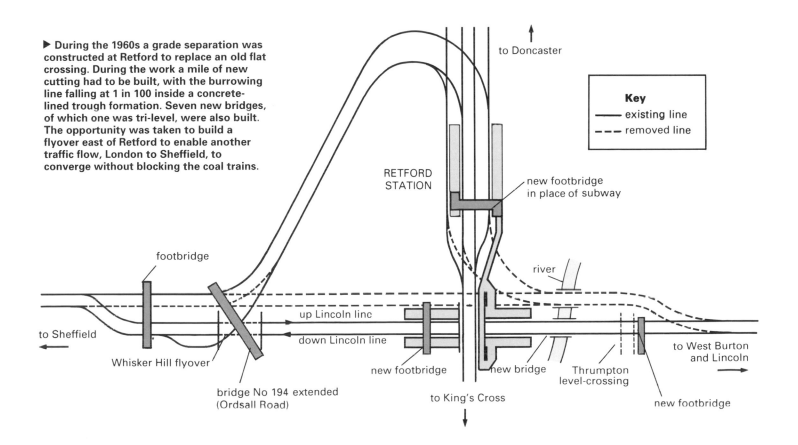

► During the 1960s a grade separation was constructed at Retford to replace an old flat crossing. During the work a mile of new cutting had to be built, with the burrowing line falling at 1 in 100 inside a concrete-lined trough formation. Seven new bridges, of which one was tri-level, were also built. The opportunity was taken to build a flyover east of Retford to enable another traffic flow, London to Sheffield, to converge without blocking the coal trains.

to Doncaster

**Key**
—— existing line
- - - removed line

RETFORD STATION

new footbridge in place of subway

river

footbridge

up Lincoln line

down Lincoln line

to Sheffield

Whisker Hill flyover

bridge No 194 extended (Ordsall Road)

new footbridge

new bridge

to King's Cross

Thrumpton level-crossing

to West Burton and Lincoln

new footbridge

# Cuttings and embankments

When the canal system was built during the late 18th century, the engineers followed the contours of the landscape to avoid the need for constructing locks – although this added considerable distance to each route. Because the railways which followed wanted a more direct path, cuttings and embankments were needed. To build them a great deal of earth had to be moved – much of it by hand.

**Building embankments** Great care has to be taken with the angle of the sides of embankments. Because embankments are load-bearing and manmade, their slopes must be relatively gentle. Ideally, the soil used to build an embankment would come from a nearby location – preferably from a recent excavation on the same

railway. When the Great Central Railway was built in the late 19th century, spoil from one cutting was used to make a nearby embankment. After the line closed seventy years later, the same spoil was used to re-fill the cutting.

The stability of embankments is affected by water, but drainage is relatively easy to manage. Embankments are more at risk from major floods and in countries where there is sudden heavy rainfall, many have been swept away.

When building an embankment, care has to be taken to ensure that the ground will bear the extra weight. Stephenson's famous method of using brushwood to support the Liverpool & Manchester's line across Chat Moss is well known.

In 1979, when the Penmanshiel diversion was being built, it was found that in some places the ground was not strong enough and peat beds were completely removed and replaced with fill.

In the 1980s, the East Coast main line was diverted across the Plain of York – called the Selby diversion – and the new track called for the use of embankments.

The spoil material used in construction contained water and to ensure that it was steadily squeezed out, the rate at which the foundation material was dumped was carefully monitored.

When the early railways were built, small coals, too small to be sold, were sometimes used in the construction of embankments. Over the years, spontaneous combustion has occurred in some of them and smouldering fires like this are difficult to extinguish without rebuilding the affected area completely – a solution which involves closing the line for some time.

**Constructing cuttings** Water is a problem in cuttings, particularly where they have been built through rock. Water trapped in cracks, freezes and expands during a hard frost causing the rock to split and become unstable. Where the Hull & Barnsley Railway passed through the Yorkshire Wolds, chalk particles were constantly being dislodged from the steep sides of the cutting and these had to be removed regularly.

Precautions must, therefore, be made to prevent seepage by providing a ditch along the top of the cutting. If too much water gets into the face of a cutting dug through soil, it can cause it to slump downwards towards the track. In extreme cases, a pile of spoil can block the line and there have even been instances when the track bed has been forced upwards by debris pushing against the sides. Piles of rock or concrete placed near the foot of the cutting can stop this movement of spoil. Rock filled vertical, or Y-shaped, drainage channels running down the sides help to channel water down the cutting face.

Drainage in a cutting is also necessary to remove water at track level. If the track is completely level, there will be difficulty in getting the water to drain out of a cutting. Ordinary ditches were adequate at one time, but piped drainage is now provided on most main lines.

▼A locomotive hauls spoil through a London & Birmingham Railway cutting at Berkhamsted in 1837. Much of the earth was removed in barrows, wheeled up planks of wood on the side of the cutting by the strongest men. If they slipped – as they frequently did – a fatal accident could follow should the barrow overturn and its load fall on top of them.

▶ If water is not drained away properly from a railway cutting, seepage causes the soil face to loosen and slide downwards. It is possible for spoil to block the line and even force the track upwards. To prevent this, drainage ditches are dug along the top and at the bottom of the cutting, and sometimes piles of rock or concrete are placed near the foot to stop spoil movement.

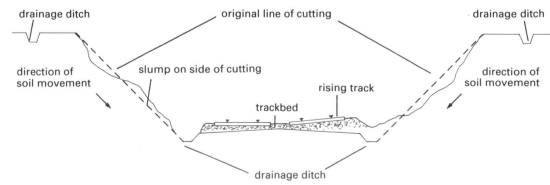

drainage ditch

original line of cutting

drainage ditch

direction of soil movement

slump on side of cutting

rising track

direction of soil movement

trackbed

drainage ditch

# Mileposts

In the days when passenger fares and freight rates were calculated at so many pence per mile, one Victorian Act of Parliament which regulated the railways required markers to be fixed along the track at quarter-mile intervals. If these were not provided, the railway could not insist on being paid for carrying passengers or freight over that stretch.

So important was this rate to those deciding how to move their goods from one part of the country to another, that commercial publishers produced thick books, listing the distances between any pair of stations in the country by every possible route. However, when the building of a line involved particularly expensive major engineering works – the Forth Bridge or the Severn Tunnel, for instance – Parliament agreed that, for charging purposes, a fixed extra mileage should be allowed, over and above the actual distance.

## Different types

Many railways evolved their own distinctive types of milepost. Quite often the actual mileposts were larger or more ornate than the intermediate quarter posts, and some posts showed where the zero point of the series was located. For many main lines this was London, but the starting point for those posts on the Midland's line through Birmingham to Bristol was at Derby.

It is unusual for there to be an actual zero post, but the one at Derby can still be seen. Another such post was installed quite recently at Moorgate, close to the buffers in Network SouthEast's Thameslink platforms. On branch lines, practices differed. Sometimes the mileposts were numbered continuously from the series on the main line, but elsewhere they may start from the junction at zero.

Quite often the distances at the quarter, half and three-quarter miles are not shown in full, but special designs of marker are used for each. The Great Eastern used one, two or three small discs on a vertical post, while the North Eastern had cast-iron posts with one, two or three points radiating from the circular top, with the fraction shown in the centre. Some BR ones have the appropriate number of dots or vertical lines on the bottom half of the plate, with the actual mileage above it. Some pre-Grouping designs are sufficiently distinctive to enable today's traveller to work out which company constructed that particular line.

Our railway civil engineers now

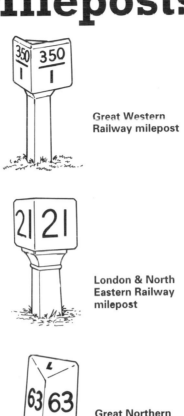

**Great Western Railway milepost**

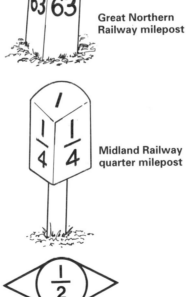

**London & North Eastern Railway milepost**

**Great Northern Railway milepost**

**Midland Railway quarter milepost**

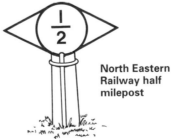

**North Eastern Railway half milepost**

**London & North Eastern Railway half milepost**

measure distances in kilometres and metres, rather than miles and chains. Accordingly, many mileposts now have the metric equivalent stencilled on them, but there are a few places where there is a separate series of kilometre posts.

London Transport installed such a system several years ago, the zero being at the most easterly point on their railway – Upminster. The BR lines out of King's Cross to Hitchin via Welwyn and Hertford have small blue markers at the kilometres and half-kilometres, and, at the other end of InterCity's East Coast Route, the Scottish Region installed similar orange markers northwards from Berwick during the electrification of the line. Although the old North British Railway's mileposts on the other side of the tracks were measured from Edinburgh, the kilometre ones have their zero at King's Cross.

## Flexible miles

The position of a particular milepost is often not quite correct, and those who regularly use them to work out the speed of trains know those which are out of position. Particular difficulties arise when the alignment is altered, one example being just north of Durham on the East Coast route. A short cut-off was constructed in the 1960s, which shortened the route by 140 yards, and upset the milepost distances. In contrast, the deviation around the collapsed tunnel at Penmanshiel in Scotland is longer than the original line.

However, there is one railway where the mileposts are particularly accurately positioned. This is the Ffestiniog in North Wales, where members of the Railway Performance Society remeasured the line in 1991, and later fixed the quarter-mile posts in the correct positions.

### Moving the mileposts

Before the line over Stainmore was closed, there used to be a movable milepost at Barnard Castle. Built by the South Durham & Lancashire Union Railway, which was a stickler for accuracy, the milepost was fixed to the doubletrack level crossing gates just east of the station. Every time the gates opened and closed the post moved its position. The gate was still in use up to the time the line was finally closed to all traffic in 1962. Some mileposts have now become collectors' items.

# Lineside signs

Numerous different signs are provided on the lineside for the information of drivers. The oldest type are known as **gradient signs**, which indicate whether the line is rising or falling, and how steeply. This information used to be vital in the days when loose-coupled goods trains, without continuous brakes, were hauled by steam locomotives.

The driver and guard had to work together to prevent the wagons closing up violently and to keep the train under control downhill. On particularly steep descents there would be large signs indicating where the driver had to stop to let the guard apply the brakes on some of the wagons.

On steep climbs, catch-points were frequently installed to derail any wagons which might break loose from the rear of the train and run back down the gradient. It was vital for the driver not to stop with the train on one of these spring-operated switches, and large signs indicated where these were.

In Britain, the gradient signs have arms inclined up or down to indicate whether the line is rising or falling, and there is usually a single figure on each arm. If this is the number 200, for example, it means that the line rises or falls one foot for every 200 feet travelled forward. Railway gradients are modest compared with those on our roads, but the weight of a train is vastly greater than that of a car or lorry.

In the days of steam, **speed restriction signs** were rare in Britain. As late as 1950, only 12 such signs were installed on the down line between Totnes and Penzance – a distance of 104 miles. If the driver adhered to the times in the timetable he would not need to travel faster than was safe. As train speeds increased, it became important to lay down fixed limits, but, while lists of these were read by drivers, relatively few of them were marked on the lineside.

The four Grouping companies used different types of speed restriction signs, but BR adopted the London & North Eastern Railway (LNER) design as standard. This had large cut-out figures, painted white (later yellow) on the side seen by the driver. Originally a sign was only to be put up where the speed had to be reduced below the overall maximum for that particular line. After 100mph running began, the practice developed of showing every speed restriction. For instance, there are now 125mph signs at the exit ends of the 100mph restriction over the flat-crossing at Newark.

## Rail side road signs

In recent years there has been a change-over to circular road-type signs, with a reflective finish which shows up in the high powered headlights fitted to fast trains. Where there is a sudden marked reduction in speed, it is usual to provide an **advanced warning sign** in the form of a triangle with the point facing downwards. The ordinary circular ones are now installed in considerable numbers, with small **repeater signs** in places,

where, for example, a train comes out of a loop to join the main line.

Another type of sign tells the driver the frequency to which the cab radio telephone should be tuned. These are used widely, appearing also on remote lines provided with radio electronic token block signalling. Such branches have a whole series of their own lineside signs, telling drivers where the different tokens must be obtained and given up.

On some electrified lines special **warning signs** are used to tell drivers not to attempt to take electrically hauled trains on to lines where there are no overhead wires. As speeds are low at such places, the message is spelt out at length, rather than being conveyed in an abbreviated form.

There are, however, some similar written signs in places on fast sections of the East Coast route telling drivers that they are two miles from stations such as Grantham and Newark. At night there are no obvious landmarks, but the white-painted board on the lineside indicates to the driver when he should start braking.

---

### Temporary speed restrictions

Sections of track disturbed during civil engineering work are marked by temporary speed restriction signs. Normally these are listed in the weekly notices read by the drivers, but it is sometimes necessary to introduce one at short notice. Until a notice was put up in the driver's signing-on point, a hand-signalman on the lineside would place a detonator to warn each train.

 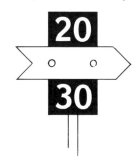 

---

gradient sign – line decends 1ft for every 490ft travelled

LNER speed restriction sign; 50mph is maximum limit

advanced warning for a speed restriction

sound whistle or horn as warning

# Locomotive water supply

When working an express train, a steam engine would use 30-50 gallons of water per mile; on heavy freight work 50-70 gallons a mile was typical. Water stops had to be brief, but 2000 gallons could be taken in a four-minute halt.

There were five main types of water supplying device: the **high capacity storage tank**, a large water tank, often placed above a locomotive depot's coaling stage, which fed water directly through a pipe to an engine; the **fixed stand-pipe**, positioned between two tracks and useful where space was limited; the **fixed water column**, a vertical post with a flexible hose at the top; the **water crane**, a water column with a horizontal swinging arm at the top which could be swung across to reach the water tank of an engine; and the **parachute tank**, a round tank of around 2000 gallons capacity with a flexible hose placed at the top of a column.

A swinging arm allowed the driver more room to manoeuvre when positioning the tender in the correct place by the column – never an easy task when running a train into a station.

All the main types of water facility needed a flexible hose to reach the filler hole in the locomotive's tender or tank. The hoses were usually made of leather with copper rivets and were heavy to handle. Most crane arms rotated on a ramped surface. This ensured that they would return to the standby position parallel with the track after use. It was important to secure the hose after use in case it was blown in front of a train.

As tenders grew in height and size, water cranes were sometimes given an additional swan neck to provide sufficient clearance over the tender.

## Operation

The water was usually turned on at a stop valve at ground or platform level. This procedure occupied both driver (at the valve) and fireman (up on the tank watching the water level). Some railways provided a pull chain on parachute tanks, or a wheel on the end of water crane arms, so that the fireman could control the water. Good drainage was required under the hose when standing idle.

In winter, steps were necessary to prevent water in columns and tanks from freezing, which could cause costly damage. In Britain, it was normal to place a coal fire in a brazier, or a fire cresset with a long chimney, at the foot of the column to radiate heat. At least one railway, the Highland, built a small firebox into the column itself, its heat passing up within the column round the central water main.

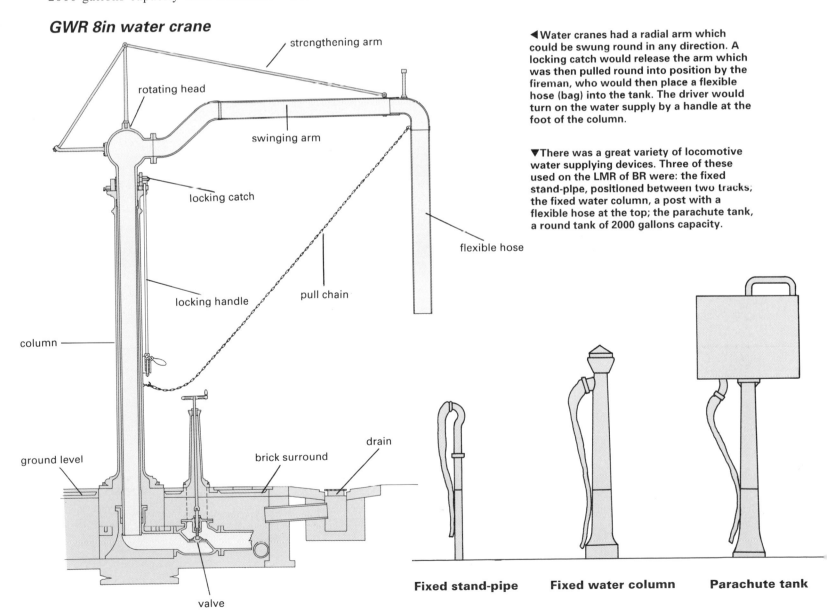

**GWR 8in water crane**

◀Water cranes had a radial arm which could be swung round in any direction. A locking catch would release the arm which was then pulled round into position by the fireman, who would then place a flexible hose (bag) into the tank. The driver would turn on the water supply by a handle at the foot of the column.

▼There was a great variety of locomotive water supplying devices. Three of these used on the LMR of BR were: the fixed stand-pipe, positioned between two tracks; the fixed water column, a post with a flexible hose at the top; the parachute tank, a round tank of 2000 gallons capacity.

**Fixed stand-pipe**   **Fixed water column**   **Parachute tank**

# Mail on the move

During Queen Victoria's reign the government often required railway companies to carry the mail at low rates, while imposing high standards of speed and punctuality. The mail train became synonymous with speed.

The Travelling Post Office (TPO) dates from 1838 and later featured sorting vehicles in which Post Office staff would sort letters en route. Further time-saving resulted from a method of picking up and putting down mailbags on the move. After wrangles over patents, an apparatus came into general use in the 1850s.

With this system, a sliding door on the side of a sorting coach could be opened and a net extended outwards. This net would catch one or more leather mail pouches suspended from a lineside post and then retract automatically – the pouch deposited on to the coach floor. The pouches had a short working life and occasionally split on hitting the floor. A similar apparatus could also deposit mailbags. The corridor connection on the Post Office owned vehicles was uniquely offset in order to make them non-compatible with passenger stock for security.

Within a few years, a network of night mail trains was established, with links so that one train could exchange mailbags with another during halts at a handful of key junctions. The key to this network was the West Coast Postal service, running between London and Aberdeen. By the turn of the century this train had nine vehicles. Parcels vans were at the front and rear while the centre was occupied by three letter sorting vans. Between London and Crewe the train stopped at Rugby and Tamworth; in other places mail exchange was by pouch apparatus. Crewe was then the hub of the system, with mail trains converging from around the country.

This system made it possible for most people to receive letters posted late that afternoon by the following morning. Each TPO provided a red letter-slot in which, for an extra stamp, anybody could post a letter when the train was in a station. Now small towns are served by road transport, the mail exchange apparatus is no longer used.

When road and air transport took away some of the railway's mail business, the system nevertheless continued very much as before. Derby – where air, rail and road interchange – replaced Crewe as the main hub. Sorting was still done on the TPOs, but the sorting cars were dispersed down the train, separated by stowage cars where the sorters drew unsorted mail and deposited the freshly sorted post.

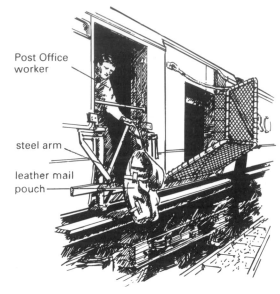

Post Office worker

steel arm

leather mail pouch

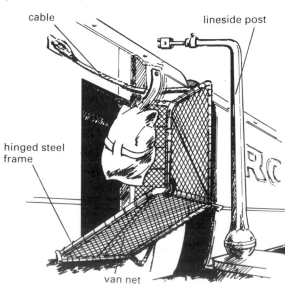

Until October 1971, mail could be picked up and delivered at certain lineside locations by special Travelling Post Office (TPO) trains. To set the mail down, a Post Office worker would hang a strong leather mail pouch on a retractable steel arm (traductor) and suspend it over the side of a coach fitted with exchange apparatus. As the train passed the pick-up point, the bag would be knocked off by a lineside net.

When the mail was picked up, a net was let out on a hinged frame. A cable suspended between the coach and the net, knocked the bag hanging from a lineside post (standard) into the net.

cable

lineside post

hinged steel frame

van net

# Steam locomotive depot layout

Steam depots were usually built near stations, goods depots and marshalling yards. They provided the facilities to prepare locomotives for work, to service them when they had finished and to carry out minor repairs. The aim was to have the locomotives available for work for the maximum time each day. This meant getting each locomotive to and through the depot as quickly as possible, using mechanization to cut servicing time to a minimum.

When an engine arrived at the depot after working a train, a number of tasks were performed: coal and water were taken on; the smokebox emptied of ash and char; the fire and ashpan cleaned; the engine turned if necessary and minor repairs carried out. Of these tasks, cleaning the fire and ashpan were the

most time consuming. The time allowed to prepare an engine for work was the subject of fixed national agreements with the trades unions.

After servicing, operations were affected by the layout of the depot and its buildings. There were three types – straight dead end, straight double end and roundhouse.

Each layout had advantages and disadvantages. Dead-end buildings, with one entrance, were suitable only for small or medium sized depots with limited space. Engines had to be stabled in reverse order until they were needed. The straight double-ended shed, in which engines passed through in one direction, was cheap to build for the greater flexibility it provided. The roundhouse, with engines grouped round a central turntable, was

also quite flexible, but expensive to build and vulnerable if the turntable was damaged leaving engines unable to enter or leave the shed.

In the depot yard, the best layout allowed locomotives to move through the various operations without reversing. Many depots could not follow this pattern, resulting in delays and conflicting engine movements.

It was desirable – though not always possible – to have separate entrances and exits to and from the main line, otherwise a derailment at the only connection would close the shed. It was useful for engines to be able to bypass the coaling point and the ashpit – the slowest operations. It was also important for coal and ash wagons to be shunted without disrupting engine movements.

Many depots failed to meet these guidelines. But the possibility of meeting them was shown by results on the London Midland & Scottish Railway. After carefully analysing how depots operate and making some of the recommended changes, its average daily locomotive hours in traffic improved from 11.7 to 14.4 (December figures) between 1929 and 1936.

In the 1930s, the London Midland & Scottish and London & North Eastern railways in particular, authorized massive programmes for modernizing depots.

◄ **In 1961, Bristol Barrow Road shed conveys the atmosphere typical of a steam engine depot. The line of wagons contain locomotive coal and it was important that these wagons could be shunted without interfering with any engine movements.**

## *Ideal shed layout*

A double-ended shed allowed the locomotive to enter the depot by an entrance road, travel to the coaling plant and then to the water crane. At the ash pits, the engine would have its smokebox emptied and its fire cleaned. If turning was necessary the locomotive would then proceed to the turntable, after which it could enter the shed on a designated road. Inspection pits in the shed enabled the locomotive to be checked for defects. At the front of the shed, preparation pits allowed the crew easy access underneath an engine. The locomotive would leave the depot by a separate exit.

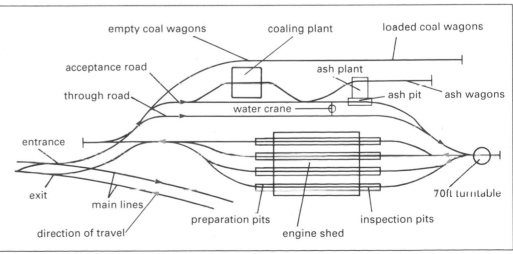

# Steam depot equipment

Steam locomotives needed to be regularly serviced and maintained, and locomotive depots contained various devices to carry out these tasks.

### Ash disposal

A steam locomotive could produce up to half a ton of ash and clinker by the end of a single journey. These deposits always presented the depot with a disposal problem.

In the 1920s and '30s, mechanization programmes tackled ash handling in one of two ways. The London Midland & Scottish Railway favoured cleaning fires and ashpans into **tramway tubs** running in, and alongside, the ashpit. These tubs were tipped into an underground skip, positioned towards one end of the ashpit, from where the deposits were raised by bucket conveyor to an elevated bunker and dropped into wagons to be taken away. On the London & North Eastern Railway (LNER), ash and clinker were dropped from the locomotive, through grids into a deep **wet-ashpit** below the rails – wet ash being easier to handle. The wet-ashpit was regularly cleared by lifting the grids and removing the deposits with a grab-crane.

One of the last big re-equipment schemes, at Polmadie depot in Glasgow during World War II, combined wet-ashpits with full-length submerged belt conveyors, taking ash into the bunker.

### Washing out

Locomotive boilers needed to be washed out regularly to prevent the build up of scale which impaired steaming. If washed out hot, the boiler was emptied of steam and hot water through a hose from a blow-off cock at the base of the firebox, into a static plant. The hot water, under pressure and after filtration, was used to wash out the boiler. Steam heated cold water was then used for refilling the boiler after washing out. High pressure (about 60lb psi) water mains were required at the washing out points for washing out cold; a suitable booster pump fed these mains.

### Sand drying

Steam engines used sand to give a better grip on wet or greasy rails. The sand had to be dry and free from stones if it was to flow freely from the locomotive's sand-boxes on to the rail surface. Sand was kept dry in the depot's sand furnace; many of the old furnaces were brick-built and wasted fuel. When a depot was modernized, this building was replaced by a semi-automatic coke-fired drying plant. These were more efficient and needed less attention than the older furnaces. The sand was filtered through gratings which removed any stones.

Traditionally, sand was carried by the crew from the furnace to the locomotive in buckets with large pouring spouts. But some larger depots, notably on the LNER, installed overhead hoppers above the preparation pits from which the sand was drawn through hoses. Sand was blown by air through a pipe to the hoppers.

### Wheel drops

One of the heaviest tasks undertaken at any depot was the removal of wheels from a locomotive. Any case of a hot axlebox required removal of a pair of wheels. Lifting the engine, particularly by hand-operated sheerlegs or gantry, which were all that were available at many larger depots, was time consuming and imposed extra stress on the frames. Major depots were normally equipped with a wheel drop, either electrically or hydraulically powered. The locomotive ran over the drop table and the affected wheels were lowered well below rail level. Temporary rails were positioned to bridge the gap, and the engine drawn clear. The wheels could then be raised and rolled away for attention. Where possible, the wheel drop table was long enough to drop a complete bogie.

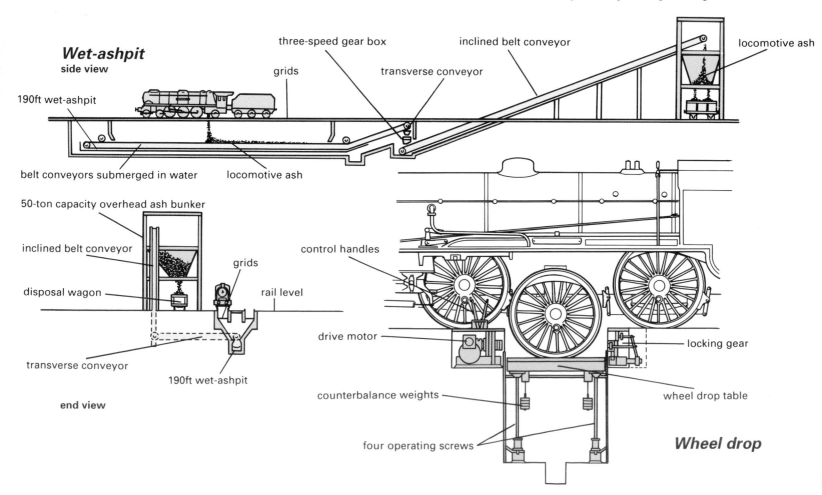

**Wet-ashpit**
side view

three-speed gear box

inclined belt conveyor

locomotive ash

grids

transverse conveyor

190ft wet-ashpit

belt conveyors submerged in water

locomotive ash

50-ton capacity overhead ash bunker

inclined belt conveyor

disposal wagon

grids

rail level

transverse conveyor

190ft wet-ashpit

end view

control handles

drive motor

counterbalance weights

four operating screws

locking gear

wheel drop table

**Wheel drop**

# Testing stations

In the early 20th century, the scientific testing of steam locomotives in Britain, with a view to improving their design, generally relied on measurements being taken in a dynamometer car coupled behind the locomotive. While the locomotive was hauling a train, power outputs were plotted against distance, on a moving paper band.

But testing locomotives on the track (line testing) had the disadvantages of variable weather, changing gradients and signal delays. To get results upon which new conclusions and theories could be based, it was desirable to supplement line testing with studies at stationary testing plants. Here, locomotives could run continuously at fixed speeds and power outputs.

## Rugby and Swindon plants

The first testing plants were built in Russia and America, but in 1905 the Great Western Railway (GWR) opened its own plant at Swindon. This remained the only British example until the London & North Eastern Railway (LNER) and London Midland & Scottish Railway (LMS) combined to build a testing station at Rugby. However, because of the war, it was not completed until 1948. Its first task was to investigate the effect of variation in valve events on power output and fuel economy of locomotives, so as to provide data for the design of the BR Standard locomotive classes.

The Swindon plant, although rebuilt in 1936, lacked the means of measuring and plotting drawbar pull on a recording table. Instead, indicated cylinder horsepower was used. But this limited the plant's applications and the GWR engineers tended to use it more for running-in repaired locomotives. When Nigel Gresley of the LNER wanted to test his P2 class 2-8-2 *Cock o' the North*, he sent it not to Swindon, but to Vitry in France.

## Plant machinery

In the testing plants, a locomotive under trials was coupled to the plant drawbar. The supporting platform was then lowered and the wheels settled on rollers that had been accurately placed at the appropriate positions.

The rollers under the driving wheels were coupled to power-absorbing brakes. The resistance of the brakes could be adjusted to impose the appropriate load, so that the power transmitted by the driving wheels could be absorbed at any speed. With the locomotive pushing against this resistance, the natural tendency for it to move forward was restrained by a drawbar coupled to the rear of the engine.

## Scientific methods

At Rugby, the drawbar was attached to a hydraulic dynamometer, the oil pressure of which was transmitted to a sophisticated recording table located in the sound-proofed control room, so that the wheel rim tractive effort was recorded on a moving paper roll.

Wheel-rim speed was transmitted electrically to this table from a roller engaging the rim of one of the engine's wheels. The apparatus of the table also calculated and recorded the power developed by the engine. Other records made included temperatures, pressures, vacuum, and water and coal consumption.

Within a few years, Rugby developed the Farnboro electric indicator in a form suitable for steam locomotives, which had various advantages over the mechanical type and produced much larger indicator diagrams.

### Rugby plant

The delay caused by the war meant that by the time the Rugby plant had overcome some teething troubles and established really reliable testing procedures, the design of most BR Standard classes was well in hand. With the announcement of the Railway Modernization Plan in 1954, the will to make substantial modifications to improve steam locomotives steadily waned. The plant was closed to testing in 1959.

▶ There were two testing stations in Britain: the GWR had one at Swindon and the other, built jointly by the LMS and LNER, was at Rugby. The locomotives under test ran on rollers and were restrained from actually going anywhere by a dynamometer, which was attached to its drawbar. This was used to calculate the power developed. Other separate recording instruments in the control room made continuous records of temperatures, pressures and vacuum at selected locations on the engine. Water fed into the boiler was metered, and the coal fed into the firebox was extracted from a self-weighing hopper, so that consumption was regularly noted. A chemist carried out analysis of the coal and exhaust gases.

In the 1950s, Rugby Testing Plant was host to ex-LNER D49/2 Hunt class 4-4-0 No 62764 *Garth*.

# Hump yards

Until the 1960s, a succession of trains was required to get each freight wagon to its destination. Wagons would be added to, or detached from, trains in a variety of shunting yards, ranging from wayside freight stations to huge marshalling yards. This repeated shunting was expensive, time consuming and produced no revenue. To reduce costs and speed up operations, the railway companies mechanized the biggest yards.

One form of mechanization, which appeared after World War I, was the creation of hump yards. These were faster than conventional marshalling yards and needed fewer locomotives to move the wagons. The trains arriving at the yard were pushed over a hump (a section of track on a raised piece of ground) so that the individual vehicles, or cuts (groups) of vehicles with the same destination could roll into the appropriate siding. In each siding a new train was made up ready to be taken to its destination – often another yard.

## Slowing down

To avoid high impacts between wagons in the sidings, the speed of cuts was controlled by retarders. These were pneumatic or electro-pneumatic jaws on each side of the rail that could briefly grip the wheel flanges and slow the vehicles down. Usually, each cut passed over two sets of retarders, one at the bottom of the hump (primary or master retarder) and one on the track leading to a group of sidings (secondary or group retarder). Primary retarders were typically 72ft long, and the secondary retarders were 36ft. Both were broken down into 12ft sections and each was operated by its own motor.

Overlooking the yard, near the hump, was a control tower. This had a control panel with a track plan, buttons, switches and indicator lights needed for operating points and retarders.

Over the years, hump yards became more mechanized and automated. Post-war yards made use of radar and computer techniques. The retarder and point systems accepted information that gave the order of wagons being pushed over the hump, the track into which they had to be directed, their weight (essential for instructing the retarders) and the totals of wagons already in each sorting siding. Trackside radar installations not only measured the speed of descending wagons, but also indicated how easily they rolled. This information enabled the retarders to slow them down just enough to ensure that each cut would have enough momentum to take it gently up to the vehicles already in the siding.

## Operating sequence

Sorting the wagons began when an incoming freight train entered the reception sidings. Here its locomotive and brake van were detached and a powerful hump shunting locomotive was positioned at the rear. A shunter, meanwhile, walked along the train, noting the destination of each wagon and the siding into which it had to be directed. Each cut was uncoupled and the shunter's list sent to the operator in the control tower.

Using this list, the operator pushed the appropriate button for each cut. Each button set the points needed to route a cut into one particular siding. In modern installations, the operator could push the buttons in the correct sequence directly from the list; the information was stored and brought into play as each cut proceeded down the hump.

Having entered the information for all the cuts, the operator released the signal to proceed. Signal indications at hump yards were **stop**, **slow** and **normal**, and might be given by a row of three white lights (horizontal, 45° and vertical), or by a three-position semaphore signal. The hump locomotive would then push slowly, and successive cuts would go over the hump and gather speed. A complex system of electric track circuits registered the progress of each cut, enabling the points to be set for the next cut while preceding cuts were still on their way.

Vehicles passed over the hump at about 3mph. Sometimes a second hump locomotive was provided so that once one train had been cleared, the next would be ready immediately. The bigger post-war hump yards processed about 3000 wagons daily, although at peaks over 4000 might be handled. There were also more modest hump yards, where the hump was low, speeds slower, and instead of retarders, athletic yardmen would chase after cuts to slow them down by applying the brakes manually.

In Britain, the large yards became redundant after the 1960s, as their humps were unsuited to long-wheelbase vehicles. Some yards reverted to conventional working and gradually grew smaller, while others were entirely abandoned, releasing huge acreages that were sold.

▼Hump yards were sometimes huge, with some able to process up to 4000 wagons a day. In 1929, a solitary wagon rolls down the hump at Whitemoor towards a wagon retarder which will slow the vehicle down on its way to form another train. The control tower is located in the centre, giving an excellent view of all activities.

# Manual signalboxes

Manual signalboxes, which may still be found on preserved lines, originated in the middle of the 19th century when signal and points levers were first grouped together at stations and junctions, and their design remained virtually unchanged.

Signalboxes varied in design according to the company or contractor that built them. Some were mainly of timber, others were constructed from brick, some were a combination of the two. They were usually built on two levels, the operating floor upstairs where the signalman worked, and the locking room downstairs. On the upper floor a line of windows at both ends and stretching along the side facing the railway gave the signalman a good view of the trains and signals.

The first thing a visitor noticed inside was the row of large, numbered steel levers, each controlling a signal, a set of points or a point lock. They stood about 4ft (1.3m) high, most leaning away from the signalman. Levers were pulled towards the signalman for the reverse position. The rounded top of the lever held by the signalman was usually polished steel rather than painted. The signalman always used a duster when pulling these, as the steel would soon rust from hand perspiration.

Behind the main lever handle was a second one – the catch handle – which controlled a weighted block or spring near the bottom. This held the lever in either the normal or reverse position. The levers extended through slots below the floor to a pivot in the frame downstairs. An extension at right angles was attached to the signal wires or the point rods. Bars attached to the front of the levers also passed into the interlocking frame. This consisted of horizontal and vertical slides which ensured that signals could not conflict with other signals or points.

The block shelf with its array of instruments was set above the levers. These included bells for operating the block system, the block instruments themselves, and indicators showing whether out-of-sight signal arms had responded to a lever movement or whether signal lamps were alight.

Above the block shelf was a track layout diagram showing the positions of signals and points and the lever numbers. Some diagrams were illuminated by red lights along the tracks to show if a train was occupying a section of line. In some signalboxes this indication was shown on a separate track circuit indicator on the shelf. Finally, there were plungers which had to be pressed to release electric locks on levers.

Furniture was sparse – a chair and table for meal breaks, a desk for the train register book where all signalling movements were recorded, and various operating notices and timetables. Depending on location, the lighting was by oil or electricity and inevitably there was a stove, usually fired with solid fuel, on which the kettle was always ready to make tea. The floor lino was washed daily, the brass on instrument cases polished and all operating equipment kept clean and tidy.

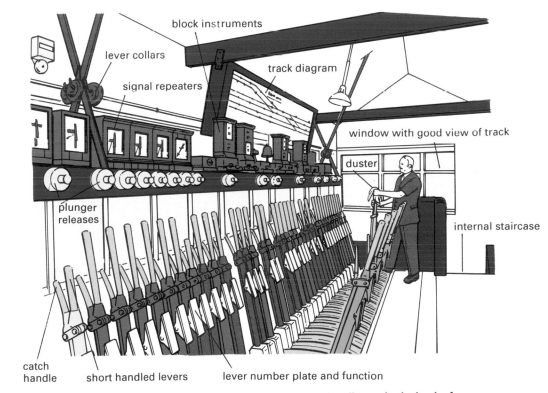

All manual signalboxes had a bank of levers controlling signals, points and point locks. Each lever was painted in a specific colour to identify them: red for stop signals, yellow for distant signals, black for points and blue for facing point locks.

◀ Signalman Rogers waits intently for the 10 o'clock time check in Liverpool Street station box. It was vital that signalmen all worked to the same time. On the LNER two time signals were sent out every day by special code, so signalmen could co-ordinate their clocks.

# Manual level crossings

Ever since the beginning of the railways, gates have been provided which close off roads from the railway line. This was originally to ensure that cattle, sheep and horses passing over the crossing couldn't stray on to the tracks. When a train was due, the gates were swung across the road by a gateman to stop traffic.

The gates were wooden and of open style with top and bottom rails braced by diagonal members. Later on they were covered with wire mesh to stop children and small animals climbing through the bracing. The timber was painted white, with black ironwork for hinges and strengthening pieces. A large red warning disc was placed at the centre of the gates.

By the time the block system was made compulsory on passenger lines in 1889, level crossings were controlled in a number of ways. This depended on the location relative to stations and signalboxes; whether the line was single track or not; and how much traffic used the road (this became much more important with the growth of motor traffic).

On a double track across a road there were usually four gates, each of which covered one track or half the road on each side of the crossing. They could be linked together by rods passing through a trough under the road and connected via another master rod to the gatekeeper's hut or signalbox. Unless the gates were worked by hand, this was attached by gears to a hand wheel, rather like that on a ship's bridge.

To operate the gates, the signalman or gatekeeper first pulled a gatelock lever back part way to release stops which prevented the gates from swinging in a wind. After checking for road traffic, he wound the wheel around several times to swing the gates and close off the road. The gatelock lever could now be pulled back fully, raising the gatestops on the road and holding them in position. This released the interlocking with the signals protecting the crossing, allowing them to be cleared for an oncoming train.

Gates were controlled either from a signalbox operating the block system, in which case the signalman knew where the trains were, or by a gatekeeper in a simple crossing hut. A gatekeeper had to be advised via a system using repeater block instruments, bells or a telephone.

The train drivers knew that the crossing was open if the signals were clear – provided the gatebox had signals to protect the crossing. Sometimes though, no signals were provided. In this case a large red disc was placed on the side of the gates facing the trains as well.

If crossings were near to signalboxes, but too far to be worked directly, a gatebox was sometimes provided with controls released from the signalbox. This method was very costly in terms of staff, however, and automatic crossings were introduced in the 1960s.

▲A double tracked line usually needed four gates controlled from a signalbox to close off the road. The colour red was standard to ensure quick recognition for oncoming traffic, with black hinges and posts, white gates and red warning discs.

▶ To operate double gates from a signalbox, a lever had first to be pulled halfway back to release the gatelocks. The gates could then be swung round with a few turns of the wheel. Finally the lever was pulled back fully to lock the gates across the road. This allowed the signals to be cleared via the interlocking system so a train could safely pass over the road.

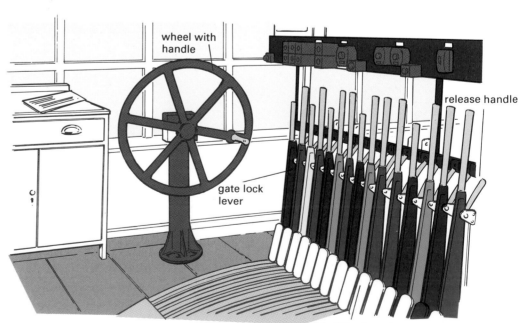

wheel with handle

release handle

gate lock lever

identification plate

# Automatic crossings

In 1957, BR was authorized to use automatic barriers controlled by the trains themselves – although the crossing would still be monitored by a signalbox. The first automatic half barrier crossing (AHB) was installed in 1961. The barriers blocked off half the road on the entry side, leaving the exit side completely open. Special traffic signals stopped cars before the barriers were lowered, 20-30 seconds before a train approached.

The traffic signals are usually unlit, but when a train approaches it triggers the crossing sequence. First the road user sees a steady amber light for three seconds. Then two red lights flash alternately – a mandatory stop indication for road traffic. After seven seconds with the red lights flashing, sometimes accompanied by warning bells or a yodel alarm, the barriers descend, taking about seven seconds. After a further 12 seconds, the fastest train will have reached the crossing – a minimum of 29 seconds in all.

Another type of automatic crossing is the automatic open crossing – locally monitored (AOCL). No signalbox is present and the crossing is checked by the driver of an approaching train. To the road user the main difference is that there are no barriers, but the lights are the same. However, the train driver has warning and speed restriction signs, and signal indications to advise him whether the crossing road lights are working: a flashing red light to remind him to check that the crossing is clear, and a flashing white light to indicate that the road signals have operated correctly.

A newer type is the automatic half barrier crossing – locally monitored (ABCL). It has the same rail and road signals as an AOCL, and again is unsupervised by a signalbox.

Normally, the driver of a long, slow-moving road vehicle must telephone the supervising signalbox for permission to cross an AHB, but not an AOCL or ABCL crossing. In these locally monitored crossings, the train driver must check that the crossing is clear. Train speed is limited to 88km/h (55mph) and the driver must have a good view of it.

Controlled full barrier crossings, consisting of entry and exit halves on both sides of the road, are often worked remotely from signalboxes using closed circuit television. The same road traffic signals as for automatic crossings are used to stop cars, although without the precise timing sequence. On either side of the road, the entry barriers start to lower first and then the exit barriers, although the signalman has some control and can stop them if necessary.

Normal rail signals are always provided to protect controlled barrier crossings. Once the barriers have lowered, the signalman must look at his TV monitor to ensure that the crossing is clear. He must then press a crossing clear button before he can clear the rail signals.

▼Many automatic crossings block off only the entrance side of the road. Some half barrier crossings are monitored by a signalbox and others have to be checked by the train driver.

▼As a train driver approaches an open crossing he sees three caution signs: first, the warning of an open crossing ahead; next, the speed limit board and finally the signal. This flashes red as a reminder to the driver to check that the crossing is clear and see that the white light is flashing, meaning that the road lights are at red.

▶▼An automatic open crossing, locally monitored (AOCL) is not protected by barriers. A set of signals is operated by an approaching train which activates a treadle. Road lights give a steady yellow for three seconds, then flash alternate reds which is a compulsory stop signal. The whole sequence takes almost half a minute.

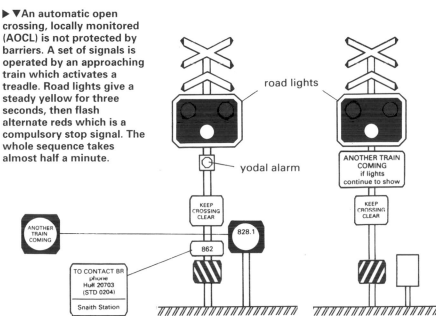

# Bridges and viaducts

Most early railway bridges were modest structures, many being simple arches built from brick or local stone. In some cases metal was used, but the only material available in any quantity was cast-iron – which had severe limitations.

The early engineers were cautious and usually allowed large margins for safety, making bridges stronger than they needed to be. Many of these are still in use, carrying heavier loads at much higher speeds than planned. Many people thought that the stone arches of Brunel's viaduct across the Thames at Maidenhead were too shallow, and cracks soon appeared in them. Later, the contractor admitted that the supports had been removed too soon, and, after the bridge had been repaired, Brunel ordered the scaffolding to be left in position, but no longer supporting the bridge. During a storm, it was the scaffolding that blew down. The bridge still stands today, taking far heavier loads at speeds which even its designer did not consider.

Some early bridges did need to be replaced quickly or strengthened, and a few even collapsed. The best known example is the Tay bridge, which was destroyed in a storm because the designer did not allow enough strength for the effect of gales, which was made worse by poor construction and maintenance.

Wood was also used in bridge construction, even for viaducts, and Brunel built outstanding examples in Devon and Cornwall. The piers were built of stone, but wooden timbers fanned out to support the track. Wood has a limited life as a building material, but Brunel's structures were designed so that individual timbers could be restored and renewed. In the last part of the nineteenth century, steel was often used for bridge construction, the Forth Bridge being a famous example.

With the invention of concrete, new construction methods were introduced. The first concrete viaducts used separate blocks made to size, but later the whole bridge structure was cast on site. A notable example is the Glenfinnan viaduct on the line from Fort William to Mallaig.

Reinforced concrete was followed by prestressing, a technique also used for making sleepers. Advanced designs using concrete included one viaduct that had a continuous span cast at one side of a gap and then pushed over the top of the piers to form the bridge.

Many bridges crossing waterways had to be built high enough for tall ships to pass underneath. Another solution was the swing bridge, where one span pivots about its centre point to provide an opening.

---

### Foot bridge
Almost every type of bridge has been used with success on the railways, except for suspension bridges. As early as 1830, the Stockton & Darlington Railway built one across the Tees on the line to Middlesbrough. But it did not inspire confidence, and one driver was so distrustful of it, that he would set the locomotive's controls so the train took itself across, while he crossed on foot.

LMS 4-6-0 No 5407 crosses Griseburn Viaduct in Cumbria with a steam hauled excursion in the 1980s. Griseburn Viaduct is 142yd long and 74ft high and is one of 21 such structures on the 72 mile Settle – Carlisle line. Although graceful, bridges using arches are not easily built without considerable disruption to traffic.

# Swing bridges

In Britain, the network of canals and navigable waterways was largely developed before the coming of the railways. When the railways were built, they had to find the cheapest way of crossing the older rights of way. To obtain permission to start building, a railway company had to satisfy all the owners and users of the waterway that any crossing would not impede the traffic.

Most of the barges using the canals had to pass through small tunnels, so it was usually necessary for the railway to build a low bridge. This reduced considerably the cost of railway construction. Difficulties arose on larger waterways when vessels with higher superstructures or masts had to pass underneath.

In many cases, particularly in flat parts of the country, a bridge which could be opened to enable the occasional high vessel to pass was a cheaper solution than making the structure high enough to clear the tallest mast. Many such bridges were built, mainly of the swing variety.

## Balancing act

The opening span of a swing bridge is usually symmetrical, so it will balance on its central pivot when it rotates. The pivot has to be a substantial structure to support the span when it is open. The wider the channel that has to be crossed, the longer – and heavier – this span must be, and the further the central pier will be away from either shore.

This pivot also houses the mechanism required to turn it. In the last century, a small steam engine with its own boiler was often installed in a machinery room in the central pier.

When trains cross a swing bridge, the opening span must be firmly supported at both ends. Means must then be provided to lift it slightly so it is free to rotate and this is done with hydraulic rams, powered by the steam engine. Nowadays such bridges are usually worked by electricity.

## Protecting signals

Usually rail has to give way to ships at a swing bridge. As it is not easy to stop a ship, the bridge has to be opened well before it arrives. The signalman in the cabin of the bridge at Goole, on the line between Doncaster and Hull, is provided with a brass telescope so that he can see the approaching ships in good time. But this has not prevented a number of vessels hitting the structure in recent years, even when the bridge is open. This has put the line out of action for months at a time.

Overhead electrification wires present another problem at a swing bridge. This is because of the difficulty of fixing and tensioning the short length of wire, as well as ensuring that there is no gap at either end. When the line to Norwich was electrified in 1987, the new swing bridge at Trowse, on the outskirts of the city, was provided with a fixed conductor, rather than the usual suspended wires.

It is not surprising that the railways take every opportunity to convert swing bridges into fixed spans, and many have now been altered in this way.

### Heat troubles

When a swing bridge is being used by trains, only a small gap can be permitted between the rails on the bridge and those on the fixed sections at both sides. Trouble can arise if heat causes the bridge to expand too much while it is open for water traffic – making it too long to fit the gap. For this reason water sprays are often provided to keep the bridge cool in hot weather.

**Swing bridges were constructed by railway companies as a cheaper alternative to building a structure high enough for tall-masted ships to pass underneath. Many such bridges were built in flat areas of land, such as in the east of Britain. The swing bridge at Selby, North Yorkshire is a fine example.**

# Tunnels

Tunnels are slow, expensive and dangerous to construct and railway engineers only build them when there is no other option.

Railway companies have built tunnels in many locations: through coastal headlands, rocky outcrops in valleys and even under rivers and seas. In Switzerland, spiral tunnels are built into the mountain sides to gain height.

Hazards await the tunneller through high mountain ranges. Workers in the 12 mile Simplon Tunnel, between Switzerland and Italy, faced temperatures up to 127°F (53°C), while in one place the pressure of the rock caused the tunnel supports to splinter. The tunnellers remedied this problem by using more beams.

In 1908, when the Lötschberg, another Swiss tunnel, was being built, a blast holed a deep fissure filled with water. The sudden inrush drowned 25 tunnellers and flooded over a mile of the tunnel, which finally had to be diverted round the affected area.

Most tunnels are wet inside because water seeps down from the ground above, making drainage essential. The gradient inside the tunnel must slope gently towards one or both ends. The three Standedge Tunnels, between Huddersfield and Stalybridge, are exceptions to this rule and are entirely level. This is possible because a canal tunnel runs parallel to the railway and drains off the water. Because the railway tracks are level, there were water troughs inside one tunnel during steam days.

The Channel Tunnel is the most outstanding example of an underwater crossing, but when the GWR built the 4½ mile Severn Tunnel, over 100 years ago, it was the longest underwater tunnel in the world. Running below the Bristol Channel, it took more than 13 years to construct and additional difficulties arose when fresh water, from an underground source, frequently flooded the workings.

In recent years, many changes have taken place in tunnelling methods. When materials like soft chalk marl were encountered under the Channel, massive Tunnel Boring Machines (TBMs) cut through the ground easily, positioning the lining segments behind them as they worked. The TBMs advanced as much as a quarter of a mile in a week.

The tunnel lining, made from reinforced concrete, has to resist massive pressure from above, but sometimes there is also significant pressure from below. To help deflect these forces, most tunnels are circular in cross section or arched top and bottom with curved sides – the track bed built up on the curved floor. Altering the floor when lowering the track in a tunnel to increase clearances can be difficult. It was during such an operation in 1979, that Penmanshiel Tunnel on the East Coast main line collapsed.

Some tunnels are bored through rock so solid that it does not need any lining, but explosives are required to break up the material for removal. To speed up the construction of long tunnels, intermediate shafts are sometimes sunk from the surface to the track level, each of them opening up a new pair of working faces. All the spoil and materials have to travel up and down the shaft, and water has to be pumped out instead of drained.

Simpler tunnels are constructed on the cut and cover principle. A deep cutting is made, lined and then covered over. This was used to prevent a line being seen from a wealthy landowner's house. Nowadays, such is the influence of environmentalists, that German Railways have built much of their Neubaustrecke (new high speed line) in tunnels.

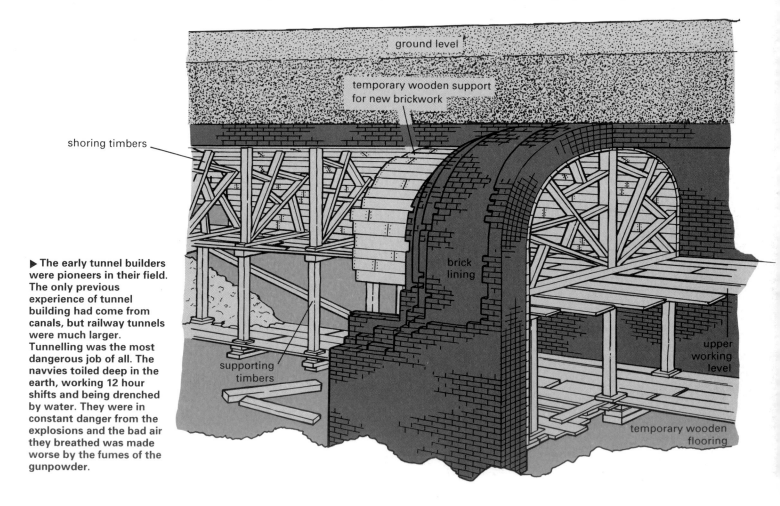

▶ The early tunnel builders were pioneers in their field. The only previous experience of tunnel building had come from canals, but railway tunnels were much larger. Tunnelling was the most dangerous job of all. The navvies toiled deep in the earth, working 12 hour shifts and being drenched by water. They were in constant danger from the explosions and the bad air they breathed was made worse by the fumes of the gunpowder.

ground level

temporary wooden support for new brickwork

shoring timbers

brick lining

supporting timbers

upper working level

temporary wooden flooring

# Turntables

Turning a locomotive requires either a turntable (a small section of track on a rotating table), or a turning triangle (an area of track laid out in the shape of a triangle).

Until the end of steam, turntables were usually found at depots or station areas, and turning triangles were either installed at depots or laid out as triangular main line junctions. Although turning triangles with automatic trailable points were cheaper, quicker and more reliable than turntables, space for them was seldom available on Britain's railways.

Turntables consist of a line of rails supported on a girder structure, pivoting in the centre and resting at each end on a pair of wheels running on a circular race rail. Locking bolts engage in sockets in the surround to hold the rails in alignment with the approach tracks.

Until the 1920s, all turntables were centrally balanced and the weight of table and locomotive was carried on the central pivot. The race wheels ran just clear of the race rail, providing the minimum resistance when turning. Enginemen

would inch their locomotives on to the table until they felt the slight movement on reaching the balance point.

Balanced turntables were of two types: those with the main girder structure under the rails, which needed a deep pit, and those with side girders above the rails, for which a shallower pit sufficed. The type with side girders was wider and heavier due to extensive cross-bracing and found favour with the GWR.

As locomotives grew larger, balancing became increasingly difficult. This was particularly a problem when the tender was low in coal and water, causing it to be much lighter than the locomotive, and extra table length was needed to reach a balanced position.

To solve this problem, two types of turntable were developed. The first, dating from the 1920s, was the Vogele articulated table, made by Cowans Sheldon. Shallow, half-length undergirders were joined by flexible attachments near the centre pivot, so at least half the weight was carried by the race wheels and the centre pivot could be lighter. The LMS

and L&NE used this type extensively.

The alternative to the Vogele was the Mundt turntable, invented by a Dutch engineer, built by Ransome & Rapier and first installed in Britain in 1930. The Mundt was based on a shallow half-girder structure which was flexible in the centre and spread the weight between pivot and race wheels.

When turntables first appeared they were pushed round by the crew, but in the mid-1930s vacuum powered turntables were introduced. The engine's vacuum brake pipe was attached to a motor on the turntable which turned one race wheel – so the locomotive turned itself. The LNER provided large vacuum reservoirs on their turntables so that freight engines not fitted with vacuum brakes could be turned – courtesy of the previous engine.

▼On 4 August 1962, Duchess class 4-6-2 No 46238 *City of Carlisle* is turned at Camden shed, outside Euston. The turntable is one of the 70ft vacuum powered examples, in which the locomotive uses its vacuum system to turn itself.

# Modern traction depots

Two basic changes have taken place in locomotive depots since the days of steam. Firstly, clean, well-lit interiors are now the rule. Modern traction not only heralded the end of steam's grime, but made cleanliness essential due to dirt's disastrous effects on electronics.

The second change is the move towards long sheds, purpose-built to accommodate whole trains. Though not universal, they are becoming more common with the increasing importance of fixed formation self-powered trains. Such depots were first introduced by the Southern Railway for its multiple-unit electric trains.

In steam days a distinction was made between the running shed, responsible for daily preparation and running repairs of locomotives, and the workshop, where the locomotive went for varying degrees of repair, depending on the size of the shed. This distinction is now blurred after BR reorganized all depots in the 1980s into a system which uses five levels of depot.

At the bottom of the list is the fuelling point, which has rudimentary facilities sufficient to keep a locomotive in service between examinations. Level 2 is slightly more ambitious and includes a servicing shed; besides fuelling, locomotives can also undergo basic periodic examinations. The next two levels offer more intensive maintenance, while Level 5 tackles all maintenance jobs short of the complete overhauls for which main works are responsible.

The key to this system is the influx of modern rolling stock, which is designed both for minimal and easy maintenance. The ability of the old steam depot to repair parts using a machine shop has been replaced by component exchange, which reduces repair time.

Level 5 depots can exchange all components, including traction bogies and diesel engines. Their distinctive feature is the overhead lifting gantry, aiding bogie exchange and essential for diesel engine changes. Other necessary features are generous provision of inspection pits and, ideally, platforms giving easy access to the upper parts of vehicles.

Outside, plenty of stabling track gives operational flexibility and there is usually a washing plant and a sanding point, sometimes incorporating a sand drier. Where diesel traction is handled, there must also be a fuelling point.

The layout varies according to how much existing buildings and land are used, and the main type of rolling stock handled. Straight road layouts are preferred, while through roads, with entries and exits at both ends, are more flexible.

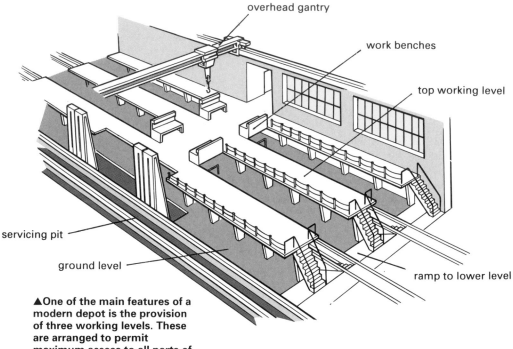

overhead gantry

work benches

top working level

servicing pit

ground level

ramp to lower level

▲One of the main features of a modern depot is the provision of three working levels. These are arranged to permit maximum access to all parts of the locomotive: underneath for brakes and traction motors; ground level for work on springs, bogies and external equipment below the footplate; and above (the main working level) for attention to the engine, generators, batteries and cab.

▼A typical modern depot tries to make use of straight road and through road track layouts. These dispense with turntables and allow locomotives to enter and exit from both ends of the sheds. The difference between a convenient and inconvenient layout usually only becomes obvious at times of crisis, when carefully designed sequences and routines have to give way to improvisation.

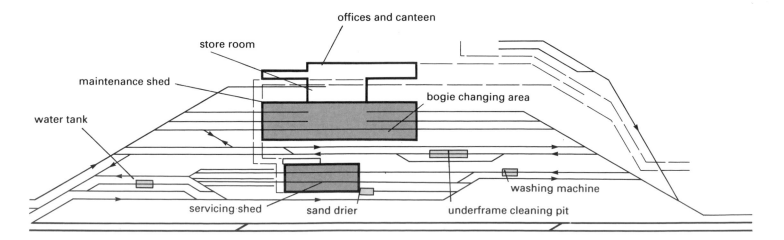

offices and canteen

store room

maintenance shed

bogie changing area

water tank

washing machine

servicing shed

sand drier

underframe cleaning pit

# Times and timetabling

Pre privatisation, timetables were of two types – those available to the public and those issued to employees as work programmes.

Employee timetables – known as **working timetables** – included regular freight trains and provided operational information, for example on attaching and detaching vehicles en route. This information also included the times when trains passed particular points as well as their arrival and departure times.

For passenger services, the working timetables gave actual schedules and the printed **public timetables** gave 'advertised' times. These times could vary slightly from one timetable to the other. For example, sometimes it was thought sensible to advertise arrival times later than actually scheduled to deter passengers from planning connections that were too tight.

The public timetables were issued twice a year, the working timetables more often depending on the changes in train operations. The basis of both these timetables was the train graph – the document on which timetablers plotted each train movement. The advent of computers did not affect basic procedure – the train graph appeared on screen rather than on paper.

The graphs were produced in varying degrees of complexity, depending on the railway system, the type of line, and the complexity of operations. A very busy line might need several pages to cover the 24 hours. On British Rail, graphs covering most routes were produced in three versions – Monday to Friday, Saturday and Sunday.

Gaps between trains were built in to allow for stopping distances. Even with colour light signalling there had to be horizontal intervals of about four minutes between trains. There were still some routes in Britain where fitting in all the desired trains at the desired times was near impossible and the timetabler juggled on his graph with the various possibilities to find the best compromise.

On BR, InterCity requirements took precedence. InterCity trains were entered on to the clean graph which was then passed on to Regional Railways to plot paths for its passenger services. Freight trains – except for a few specialized services – were squeezed into the spaces that were left. Inevitably, there was more space on the graph at night and, being slower, freight trains tended to spread across the graph during the late and early hours.

Only when the graphs were agreed were timings transferred to the public and employee timetables. But BR sometimes had to print its public timetables before the graphs were finalized which meant that very unwelcome supplements had to be printed and distributed later.

The pre-nationalization passenger had access to several types of timetable. The companies displayed poster sized time sheets at their stations and sold their own timetable books.

Many cities had their 'ABC' guides, which provided alphabetical lists of destinations with departure and arrival times. This format avoided the traditional column arrangement of tables, where a train's timing was displayed down a column, with the stations arranged vertically on the edge of the page. Station displays of the column type timetables have now disappeared, although BR used to publish its own timetables similar to the earlier versions.

## Principles of timekeeping

The train graph is the basis for all train timetables. Originally drawn as here, it is now done on computer and shows an immediate visual representation of where the trains are scheduled to be at any one time.

This graph plots the distance covered and time taken by three trains – two local services and an express – travelling between three stations. As the up and down services travel on different tracks there is no danger of collision.

Train one is a down local passenger service and takes 15 minutes to cover the nine miles to station C including a wait of two minutes at station B. Train two is a very fast up service which leaves station C at 12.00 and runs directly to station A without stopping at station B; it then returns in the down direction to C. Train three is an up local stopping service.

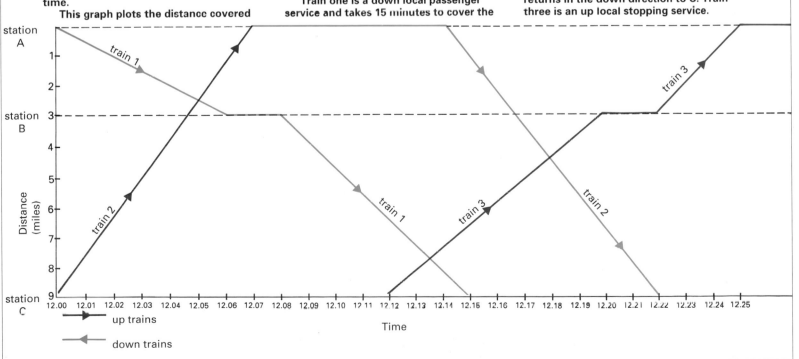

# Railway company timetables

All railway companies operating passenger services published a timetable showing the times and destinations of their various trains. These timetables could range from sizeable volumes to leaflets and single cards. The larger railway companies with complex systems of many lines usually published a complete list of services bound into a book with paper covers.

This normally appeared twice a year, in summer and winter, and throughout most of the 1930s and 1940s was priced at 6d. Any changes in service unforeseen at the time of printing would be accommodated in supplements which would be published as required throughout the year.

Even some of the smaller companies issued book timetables, though these hardly bore comparison with the volumes published by the large operators. The timetable issued by the Belfast & County Down Railway in September 1916 comprised 48 pages giving full details of all rail and steamship services, motor car road services, bye laws and conditions, fares and many other facts and figures. It also included the customary map.

The Eastern & Midlands Railway, forerunner of the Midland & Great Northern Joint Line, produced its 1888 timetable in the form of a broadsheet 20in (508mm) by 15in (381mm). This was folded into eight, each face of which carried on the reverse a separate handbill-type advertisement for various excursions and cheap fares.

In addition to the main timetable book, many companies also issued booklets and leaflets giving details of services over specific lines, or covering a particular period such as a Bank Holiday weekend. The Great Western Railway published wallet-sized single cards 3in (76mm) by 4in (102mm). A typical example gives details on one side of a half-day excursion from Exeter to Truro, St Ives, Penzance and Land's End on Wednesday, 2 September 1931. The return fare from Exeter to Penzance was 7s 6d. On the reverse side were details of a similar excursion to Plymouth and Falmouth on 6 September.

The Great Northern Railway provided commuters with a folded paper sheet giving the October 1913 timetable for the High Barnet and Edgware Branches. Some timetables appeared as small hanging cards which were to be found displayed in shops, offices and pubs near the station. Others took the form of posters displayed on station platforms and sometimes in the centre of towns. A novel timetable was put out by the Isle of Man Railway in the 1880s. This was a paper disc, 1¾in (43.7mm) in diameter, which fitted inside a pocket watch case.

For all but the most enthusiastic timetable fanciers, the cover of a timetable is often more interesting than the contents. Certainly, in the period from 1880 up to the 1923 Grouping, the timetable cover was seen as an excellent form of sales promotion, and the railway companies spared no expense in creating attractive, eyecatching designs.

The Midland Railway (MR) adopted a classical style with a map of the British Isles framed in an arch. For its Irish lines of the Northern Counties Committee, the MR employed a different but equally attractive design.

## Collecting railway company timetables

Timetable books still exist in considerable quantities, particularly from the later pre-nationalization and early British Railways periods. But the plain covers of these books are not nearly as attractive as earlier examples, and they can usually be bought fairly cheaply. The pre-Grouping volumes, being much rarer, will cost more, those with attractive covers, in good condition and from the smaller companies commanding the highest prices.

Booklet and leaflet timetables from the large companies can be found for a few pounds, while those from the smaller lines will cost rather more, depending on the scarcity of printed material from that particular company.

The most likely sources for timetables are the various ephemera and book fairs. Regular railway auctions may also come up with some interesting material. Antiquarian and second-hand booksellers are another possible source. Patience, stamina and a sharp eye are vital.

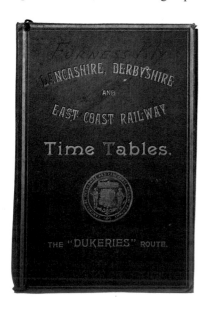

◀ From left to right: a binder from the timetables of the LD & ECR, which appears to have been held by an office of the Furness Railway; a gratuitous copy of the LYR timetables for July-September 1910, decorated by the two counties' white and red roses; and the Cambrian timetables, also gratuitous, from 12 July 1913.

# Station clocks

The advent of the railway age highlighted the importance of knowing the correct time and as a result the station clock became an integral part of the station scene. Before this, towns kept 'local' time – for example passengers travelling from London to Bristol might arrive to find a ten minute difference even though the train was on time. In 1847, the London & North Western Railway (L&NWR) introduced standardized Greenwich time throughout their system and other companies soon followed suit.

Clocks on station platforms often incorporated two faces at angles to enable train drivers as well as passengers to read them. It was usually the duty of the guard of the first train of the day to regulate the clocks.

Some railway companies used the clock as a status symbol. London's King's Cross and St Pancras have large turret clocks incorporated into the architectural design. Other main stations had huge, multi-faced clocks suspended from the roof. Because they played such an important role, several of these clocks

have remained in place, since to replace them would mean a major task and require structural modifications. But some of these survivors are no longer still in daily use – in many cases digital clocks have replaced them.

The status symbol clocks, by their very size, are beyond the scope of most collectors. However, there are numerous smaller clocks found on stations, ranging in diameter from 8-14in (20-35cm) – and these are highly collectable.

Many private firms – such as Joyce of Whitchurch, Shropshire and John Smith of Derby – supplied clocks to the railway companies, while other companies, such as the ever independent Great Western, manufactured their own.

Station clocks are very appealing, with their English dial faces, polished wood cases and brass surrounds. Some have extended cases to allow for a longer pendulum, ensuring more accurate timekeeping. Company offices also had shelf or mantelpiece style domestic clocks encased in marble, metal or wooden cases.

There are many variations to be found and such clocks appeal to general antique collectors as well as railway specialists. Since every station had at least one clock the number of survivors is quite large and they tend to be well preserved.

## Where to look

Many collectors purchase items relating to specific companies, but generally clocks are priced according to style and condition. Beware – non-railway clocks with company initials added to make them look like the real thing are not unknown. Railway auctions and specialist dealers are the main sources of supply for station clocks.

▼Many companies had mantelpiece clocks in their offices. Made from golden mahogany, this clock, with a 6³/₄in dial, probably stood above the fireplace of a prominent Great Northern Railway official.

▲This oak cased Midland Railway station clock with painted dial was made by Robert Thompson of Queens College, Birmingham.

▶ Some clocks were fixed to the walls of station booking offices. This 13in dial longcase mahogany wall clock was supplied by James Ritchie & Son to the North British Railway.

# Steam speed records

In 1804, when Richard Trevithick's pioneering locomotive made its journey along the Penydarren tramroad, its inventor operated the controls by walking along the track in front of it. In a letter the following day, Trevithick recorded that 'The engine while working went nearly five miles pr hour' – no more than a brisk walking pace. This was perhaps the first ever steam speed record.

When *Locomotion* ran from Shildon to Stockton 21 years later, it could only out-distance riders on horseback because marshes alongside the line impeded the horses. At full speed the locomotive could just manage 15mph.

At the Rainhill Trials in 1829, Stephenson's *Rocket* achieved 29mph. This was eclipsed in tragic circumstances the following year, when *Northumbrian* reached 36mph as it conveyed the dying MP William Huskisson to Eccles after he had been run over by *Rocket* at Parkside.

The contestants' achievements at Rainhill were carefully recorded. Later, it became difficult to establish accurate claims as speeds increased and railways spread throughout the world.

Unlike world speed records on land and in the air, there are no international standards for railways. For example, the effect of a strong following wind has never been taken into account and on almost every occasion a record breaking train was appreciably assisted by gravity. This applies equally to the TGV's present world record of 320.2mph as to *Mallard*'s 126mph in 1938.

Speed records were usually obtained by stop-watch measurements from mile or kilometre posts. In some cases the speed claimed at the time was later adjusted after the information had been examined further.

The performance of the Milwaukee Road's Hiawatha expresses in the 1930s was accurately measured and the 112mph record by the streamlined Atlantic No 2 in 1925 was adequately proved.

During the 1930s, there was considerable rivalry over maximum speeds between the LNER and the LMS. In 1937, the LMS claimed a maximum of 114mph on the press run of their Coronation Scot streamliner train. This would have beaten *Silver Link*'s record but the figure was not confirmed by a number of experienced recorders on the train. This left *Coronation* sharing the record of 112mph with the LNER A4 and Milwaukee Atlantic.

By 1936 the German Pacific No 05.002 reached 124.5mph and in 1938, *Mallard* achieved an historic all-time record for steam of 126mph.

| Date | Wheel arrgt | Name/No | Country | Railway | Speed mph (km) |
|------|-------------|---------|---------|---------|----------------|
| Feb 1804 | 0-4-0 | Trevithick's Penydarren Locomotive | GB | Merthyr tramroad | 5 (8) |
| Sep 1825 | 0-4-0 | *Locomotion* | GB | Stockton & Darlington | 15 (24) |
| Oct 1829 | 0-2-2 | *Rocket* | GB | Liverpool & Manchester | 29 (46) |
| Sep 1830 | 0-2-2 | *Northumbrian* | GB | Liverpool & Manchester | 36 (58) |
| Nov 1839 | 2-2-2 | *Lucifer* | GB | Grand Junction | 57 (92) |
| June 1845 | 2-2-2 | *Ixion* | GB | Great Western | 61 (98) |
| June 1846 | 2-2-2 | *Great Western* | GB | Great Western | 74 (119) |
| May 1848 | 4-2-2 | *Great Britain* | GB | Great Western | 78 (125) |
| June 1854 | 4-2-4WT | No 41 | GB | Bristol & Exeter | 82 (132) |
| 1889 | 4-2-0 | No 604 | France | Est | 89 (143) |
| Mar 1897 | 4-2-2 | No 117 | GB | Midland | 90 (145) |
| May 1904 | 4-4-0 | *City of Truro* | GB | Great Western | 100 (161) |
| Nov 1934 | 4-6-2 | *Flying Scotsman* | GB | LNER | 100 (161) |
| Mar 1935 | 4-6-2 | *Papyrus* | GB | LNER | 108 (174) |
| May 1935 | 4-4-2 | No 2 | USA | Milwaukee | 112 (180) |
| Sep 1935 | 4-6-2 | *Silver Link* | GB | LNER | 112 (180) |
| May 1936 | 4-6-4 | No 05.002 | Germany | Deutsche Reichsbahn | 124.5 (200) |
| July 1938 | 4-6-2 | *Mallard* | GB | LNER | 126 (202) |

▲All the fully authenticated world records achieved by steam locomotives are the maximum speed attained, rather than averages. Some top speeds, like *Mallard*'s, were sustained only for a few yards.

◄ Although a record of 74mph was achieved by a GWR locomotive in 1846, it was not until 1931 that the company ran trains at such average speeds in everyday service. The Cheltenham Flyer was the first train in the history of railways to average regularly over 70mph. On 14 September 1931, the express sweeps through Tilehurst, Berkshire on its way to London.

# World diesel speed records

The internal combustion engine has been used by railway traction since the early 20th century. Because the available power of engines was low, new diesel locomotives were intended only for light duties, particularly on branch lines where operating costs were causing concern, or for shunting. World records were set up for this form of traction, but the speeds achieved were so far behind contemporary achievements of steam that no one bothered to take any notice.

After World War I, internal combustion engines became smaller and better ways were found to transmit power to the wheels of a locomotive or train. By the 1930s, with more efficient diesel motors becoming widely available, high speed trains were developed. These mounted the first serious challenge to steam's speed supremacy.

It is not the highest speed reached that matters to the ordinary traveller, but how long the journey takes – high *average* speeds, although slower than the peak speeds, have more commercial importance. The difference between the two speeds is shown by the Burlington Railroad's high speed run with its three-coach, stainless-steel, streamlined Pioneer Zephyr in May 1934. The maximum of 112.5mph earned the Zephyr the world speed record, but it also ran the 1015 miles from Denver to Chicago non stop at an overall average of 77.6mph. At the conclusion of its run, the train was displayed at an exhibition alongside its rival, the Union Pacific M10001, which was to achieve the next world record of 120mph later that year.

Although the North American diesel streamliners quickly made their mark on the railway scene, all other world speed records with diesel power have been achieved in Europe. In 1972, the Spanish Talgo record was attained with a diesel-hydraulic locomotive, later overtaken in the UK using HSTs with electric transmissions. Ironically, the 1986 and 1987 diesel records were made by HSTs during bogie trials for the East Coast electric InterCity 225 trains.

There have also been a number of record-breaking oddities powered by internal combustion. In 1933 a German railcar, propelled by an airscrew, reached 143mph, but there are no reports on the effect that the slipstream had on waiting passengers as it passed through a station. In 1966, the New York Central mounted a pair of jet engines on top of a railcar, generating a speed of 183.9mph – and much noise. Gas turbines have also been successfully used in a number of trains propelled through their wheels.

◄ Since 1932 there have been 10 fully authenticated world speed records for diesel-powered trains. By the 1930s, mechanical methods had replaced stop-watches to record top speeds accurately, and most diesel records benefited from this new technology.

▲ In May 1934 the Burlington Railroad's Pioneer Zephyr reached 112.5mph and earned the world railway speed record. The three-coach, stainless-steel, streamlined train also ran the 1015 miles from Denver to Chicago non stop at an overall average of 77.6mph.

| Date | | Train | Country | Speed mph (km/h) |
|---|---|---|---|---|
| Dec | 1932 | VT877 railcar | Germany | 102.5 (165) |
| May | 1934 | Pioneer Zephyr | USA | 112.5 (181) |
| Oct | 1934 | Union Pacific M10001 | USA | 120 (193) |
| Feb | 1936 | Leipzig railcar | Germany | 127.4 (205) |
| June | 1939 | Kruckenberg set | Germany | 133 (214) |
| May | 1972 | Talgo 353-005 | Spain | 137.9 (222) |
| June | 1973 | HST prototype | GB | 143.2 (230.5) |
| Sep | 1985 | HST | GB | 144 (231.7) |
| Nov | 1986 | HST | GB | 144.9 (233) |
| Nov | 1987 | HST | GB | 148.5 (238.9) |

# Electric speed records

The first electric locomotive was built by R Davidson in 1842. Battery powered, it reached 4mph (6.4km/h) on the Glasgow – Edinburgh line, but the design was far too crude to be a rival for steam traction.

It was not until 1879 that Werner von Siemens produced the first recognizable electric train, drawing current from a conductor along the track. Although this machine was only a miniature gauge model in a Berlin exhibition, within 22 years a Siemens & Halske locomotive had topped the 100mph (160.9km/h) mark on the Marienfelde – Zossen Germany military railway. The same test track was used in 1903 to set up three more records, the fastest being no less than 130.6mph (210.1km/h), a speed never surpassed by steam.

The current collection methods used for the Siemens & Halske tests involved three different contact wires, mounted one above the other on masts alongside

**▼Early electric traction records were achieved during primitive experiments, but since 1954 this form of motive power has dominated railway speed records. Over the last 40 years the pace has been set by the TGVs and ICEs of France and Germany.**

the track. The vehicles sprouted a series of collectors which badly infringed the normal loading gauge and there was no way the contact wires could be continued through a junction. For this reason these trains have always been considered as oddities.

It was not until the late 1930s that the speed capabilities of orthodox electric trains started to rival steam, with a speed of 126mph (202.7km/h) being achieved by an Italian streamlined railcar in 1939. Since 1954 this type of motive power has held all the absolute railway speed records, Spanish and British diesel records being well behind the contemporary electric achievements.

Over the past 40 years, honours have been shared by the French and German railways, with their TGVs and ICEs. The friendly rivalry between the two countries stimulated German efforts to push the speed of their prototype ICE beyond the TGV's 1981 record. Seven months later, the French engineers marginally regained the lead during a test run with the prototype TGV for the new Atlantique line, but did not claim it officially.

The French were saving their efforts for a series of trials planned for the new line after it had been completed. A long

downhill stretch to the bridge across the river Loire provided a magnificent racing stretch. Between December 1989 and May 1990 no less than five new world records were set, culminating in a final speed of 320.2mph (515.3km/h).

The Japanese railways do not figure in the world record table. From 1965 their Bullet trains set new world records for commercial services, being the first to set schedules of more than 100mph (160.9km/h) start-to-stop. They have nevertheless achieved a number of national railway speed records. The new Series 300 set up a figure of 202.4mph (325.7km/h) on the Central Japan Railway in February 1991 and in March, on the East Japan Railway, the new Series 400 reached 214.4mph (345km/h).

So rapid are current world developments that a speed of 205mph (329.9km/h) was reached early in 1992 on the new Spanish AVE before the line between Madrid and Seville had been completed.

In Britain the railway speed record is still held by the APT-P, which attained 162.2mph (261km/h) between Beattock and Lockerbie in December 1979 – but the Class 91 came very close in September 1989 with 161.7mph (260.2km/h) descending Stoke Bank.

| Date | Train/locomotive | Country | Speed mph (km/h) |
|------|------------------|---------|------------------|
| 1901 | Siemens & Halske loco | Germany | 101.0 (162.5) |
| Oct 1903 | Siemens & Halske railcar | Germany | 126.0 (202.7) |
| Oct 1903 | Siemens & Halske railcar | Germany | 128.5 (206.8) |
| Oct 1903 | AEG railcar | Germany | 130.6 (210.1) |
| July 1939 | ETR200 multiple unit | Italy | 126.1 (202.9) |
| Feb 1954 | CC7121 | France | 151.0 (243) |
| Mar 1955 | BB9004 | France | 171.5 (276) |
| Mar 1955 | CC7101 | France | 202.6 (326) |
| Mar 1955 | BB9004 | France | 205.7 (331) |
| Feb 1981 | TGV33 | France | 230.5 (370.9) |
| Feb 1981 | TGV33 | France | 236.4 (380.4) |
| Apr 1988 | ICE prototype | W Germany | 240.5 (387) |
| Apr 1988 | ICE prototype | W Germany | 249.2 (401) |
| Apr 1988 | ICE prototype | W Germany | 251.0 (403.9) |
| May 1988 | ICE prototype | W Germany | 252.8 (406.8) |
| Dec 1988 | TGV88 | France | 253.7 (408.2) |
| Dec 1989 | TGV325 | France | 275.0 (442.5) |
| May 1990 | TGV325 | France | 317.3 (482.3) |
| May 1990 | TGV325 | France | 317.4 (510.6) |
| May 1990 | TGV325 | France | 320.2 (515.3) |

**▲High speed electric networks are growing all the time throughout Europe. The Spanish AVE (*Alta Velocidad Espanol*) runs at high speed on a standard gauge line from Madrid to Seville, known as a NAFA, and the Eurostar reaches 186mph (300km/h) between Paris and Calais.**

# Train resistance

A moving train encounters two main forms of resistance: gradient resistance and rolling resistance.

**Gradient resistance** is a reflection of the horsepower (hp) needed to get a train up a hill. More hp is needed to get a train to climb up a gradient than is required on level track. But hp used for taking the train up a gradient can be reused. By making the locomotive work hard on the climb, the engine stores energy that can be recovered on the descent. Provided the slope is gentle enough to make braking unnecessary, little energy will be used up when gravity, rather than horsepower, propels the train downwards.

On a steep descent, electric locomotives with regenerative braking (which slows the train by using motors as generators) can convert the potential energy of a downward moving train into electricity that is fed back into the catenary for use by trains going up.

Compared with the horsepower needed for overcoming gradients, the amount needed to overcome rolling resistance is small. **Rolling resistance**, not the same as the effort needed to start a train, comes from a number of areas: the axles encounter friction as they rotate on their bearings; the wheels find resistance at the points where they touch the rails; energy from the wheels is absorbed into the rail surface and rail joints; further energy is lost into the ballast as the rail and sleeper is pressed into it by the weight of the train. On curved track there is additional wheel resistance as flanges grind against the outside rail.

Another aspect of resistance comes from the air – **aerodynamic resistance** is largely a result of surface friction. Passenger coaches, with their large areas of outside surfaces and complex undersides, produce almost as much air resistance as the locomotive. Since the front of the engine is comparatively small, it does not meet significant air pressure except at the highest speeds.

On average, the air resistance of a passenger coach is about two thirds that of the locomotive. However, air resistance is a small part of the total rolling resistance.

Actual rolling resistance can be measured by dynamometer car trials, but good approximations can also be made by a formula. A four-axle wagon fitted with roller bearings and weighing 25 tons has a resistance of about 290lb on level track. To keep the wagon moving, the locomotive has to exert a pull of 290lb on the coupling. If the wagon is loaded with 100 tons of freight, only 525lb will be needed as the rolling resistance does not increase proportionately with the weight. On moderate grades there is less difference than might be expected in the hp needed for loaded and empty trains.

As a rule of thumb, the rolling resistance of a loaded wagon can be taken as 4lb per tonne, and of an empty wagon 11lb, at speeds of around 30mph. Gradient resistance is as much as 20lb per tonne of train on a 1 in 100 gradient, or 10lb on 1 in 200, and does not vary with train speed.

To train resistance has to be added **locomotive resistance**, which is proportionately much more. The heavier weight of the locomotive means that the resistance at the axle bearings and where the track touches the wheel is greater. There is also the mechanical friction of moving parts like pistons and valves. Large driving wheels, which imply slower movement of pistons and valves, reduce this friction.

Apart from aerodynamic drag, which is greater than that of a freight or passenger vehicle, there may be energy loss through the churning effect of wheels and (in the cast of modern traction) motor armatures. At 70mph, a typical diesel-electric locomotive requires 400-500hp to overcome all these resistances.

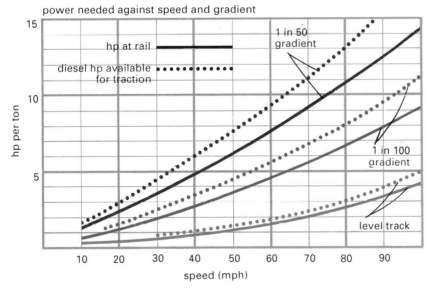

power needed against speed and gradient

hp at rail
diesel hp available for traction
1 in 50 gradient
1 in 100 gradient
level track

hp per ton

speed (mph)

▲The graph shows the power needed by a train to climb a hill at any speed. A diesel locomotive has to produce more hp than is actually used at track level to power train lighting and heating. Even on level track, the engine still has to produce two hp per ton to move it at 60mph.

▶ On level track, a train of 100 4-axle loaded wagons, fitted with roller bearings and weighing 125 tons each, would produce a resistance of 7lb per ton at 50mph. A train of empty wagons moving at the same speed produces 12lb per ton. Rolling resistance does not increase proportionately with the weight. On moderate grades the hp needed for loaded and empty trains does not change in proportion.

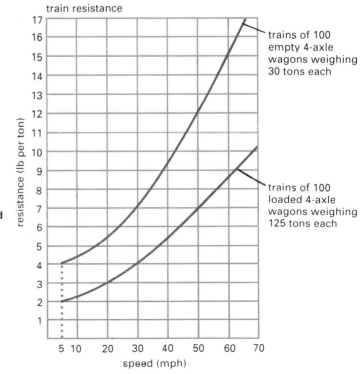

train resistance

trains of 100 empty 4-axle wagons weighing 30 tons each

trains of 100 loaded 4-axle wagons weighing 125 tons each

resistance (lb per ton)

speed (mph)

# Tractive effort

Tractive effort is the horizontal thrust exerted by the wheels of a locomotive against the rails, causing it to move. At the drawbar to which the train is coupled, it appears as a horizontal force, or 'pull'. Drawbar pull is less than tractive effort because of bearing friction and wind resistance. Both forces are commonly measured in pounds or kilogrammes.

The tractive effort of a locomotive is limited by the grip of the wheels on the rails (adhesion). In starting a train from rest, it used to be necessary to keep the tractive effort well below this limit to avoid slipping, but modern microprocessor control systems hold the tractive effort automatically on the verge of the point at which adhesion would be lost and the wheels loose their grip since this is the point of maximum point of acceleration.

When starting a train a high tractive effort is necessary to overcome its inertia. As the train gathers speed, the traction motors revolve faster and generate a 'back EMF' that opposes the flow of current. The tractive effort falls and at length a 'balancing' speed is reached at which the tractive effort and the resistance to motion of the train are equal. Train resistance is a combination of several factors, principally air resistance, bearing friction, weight and gradient.

An electric locomotive or electrical multiple unit (EMU), draws its power from the overhead wire or live rail system but the power it can develop is limited by the heating of the motors. Two power ratings are quoted. The one-hour rating is the power that can be developed for one hour without the rise in temperature exceeding an internationally agreed limit. The continuous rating is lower but is subject to a similar restriction.

In some technical descriptions of locomotives the tractive effort is expressed in a unit of force called the newton. This is a unit of the System Internationale (SI). The symbol is N and since a newton equals only .224lb it is usually combined with a multiple, for example KN means 1000 newtons.

▶ On the level of the curve at the top, tractive effort is held at an average of 4850lb while motor voltage is increased to full value. From this point the motor follows its normal full-field operating curve with speed rising to 25mph. To accelerate further, the motor switches into weak-field, increasing the tractive effort to 4500lb.

The curve at the bottom of the diagram is an example of train resistance on level track. At 65mph, it equals the tractive effort and this is the balancing speed. On a rising gradient, the train resistance would increase until a higher tractive effort struck a new balance.

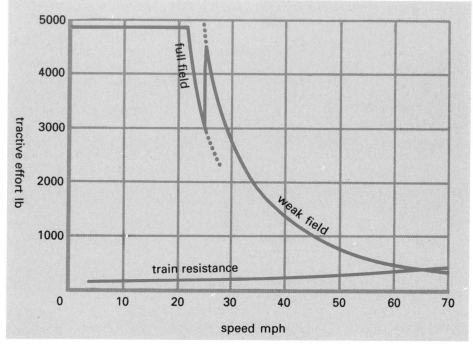

◀ Tractive effort is not to be confused with horsepower. In moving a train, a locomotive is doing work. Power is a measure of the rate at which work is done. At low speeds, the power required is small. The standard BR 350hp diesel shunter can shift heavy loads, but only in the speed range up to about 20mph.

# TE and HP – steam

The tractive effort (TE) quoted for a steam locomotive was the value at starting. It allowed for the fact that even in full forward gear the steam pressure in the cylinders was not constant, but after about 72% of the piston stroke, steam admission was cut off and for the rest of the stroke the steam worked expansively. A tractive effort formula devised by D K Clark estimated that at this cut-off, the average pressure in the cylinders was some 86.5% of boiler pressure. Cylinder volume came into the calculation and the volume occupied by the piston rods had also to be allowed for. The generally accepted figure in calculating tractive effort later became 85%.

$$\text{tractive effort} = \frac{85\% \text{ boiler pressure x the square of cylinder bore x 1}}{\text{diameter of driving wheels}}$$

**pressure is expressed in lb psi
and the other dimensions in inches**

The mathematical formula in which this appears applies to two-cylinder engines. For three or four cylinders, the result is multiplied by 1.5 and 2 respectively. Railway publicity departments were prone to quote tractive effort as power and vied with each other in claiming to have the 'most powerful' locomotive. On paper the Southern Railway's Lord Nelson class 4-6-0 of 1926 surpassed the Great Western Castle and the Gresley Pacific with a tractive effort of 33,500lb. At first, the engines did not steam well and the actual output is debatable. The Lord Nelson did not stay in the lead for long, however. The Great Western's King class 4-6-0 appeared a few weeks later with a TE of 40,000lb, a sufficient margin over its rival to allow for any shortfall of actual over calculated performance.

Quite small changes in dimensions could have a surprising effect. The TE of the Great Western King was put at first at 39,700lb. The GWR board, with an eye on the competition, asked if it could be boosted to 40,000lb. The designer, C B Collett, obliged by adding $1/4$in to the cylinder dimensions and the sum came out as desired – however, the $1/4$in was later dropped.

The King was an advance on the Castle which had a TE of 31,650lb. Collett achieved the increase by four measures: boiler pressure was raised from 225 to 250lb psi, driving wheel diameter was reduced from 6ft $8^1/_2$in to 6ft 6in, cylinder diameter increased from 16 to $16^1/_4$in and piston stroke increased from 26 to 28in.

There are several elements involved in resistance to motion, of which the most obvious is a rising gradient. Rolling stock offers resistance in axle friction, flange action oscillation and vibration (including the effect of rail joints). The strength and direction of the wind is an important factor. Locomotive resistance is also complex, including track resistance, air resistance, machine friction, oscillation and vibration.

Calculations of steam locomotive horsepower (HP) in controlled conditions on the road and on test plants have been made on many occasions. Multiplying tractive effort and speed and dividing by 375 gives cylinder horsepower (also known as indicated horsepower/ihp). Drawbar pull times speed, again divided by 375, gives horsepower at the drawbar (dhp).

In BR days, a number of the Standard and other steam classes were tested on the road and on the test plant at Rugby, and the results were published in a series of Test Bulletins.

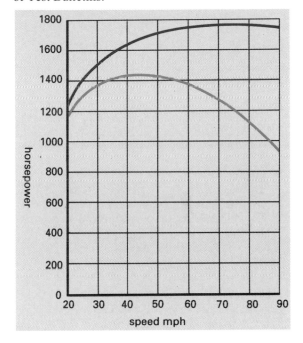

——— drawbar horsepower

——— cylinder horsepower

▶ On 5 October 1959, Standard Class 5 4-6-0 is prepared at Stewarts Lane depot, London. The diagram shows the results obtained with one of these locomotives. Similar tests of the 'one-off' Class 8 Pacific No 71000 showed a maximum drawbar horsepower of 2100 at 40mph. In its final years the steam locomotive had its performance studied intensively, using scientific resources which were not available before. Unfortunately, however, the change to diesel and electric power came before the new knowledge could be applied.

# TOPS letter codes

One of the problems of moving rolling stock on railways is maximising the use of vehicles. Traditionally, a train of wagons or trucks, once discharged of its load, was taken back empty to its starting point. Often this was because the wagons were owned privately but, more significantly, it was the only real way of knowing where they were. It became clear that a more efficient method of scheduling was needed. The answer was TOPS.

## Big brother watches

TOPS is an acronym for Total Operations Processing System, a computerised system introduced from 1973, primarily to facilitate movement of freight on the BR network but also used to categorize other rolling stock such as passenger vehicles and locomotives. TOPS' most visible aspect is the code number on each vehicle, but it is far more than just a means of keeping records. TOPS actually monitors and supervises the complete movement of vehicles from one destination to another.

Information is stored centrally on the TOPS computer, and there are terminals at major freight centres around Britain, so local users can tap into the system. The computer stores details of all rolling stock as well as the location of, for example, wagons at any given time, including when in maintenance depots and storage areas, through location codes. Timetables indicate the likely time of arrival of a particular wagon or locomotive in transit. The details of every vehicle stored also enable the computer to match a specific type of wagon or locomotive to a particular task.

## Efficient use

The TOPS system can schedule the use of each vehicle, ensuring it is used at its highest efficiency of both purpose and time in service. It avoids the previous practice of widespread storage of wagons in sidings while their next function was decided, and it has led to considerable savings as fewer vehicles are needed so operating and maintenance costs are lower. Over the years the system has been expanded and updated.

The running number of every vehicle is recorded but its type and use is recognized through the use of a TOPS code. This consists of three capital letters, displayed prominently on the vehicle; for example, a general goods van might have the code VAA. The first letter describes the wagon category; in this case V indicates a covered van. The second letter gives a further breakdown of the type of wagon with the broad category (in this case a van with full-width sliding doors) and is primarily of use when matching to load and scheduling. The final letter describes the type of braking system (in this case air braking). The full codes for the broad category and braking systems are shown in the tables.

The benefits of TOPS are many; the status of the entire network can be determined quickly, movement of freight can be planned and executed more efficiently, and customers enjoy greater reliability.

A separate TOPS numerical coding system categorizes locomotive classes – for example, English Electric Type 3 is now Class 37, and Brush Type 4 has been recoded as Class 47.

▼ ▶ The primary function of the TOPS (Total Operating Processing System) code is to oversee the movement of freight around the BR system, but it is also used to categorize other items of rolling stock. The code is made up of three capital letters. The first describes the vehicle while a second more specific letter, of which there are too many to list, helps match the load with the schedule. The third letter describes the braking system.

## TOPS third letter codes

**A** Air brake

**V** Vacuum brake

**X** Dual air/vacuum brake

**B** Air brake and vacuum pipe

**W** Vacuum brake and air pipe

**O** Unfitted

## TOPS first letter codes

| | |
|---|---|
| **A** Reserved for coaching stock | **O** Open wagon |
| **B** Bogie steel-carrying wagon | **P** Privately owned wagon except tank |
| **C** Covered bulk carrier | **Q** Ex-coaching stock service vehicle |
| **D** Reserved for DMUs | **R** Railway operating vehicle |
| **E** Reserved for EMUs | **S** Two-axle steel-carrying vehicle |
| **F** Flat wagon | **T** Privately owned tank wagon |
| **H** Hopper wagon | **U** Open bulk traffic vehicle |
| **I** Continental ferry wagon | **V** Covered van |
| **J** Bogie coil wagon | **X** Special purpose vehicle |
| **K** Two-axle coil wagon | **Y** Bogie service vehicle |
| **M** Mineral wagon | **Z** Two-axle and other service vehicle |
| **N** Non passenger-carrying wagon | |

# Cost-benefit analysis

Railway lines are expensive to build, and they have to be carefully costed before work can begin. Before nationalization it was a simple matter of economics: railway companies would estimate the projected income from passenger and freight traffic on a proposed line, and if this was greater than the operating costs and interest payments on the money borrowed to pay for construction, building of the line could go ahead. If a loss was forecast, the project would generally be abandoned.

The benefit to the public of a new railway line would be a nominal consideration in planning discussions (especially when approval was being sought from government and local interests), but this factor rarely influenced decisions to any great extent.

There were occasions when the public benefited from an investment by a railway more than the railway company itself. When the Southern Railway (SR) electrified its outer suburban routes, for example, there was a sudden increase in the value of private houses in surrounding areas, as it brought with it the opportunity for people to commute to London. The SR's outlay, while bringing in extra revenue and decreased operating costs for itself, also created wealth for local property owners.

## Costs versus benefits

With nationalization in 1948, social benefit rather than profit finally became an important consideration in railway development. Then, in the 1980s, decision-making became less socially conscious and more financially conscious, resulting in a reversal of priorities.

In Britain today road investment projects are evaluated on a cost-benefit basis, yet railway schemes still have to promise a good return on any loan before the government will allow investment in them.

For example, a proposed road by-pass scheme is evaluated in terms of the time saved by motorists and the reduction in lives lost through accidents. Assessment of a railway scheme, however, does not include the time saved by road users when a better train service encourages a proportion of drivers to leave their cars at home and travel by rail.

The approval for London's Victoria Line was held back for years because no account was taken of the benefit to those who would continue to use the roads and gain from the resulting de-congestion.

Many existing Regional Railway services that make a loss on present accounting principles are in fact viable when a value is placed on their social benefits – this can be five times greater than the revenue received from ticket sales.

## Counting the costs

There are two main factors which ought to be considered in determining whether a new railway is desirable. These are the social benefits that the new line will bring to local communities, and the financial costs incurred in building it in relation to the projected profits. If social benefits are not taken into account in this equation, far more passengers will be needed to produce an adequate return.

For example, if a new underground line is to break even purely on financial grounds, it would need to carry 74 million passengers before a profit would be made. If social benefits were included in the calculations, however, the number of passengers needed would be reduced to 18 million, making it a much more viable proposition.

### Fatal irony
It is ironic that road assessments take account of lives saved by a new road, yet railway schemes don't – despite the fact that rail journeys are 125 times safer than road journeys. Equally there is no attempt to assess the environmental costs of roads which are borne by the tax-payer.

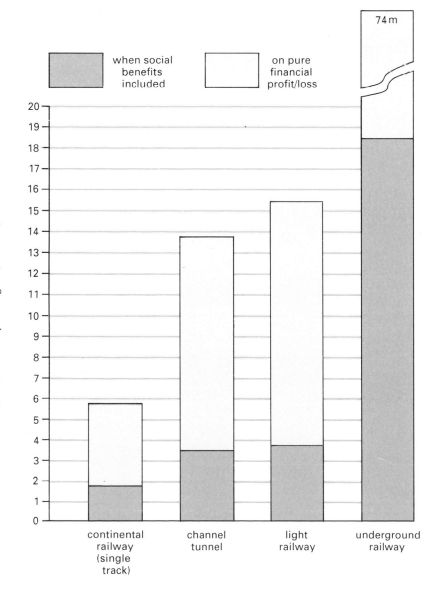

◀ Comparison estimate of passenger levels required for different types of new railway to break even, when social benefits are excluded and included from estimates.

# Picture acknowledgements

PHOTOGRAPHS:
Roger Bastin 92; John Bird 78; Ian Carr 110(t); Michael Christensen 114(cl); D Cobbe 32, 79; Collections (Brian Shuel) 129; Michael J Collins 51, 84, 88, 91, 93, 95, 96; Eaglemoss Publications (Michael Little) 37(c), 75, 114(bl, cr), 135, (John Suett) 112, (Jim Winkley) 18, 37(l), 134(c, r); Harold Edmonson 55; Mary Evans Picture Library 116; Getty/Hulton Collection 36, 57, 68, 74, 94, 120, 125, 136; Robert Harding Picture Library 63, 109, 111; John Hunt 102; Michael Little 17(r); John Lloyd 73; Hugh Madgin 49; Milepost 92 ½ 50, 127; Millbrook House 22, 60, 70, 81, 110(b), 121, 134(l), (Hugh Ballantyne) 37(r), (K Cooper) 35, (JM Jarvis) 123, (E Treacy) 20, (PB Whitehouse) 9, (JS Whiteley) 58, 69, 89; Brian Morrison 48, 80, 82, 140; National Railway Museum 67, 72, 124; Geoff Rixon 12, 131; RENFE 138; RC Riley 141; John Shuttleworth 13; Rail Archive Stephenson 33, 34; Peter J Stone 126; Graham Wiltshire 128; Jim Winkley 17(l), 27, 62, 77, 137.

ILLUSTRATIONS:
Graham Dorsett 8, 10, 14, 19, 56, 72, 76, 90, 102, 119, 120, 122, 125, 126, 127, 130, 132; Eaglemoss Publications (Paul Kellett) 6, 13, 20, 27, 30, 40, 43, 48, 57, 62, 65, 66, 80, 83, 84, 85, 92, 93, 94, 95, 96, 97, 98, 99, 100, 101, 104, 105(cl, r), 107, 108(l), 113, 121, 133, (Duncan Kitson) 11, 15, 21, 22, 23, 24, 28, 29, 31, 38, 39, 41, 42, 44, 45, 46, 47, 49, 50, 51, 54, 55(r), 58, 59, 60, 63, 64, 71, 74, 77, 82, 86, 87, 88, 89, 91, 103, 105(bl), 106, 109, 115, 116, 117, 118, 139, 140, 141, 143; Dennis Griffiths 25, 26; Kevin Jones Associates 16, 55(l), 61, 108(r); Salamander Books 7, 9, 52, 53.